Handbook for Raising Healthy Black Children (Infants to Teenagers)

by Llaila O. Afrika

A Comprehensive Holistic Guide for:

- Parenting Skills and Problems
- Controlling Teenagers
- Healthy Diets, Snacks and Recipes
- Behavior and Learning Problems
- Growth and Development
- African Centered Education
- Personality and Emotional Issues
- Discipline
- Children's Diseases and Natural Remedies
- What To Do When All Else Fails

And Much Much More

Handbook for Raising Healthy Black Children

Seaburn Publishing Group
P.O. Box 2085
Long Island City, N.Y. 11102

Graphic Art by Donald Oscar Harris

Library of Congress Cat. Num.-in-Publication Data
2009 Afrika, Llaila

ISBN 1592321879 (paperback)

Other Books by the Author:

African Holistic Health
Nutricide (Nutritional Destruction of the Black Race)
The Gullah (History Book)
Melanin

TABLE OF CONTENTS

INTRODUCTION

The Black child is a product of the Black experience of oppression, slavery trauma and White Supremacy. Oppression creates and maintains nutritional, emotional, social and psychological stressors. This causes dysfunctional thoughts, emotions, marriages, sex, feelings, behaviors and diets amongst an oppressed group and its leaders. Despite the effect of dysfunctionality, the Black child and parent must be healthy and functional by using the principles of Maat/Kwanzaa and African-centeredness. This will provide the child with the ability to achieve their highest level of humanism. This book uses step-by-step methods and practical applications and solutions that will provide the basic tools needed for African-centered parenting. The current Black parenting skills and lack of skills are based upon the child raising concepts and theories of Caucasian culture. These skills and lack of skills are a mixture of the techniques used to raise slave children. Black parents using Caucasian techniques raised children that became parents that passed on these techniques from generation to generation (hereditary). These hereditary methods of parenting have to be refined, re-evaluated and transformed into parenting relevant for the Black child.

The Black child has a different experience and culture from a White child. White oppression makes the adult, child, community, continent, education, human and natural resources directly and indirectly controlled by Caucasians, Asians and Hispanics. Therefore, the Black child and parents relationship has to function with a focus of creating social, educational, political and economic control over their destiny. This makes the Black child a cultural technology that is needed for creating a future without Caucasian, Asian and/or Hispanic oppression. Black parenting has to be commensurate and consistent with this objective.

The Slave Master's indoctrination (seasoning) caused the Black child and parent to be concrete thinkers and practical workers. In other words, they were taught to see cotton and pick cotton. The colonized and/or enslaved child/parent was not taught to be conceptual, analytical, political, self-sufficient or how to own and control their human and natural resources. In other words, the child was taught how to look for a job and not taught to look for an opportunity. Blacks were taught to be very skilled on the job market (i.e. auction block) in order to get paid more money (sold at a higher price), and taught to want to be an entertainer (i.e. actor, athlete, comedian, etc.) and not to own the entertainment industry, taught to own an automobile instead of owning an automobile factory, taught to own a diamond ring instead of a diamond mine, taught to spend their money with White businesses instead of Black businesses, etc. The Black child continues to be disciplined (seasonin) in the same manner as the slave child. The child is forced to follow Caucasian's cultural rituals, ceremonies, holidays, educational systems and rules of conduct and punishment. The slave child was beaten verbally and emotionally, sexually abused and disciplined by their slave parents and slave master in order to make them a better slave.

The purpose of disciplining the Black child is to help them to know their purpose for living, what they need to do to achieve their purpose, how to evaluate progress and what tools they need to achieve their purpose. Parenting must give the child an undistorted theoretical, rational, spiritual, military, analytical, creative, political and economic foundation.

When the parent during their childhood was raised without a holistic African-centered context, their parenting can be distorted, flawed or dysfunctional. Ideally, Black parents should have been raised with natural foods and Rites of Passage (training) for adulthood and marriage. The parents should have viewed their mate as a sexual compliment (not an opposite sex), then married and then dated each other in order to learn and become the type of person their mate could love.

The parents would have spiritualized their Regenerative and Reproductive sexual intercourse by saying a prayer and/or doing a spiritual ritual before having sex. During pregnancy, they abstained from sex and the father mothers (nurtures) the mother, while the mother fathers (nurtures) the father. This nurturing ritual is a part of the Parental Rites of Passage. The birth of the child would be a non-hospitalized and a natural birth (i.e. midwife) accompanied by a birth ceremony. The newborn would be placed on the mother's breast. The umbilical cord would be pulsating because it is providing nourishment and oxygen while the newborn is making its biological transition from living and breathing inside the uterus to living and breathing outside the uterus. If the umbilical cord is cut before it stops pulsating, it deprives the newborn of air and vital nutrients and causes sores on the brain and bonding difficulties. The newborn would be breastfed (up to 3 years old). The parents would not have sex during the breastfeeding time period. The newborn would not be circumcised because it is not needed for hygiene; it is biologically unnecessary and emotionally and physically traumatizes the male child. The child would be given its name at a naming ceremony. The child would be raised on a natural unprocessed food diet and raised in a home that was arranged using the African system (Pher Ankh = House of Life) of decorating, furniture placement and arrangement. The child would be raised without hearing or seeing pornographic type music videos, sex dancing, rap sex songs, or exposed to cursing, violence, etc. If the parents as children were not raised with the above social standards and cultural focus, then they are flawed, culturally castrated, emotionally damaged, nutritionally undernourished and are dysfunctional in an aspect of their character logic, spirituality and personality. The Black parents must be in the process of constantly working to overcome their dysfunctionality caused by Slavery Trauma and oppression.

Oppression is created and maintained by Caucasians in order for them to stay in power. Oppression requires that the Black victim be dysfunctional. Oppression is spiritual, emotional, mental and physiological. It causes the deterioration of immunity, sex organs, pancreas (diabetes, nerve damage) as well as hyperactivity, hypertension, depression, high blood pressure, self-hatred, race hatred, addiction, etc. As long as the Black race allows itself to be oppressed, it will be dysfunctional, have dysfunctional parents and dysfunctional children. Therefore, a different type of parenting is required for the Black child and parent to heal and overcome the dysfunctional ties. Caucasian culture's Parenting and Marriage Institution are in trouble (high divorce, suicide and runaway children, domestic violence, etc). Black that use Caucasian Parenting Skills are entering a house (institution) that is on fire. They cannot be a good parent and culture-less (African culture). The Black parent must create an African-centered mindset for the child and a cultural environment that will give the child the cultural program needed to access their intelligence and solve the race's problems. The parenting information in this book is designed to heal the parenting skills and define skills with a culturally relevant focus.

Parenting is a sacred privilege granted to adults. It is essentially a way to serve God and the principles of Maat and Kwanzaa. The parent's thoughts, feelings, subconscious, words, actions, behaviors, moods and parenting with the child must meet the standards of God, and the Principles of Maat and Kwanzaa. If the parent's behavior around the child and with the child does not meet these standards, then the parent must stop that behavior or behaviors. Parenting must serve the positive needs of our race and culture. Being a good parent requires holistic skills that bring joy to the child. This book is a celebration of the joy and happiness which is the child's God given right (divine).

FOREWORD

This book summarizes and briefly addresses many of the issues facing Black parents about the growth, development, education, diet and health of the Black child. I used as many charts as possible and tried to communicate information without wordiness and medical, social and science jargon. I did not go in depth about the psychological and cultural uniqueness of the Black child because there are already many books on this subject. My concern in this book is to provide the basic knowledge that a parent needs to raise a child and the parenting skills required. This book is a response to the many questions I was asked on the subject of how to parent and the best way to handle various parent/child issues and problems that arise. In researching this book, I read misinformation and disinformation about children. To be frank with you, most of the child raising literature was and is junk, with a lot of cosmetic research and statistics to back it up.

I truly hope that this book will provide you with a better emotional, spiritual and physical (holistic) understanding of the process of raising a child. It takes a village to raise a child and a village to be a parent. This book is just one voice in the village to help you.

I wrote this book as a guide so that you would gain a greater understanding, awareness and clarity on the subject of child rearing and the parenting process. It is a "how to" book (i.e. how to be a parent book). Whether you are a birth parent or not, you still need parenting skills. Each adult has to parent their friends, family or other people's children. Therefore, this book can be used by any adult or teenager that must supervise, baby sit children, or have social contact with children. Additionally, this book can help you to better understand your childhood and the parenting (or lack of) that has shaped your emotions, intellect and spirituality as well as your behavior and the strengths and weaknesses of your personality. It is an old saying that sums up parents' negative and/or positive influences on their child – "an apple (child) does not fall far from a tree." (parent's influence)

CHAPTER 1
CULTURE

"It's better to build strong, healthy children than repair a broken, dysfunctional man (adult)."

Frederick Douglas

MAAT

Maat is an African Kemetic (Egyptian) word, which means Balance, Harmony, Justice, Propriety, Order, Reciprocity and Truth. Maat is the focus of African culture, conversations, sex, actions, behaviors, marriages, spirituality, feelings, thoughts and raising of the Black child.

The main principles of Maat are control of action and thought, faith in the ability to be taught through understanding, truth and acting in truth; having the ability to know the real from the unreal, knowing right from wrong, being devoted to your life's purpose and freedom from resentment under White Supremacy, freedom from feelings that my race has made a mistake and caused their persecution.

Maat governs the parent and child relationship. The culture uses Kwanzaa principles and Maat as the center of the Eternal Relationship. Kwanzaa principles of Umoja (Unity), Kujchagulia (Self-Determination), Ujima (Collective Work and Responsibility), Ujamaa (Cooperative Economics), Nia (Purpose), Kuumba (Creativity) and Imani (Faith) are part of Maat and helps to put Maat into action. Kwanzaa principles are the center of African relationships.

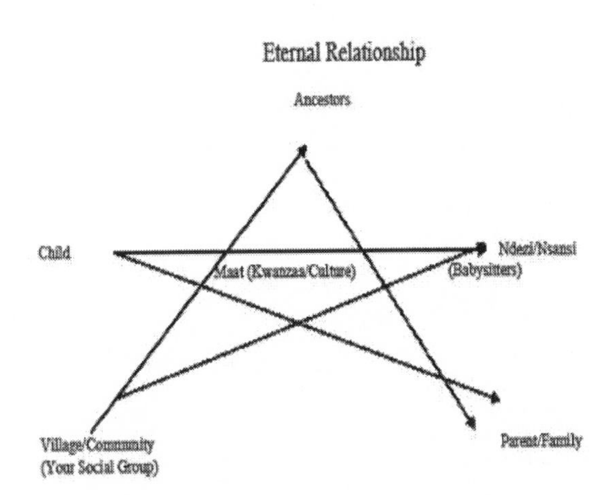

The Black child is an eternal technology of the African culture. The African culture is centered on Maat and the struggle to destroy White Supremacy. History has proven that Black folks cannot peacefully co-exist, compromise, integrate or multiculturally get rid of White Supremacy. The Black child must be raised to solve Black social and economic problems as well as understand White Supremacy. The Black child has a different culture and different social needs and educational objectives than White children. Black children require different techniques and styles for being raised. They have the fastest growth and development of all the races. The Psychomotor Development Chart comparison is a brief example of the differences between Black and White children:

PSYCHOMOTOR DEVELOPMENT

Activity	Black Child Can Do At	White Child Can Do At
Can hold self-upright	5 months	6 months
Take round blocks out its hole in the form board	5 months	11 months
Climb the steps alone	11 months	15 months
Draw up into sitting position can prevent self from falling backwards	9 hours	1-½ months
Stand up against mirror	5 months	9 months
Can support self in sitting position and watch reflection in mirror	7 weeks	5 months
Can look you in the face with head held firmly	2 days	2 months

THE PRACTICE OF MAAT

A life of practicing Maat means using the Maat Principles of Justice, Order, Truth, Balance, Harmony, Reciprocity and Propriety. When Black people practice Maat, they are able to answer The Creator when asked 42 questions. They can declare themselves innocent and say the 42 Declarations of Innocence as follows:

1. I have done no wrong
2. I have not taken what does not belong to me
3. I have not used violence to help the Caucasians or to do wrong.
4. I have not killed to do wrong for the Caucasians or myself.
5. I have not been unjust.
6. I have not deliberately caused pain.
7. I have not dishonored places of my Ancestors (home, business, history).
8. I have not lied.
9. I have not misused money, food, others, time or the community.
10. I have not used words to harm others or talk behind others back (gossiped).
11. I have not committed perverted sex.
12. I have not deliberately done things to harm others.
13. I have not done things that I will regret.
14. I have not used aggression to do wrong or help the Caucasians.
15. I have not acted deceitfully.
16. I have not ignored or wasted the wisdom and positive contributions the Ancestors have given.
17. I have not entered into a conspiracy against loved ones, the innocent or my race.
18. I did not give positive support to help others do wrong.
19. I have not been wrathful or angry except for just cause.
20. I have not condoned or positively supported others in adultery
21. I have not polluted myself (junk foods, drugs, alcohol, marijuana).
22. I have not caused terror.
23. I have not polluted the Earth.
24. 24. I have not spoken in anger in order to hurt others.
25. I have not disobeyed what is right and truthful.
26. I have not uttered curses except against evil.
27. I have not started a quarrel.
28. I have not deliberately acted out of control or in contentions to hurt others.
29. I have not prejudiced.
30. I have not been an eavesdropper.

31. I have not spoken in order to make wrong behavior seem good or spoken without control.
32. I have not dishonored my Ancestors or lied about them.
33. I have not wasted my spirituality.
34. I have not done evil.
35. I have not been arrogant.
36. I have not blasphemed The Creator.
37. I have not committed fraud.
38. I have not disrespected religious activities.
39. I have not stolen a living or dead Ancestors money or valuables.
40. I have not mistreated children.
41. I have not committed adultery.
42. I have not mistreated Nature (soil, water, plants, animals, etc.).

PRINCIPLES OF MAAT

1) Control of the quality of thought and not allowing negative thoughts to manipulate behavior.
2) Control of action and behaviors. My actions are motivated by correct principles.
3) Devotion to one's purpose by using talents and weaknesses for positive results.
4) Faith in the wisdom of our Ancestors and African centered teachers to guide us towards truth.
5) Having faithful confidence and an understanding that discipline and perseverance allows us to accomplish goals.
6) Faith in one's ability to use the knowledge of our teachers in a positive direction.
7) I use my emotions in a positive manner instead of letting anger and/or resentment use me in a negative manner.
8) I control my emotions instead of allowing my emotions to manipulate or confine me into resentment.
9) I allow the morals and ethics of my culture to determine right and wrong instead of the arbitrary situational logic of Caucasians.
10) I know what has Maat spiritual value in my life and what is real versus what is unreal.

CULTURAL VIRTUES
ETHICS, MORALS AND PRINCIPLES FOR LIVING

The philosophy, morality, spirituality and ethics that Africans use to understand themselves, relate to each other and their culture and nature is their worldview (Cosmology). This Cosmology sees the original substance that God and people are made from as the eternity of infinity. Infinity exist in a person's life if they live according to the principles of Maat. The purpose of marriage, eating, talking, sex, happiness, children or work is to serve Maat. Maat unified all African groups as one African people and you will see Maat often in the Cultural Virtues (Ethics, Morals and Principles for Living). These virtues phrases can be used a prayers, affirmations, songs or as a rap. Some phrases can be recited everyday or a portion of the virtues can be read daily. The virtues can be used to teach. You can say them when you are stressed or use them to relax. Be creative with them. The virtues incorporate the principles of the Egyptian Book of the Dead, Kwanzaa, Maat and the Zulu principles.

I;
I am;
I am alive;
I am conscious and aware of God's consciousness in me.
I am unique because God is the ultimate uniqueness.
I am who I say I am; I am an attribute of God.
I forever evolve inwardly and outwardly and grow as I face life's challenges.
I am the face of humanity;
The face of humanity is my face.
I meditate upon the Godliness in me.
I perceive; that which I perceive is God's consciousness in me.
God's consciousness is a never ending or beginning value.
Value is eternal consciousness of God.
Consciousness is that in which all things have their origins;
It does not change; it exits from eternity to eternity because it belongs to God.
It is an infinite unity of unities.
It is forever evolving to its highest good because God is the highest good.
It is a part of God.
It is God.
The value of a Godly life may take many forms;
Each form is a total form of God;
Each form of God evolves to other forms of God.

The cosmic order is an indefinite total of forms and an eternal form of life.
I am a life of God. I am a person.
I am infinite reality. I am a consciousness of God.
The infinity is a unity; it cannot be destroyed;
I am united with God and a unity of God.
I cannot be destroyed.
The infinity and I are inseparable;
I cannot exist outside of the infinity of God.
For, there is no outside of God.
Everything is inside the infinity of God.
Reality is the infinity of God.
It is a Whole;
It cannot be other than Whole; without me it cannot be Whole;
Nothing can be added to or subtracted from the Whole.
I cannot be separated or subtracted from God.
The infinity of God is alive.
There is no death within it;
There is life and perpetual consciousness and universal reality.
That which is alive has purpose;
Purpose is destiny;
I entered the earth to create Maat out of my life.
I recognize my person as a Light of God.
I pay homage to the Light;
The Light will prevail,
For I know I shall prevail,
For I am who I say I am;
No falsehood or negative force in life will conquer me.
I do unto others as God would do unto others.
I am God's constant;
A universal constant;
I am cosmic constant.
I descended from God;
And ascend to God;
Appearing in physical form follows laws;
God's laws make things appear;
Appearing is an attribute of God;
To appear is to follow God's laws.
I exist because of the Law of Appearing.
I am perpetual evolution.
My destiny is to reach my highest good.
I am an evolving attribute and value of God.
Maat is my staff (cane, scepter);
To know it is the challenge of being human;
Forever to discover it is the promise of being human.

Perfection is the continuing response to the ever moving and evolving life of Maat.
The unreal, falsehoods and negative actions and thoughts will not distort my life.
The unreal cannot sway or entice me.
I listen to the voice of Maat in me.
It tells me I am guided.
It tells me I am protected.
I walk in the shadow of righteousness, justice, harmony, truth, order, reciprocity, propriety and balance.
Maat is my eternity and rebirth.
I do not apologize for being human.
I walk in humility in the presence of God.
I worship and respect God's gift of life.
I worship no man, woman, ritual, ceremony, spirit, oracle or religion except God in my person.
I only worship God. Maat is a manifestation of God.
Maat is real.
The Maat person has compassion, wisdom and higher truths to guide them.
Crutches and excuses for not following Maat are ignorance.
Maat is the trustee of my estate; I am the master.
I grow in understanding.
I outgrow the need for crutches and excuses; I stand on my feet;
I march into the future with Maat as my guide.
Nothing can strike terror into my heart,
For I am an infinite consciousness of God.
I can count my limitations, weaknesses, strengths, ignorance and intelligence;
Maat teaches me how to count them.
To know them is to know my personality.
My personality is a genetic expression of Maat
My mother is all women; all women are my mother.
I honor and respect all women;
I cry out to them; arise, mothers of Maat!
Lead your children on a safe journey to a better future!
To all men I say: Arise, fathers of Maat!
Create the world in which it will be no WhiteSupremacy or wrongs to harm your children!
For all I desire is to realize the promise of being human as defined by Maat.
Good and evil are related;
Either translates Maat into action.
Virtue is knowledge and practice of Maat;
Vice is ignorance of Maat.

To know Maat is the glory of being human;
It is a living reality;
Perpetually to be responsible is being conscious of Maat in your daily life.
I have all I need forever to be responsible,
For I am the source of all meaning, all value and all authority because I am God's source and God is my source.
I build Maat in me in order to worship the person God has made me.
What I conceive; I believe;
What I believe; I can achieve.
That which I achieve is a manifestation of God.
That which I believe is God.
God is an unchanging part of me;
God is my eternal consciousness;
To conceive or believe is to create Godliness.
Godliness is the perpetual evolution of Maat.
That which is freely asked or freely given is love cradled in Maat.
Imposed love is a crime against Maat.
I am sovereign of my life;
My neighbor is sovereign of his or her life;
My culture is a collective sovereignty.
My culture exists to ensure that my race and I realize Maat and reach our highest level of being human.
I have no right to anything I deny my brothers and sisters.
I am all; all are me.
I come from eternity;
The present is a moment in eternity;
I belong to the past, present and future.
I can commit no greater crime than to frustrate my neighbor's attempt to practice Maat.
All of my brothers and sisters practicing Maat is our guarantee of survival.
I define myself in what I do to my brothers and sisters.
No race has any right to prescribe destiny for African peoples.
No one can challenge Maat and win;
I am not afraid of seizing my freedom;
I know my way to eternity;
My mind is capable of giving solutions to problems.
The Eternal Person is Universal Man, Universal Woman and Universal Child within the Universal God.
I am a Universal Constant; I am a Cosmic Constant.
I am All in One; I am One-in-All because I am a child of the All in All God.
I am the circle, which encompasses infinity;
I am the point that is the beginning of the circle;

I am the value behind the circle.
I am an attribute of God, the knower of all probabilities, possibilities and all that is seen and unseen.
There is nothing I cannot know;
There is no force of White Supremacy that I cannot crush.
Nothing exists anywhere, which can destroy my ability to be free of White Supremacy.
I am who I am;
I am not a creature; nothing can destroy me;
I am the self-evolving value of God; I live forever and ever.
I am a self-defining value of God.
I am a person; a reality of God.
I am a genetic code; I am part of the universe and the universe is part of me;
The ancestral genes in me have vital elements of Maat;
They are the center and core: the value of God;
The body; the aura, the Maat and Infinite Consciousness.
I am truth:
I sincerely use real facts and act upon them;
I am justice:
I use balanced righteousness;
I am propriety:
I have the quality of respecting others;
I am harmony:
I do not bring negative conflict to my relationship to others;
I am balance:
I regulate my words and deeds with equality;
I am reciprocity:
I mutually exchange and demand mutual exchange of others;
I am order:
I arrange my life so that it has regularity;
I am living truth, justice, propriety, harmony, balance, reciprocity and order;
I am Maat!
Maat and God consciousness is the environment in which I exist.
I am a reality of God.
I am adequate; I have in me all I need to be the best I can be.
I reject actions and thoughts that are not Maat.
Whoever wishes me good,
Let that good go to them;
It is their reciprocity,
Whoever wishes me to achieve my highest good;
Let them achieve their highest good,
Whoever wishes that I should die,
Let his or her wish be his or her fate,

For I want nothing to which I have no right.
I am the servant of God.
My father and mother are the messengers of my ancestors;
My ancestors are humanity;
All I live for is to be the best that I can be.
I do not prescribe destiny for my brothers and sisters;
My brothers and sisters are myself in different guise;
Equals do not prescribe destiny for each other;
They hold conversations that center around Maat;
They oppose ideas that go against Maat.
Maat is the behavior of civilized people.
My ability to use Maat makes me a value of God;
It makes me wise when strong; and brave when weak.
There are no problems I cannot solve.
For I, the person am my own challenge.
Disease has no power over me when I know;
I determine my health; I am what I want to be;
I see good health and wellness as my destiny;
Life takes many routes;
The Light of God in the person guides the routes;
God leads us along safer routes to a better future.
I join my hand with the hands of my brothers and sisters;
This is my guarantee of reaching the future I desire;
With Maat, we march confidently and triumphantly into the future;
Maat harmonized my personality and enables me to see my goal clearly;
Every moment is a rebirth and resurrection of God in me;
My duty is to guide the rebirth with Maat;
I and I alone guide the rebirth.
I;
I am a unity made by God;
I live for unity (Umoja);
I am a collective work of God;
I am responsible to God;
I am collective work and responsibility (Ujima);
God determines my destiny.
I am self-determination (Kujachagulia) in the light of Maat.
I;
I am a cooperative and economic Blessing;
I live as a cooperative economic (Ujamaa) force;
I am a purpose (Nia);
I am a created creativity (Kuumba);
My Faith is in God.
I live in faith (Imani);
I live in proportion to the degree which I practice Maat;

Knowledge of Maat opens new dimensions of my Godliness;
I meditate upon Maat to discover more of Maat;
God is my key to life;
God is the enemy of people who block me from using Maat.
For God's principles are in Maat.
I am born according to Maat;
I live, grow and die according to Maat;
My mother is Maat;
My father is Maat;
My relatives, neighbors, brothers and sisters are Maat;
We are all bound together by Maat;
My brothers and sisters are mankind;
Mankind is Maat;
Life separates and unites according to Maat;
Conflict is an aspect of Maat;
Conflict is a moment of being unconscious of Maat;
Problems arise due to the person failing to serve God.
Harmony and balance are the fulfillment of Maat;
Problems are an inadequate use of Maat;
The world is Maat;
Everything is Maat.
I am Maat.
Maat is my and my brothers and sisters will;
I am a value of God; I have all the power to be what I want to be;
There is glory in being human; in being a self-defining value of God.
I formed myself out of the consciousness of God;
My destiny is written by how well I use Maat;
I entered upon the earth as an act of the will of God.
I came to realize the promise of being a value of God.
To realize the glory of being human is only to use Maat to serve God.
To discover more satisfying dimensions of being a person; I must use Maat.
I am not alone; I have never been alone;
I shall never be alone,
I exist because we exist;
We exist because I exist;
I am the village and the village is me;
I exist as a unity and the unity is me.
I am Father-Mother-Child of the unity,
I am the past, present and the future.
I have no beginning and no end;
I am the universe in which the Father and Mother merged to become Me.
I extend myself into the child.
The child's genetic code is from the eternity of God.

I am the Eternal person that evolved from the Eternal God.
I outgrow the use of excuses and do not hide behind Ignorance;
I face the challenge of being the eternal child of God;
I use Maat to align the cells in my body;
I know each, by name;
I am self-knowledge without end because I am God's knowledge realized in a person;
That which I eat, drink, hear, touch, see, smell or learn becomes part of Maat in me;
I walk in humility in the presence of Maat glorified in my brothers and sisters;
I can afford to be humble; I am not afraid; I am adequate because Maat makes me adequate.
I reject White Supremacy; it creates disorder in my personality;
I am the enemy of all White Supremacy, for White Supremacy is an attempt to destroy Maat;
I am the egg in my mother's womb;
I draw to myself that which I need to evolve;
Every moment of my life I evolve to higher levels of Maat,
For perpetual evolution of Maat is God's destiny for me.
I am the person who extends themselves into my brothers and sisters path of Maat;
The mind of my brothers and sisters understands and uses Maat;
They are my humanity; if and only if; they follow Maat;
Maat moves our humanity;
It is the face of the infinity, which sees itself.
For Infinite Consciousness of God knows itself in me;
It knows its nature;
It knows its destiny;
It has within itself everything that satisfies Maat;
It is itself;
It has races and colors because race and color are a design of God;
The human value of God must respond to life with Maat;
Behind each change in life is Maat;
Inadequately serving Maat causes changes, as well as adequately serving Maat causes changes;
In each change is an aspect of Maat;
Maat is holistic.
Infinite consciousness is a unity of reality;
Life is a unity;
Maat is a unity;
So is Energy;
So are others, known and unknown, seen and unseen and incapable of being seen;
Your destiny in life is to know your unity;

To understand your unity with God's creations.
You move from eternity to eternity to understand them.
Your journey on earth is a never-ending journey of spirit.
Your destiny is to be spiritually uplifted by Maat.
You have all you need for your spiritual journey;
You move freely from your spiritual and human journey on the path of Maat;
In everything you think and do, you define and describe yourself;
You demonstrate how well you use Maat to face challenges.
Maat is part of your spirit and consciousness.
It has an infinite number of aspects;
The aspects interact on each other;
The interactions produce thought and more Maat;
Maat interacting on itself in you creates thoughts;
You evolve your thoughts into actions of Maat;
You create your reality and life through your actions;
You evolve to life's challenges by responding with Maat.
You and your brothers and sisters purpose are one with Maat;
Maat is placed within us and provides all we need;
To discover satisfying dimensions of being human;
To realize the promise of attaining your highest good.
You are living within God's eternity;
So are your brothers and sisters;
We are witnesses of what we are;
We are living moments in the eternity of God.
I am a tiny attribute of God.
I am an element, a substance and an incarnation of God's consciousness.
I am an incarnation of Maat;
I live in Maat; Maat lives in me;
It acts through me and fulfills itself through me.
When I know, Maat fulfills itself and God is in my destiny;
When I am ignorant, I disorganize Maat and fail to use Maat;
I create disharmonies in my personality;
I hurt my brothers and sisters;
I cause problems in the village;
I frustrate life's purpose for my brothers and sisters.
I confuse others.
I live in terror of myself;
I plant terror into my brothers and sisters life;
I terrorize all African peoples;
I move our race in cycles of conflict to catastrophe;
I collapse in the ignorance I build;
I rot in the state of mind I created;
My brothers and sisters see I have failed the race;

They say that I fled from the challenge of life and did not use Maat;
I create my destiny in everything I do;
I and I alone know this destiny.
The challenge of being human is forever to use my Godliness to serve Maat;
It is forever to understand my brothers and sisters journey of Maat;
Forever to reveal the power of God within me.
White Supremacy is the enemy of Maat;
It is the collective passive and active will of White people as a group to be supreme;
To define and control my destiny and my race's destiny with God.
White Supremacy uses institutions, systems, politics, laws, chemicals, economics, food, natural resources and military to stay in control of others.
It is disguised as democracy or freedom or peace;
White Supremacy uses freedom and peace to deny African peoples their human rights.
Freedom is practicing your culture at all times and in all situations;
White Supremacy denies us our rights to our culture;
Freedom is Maat in action;
My actions are Maat.
White Supremacy denies Maat;
It denies my right to be an aspect of God;
It is the enemy of my human value;
It cannot defeat an African people organized by Maat and united with God.
It cannot defeat me.
Perpetual evolution is the destiny of Consciousness;
Consciousness evolves in response to the challenge of the God force in consciousness;
Maat regulates evolution;
It is an aspect of Consciousness;
It is the will of the Infinity;
It is your will; it explains everything, for everything follows the Laws of God and there are no mysteries;
Mystery is ignorance of God and failure to be conscious of Maat.
Everything, everywhere, evolves according to God.
Maat is knowable;
You cannot violate Maat no matter what you do;
You incarnate Maat;
Everything you do translates into actions of Maat or your failure to use Maat;
The processes of Maat are irreversible;
Ignorance is trying to make Maat over in order to serve your selfishness;

If you destroy Maat in you, it will cause the race to suffer;
It is a crime against the ancestors and God;
Maat can balance and harmonize all conflicts and contradictions.
Consciousness, Maat and you together are the eternity of God;
Nothing can separate Maat from God.
You live in the eternal Now.
You will forever live in God's eternity;
It is your destiny;
It is how you achieve your highest level of humanism;
For, you are an attribute of God;
You are eternal.
Perpetual evolution to higher achievements of Maat is your destiny;
You evolve forever, in response to the challenges of life.
The light of God guides your path.
Your mind has many thoughts that live in Maat;
It comprehends all things;
It establishes truth, justice, reciprocity, harmony, propriety and balance;
It makes you feel Godly.
Your brothers and sisters have the same mind;
You understand all because it is all.
Your brothers and sisters and yourself originate from God;
You have the same life experience and a common destiny;
You are the obverse and reverse sides of one entity;
You are unchanging equals;
You are the faces, which see themselves in each other;
You are mutually fulfilling complements;
You are simultaneous attributes of God;
Their sorrows are your sorrows;
Their joy is your joy;
You are mutually fulfilled when you stand by each other in service of Maat.
Your survival is their survival.
They are never beyond rehabilitation and saving;
They are not good or evil, the village is good or evil, and it is the village's failure to provide Maat;
Failure of the village to create Maat conditions for your brothers and sisters survival makes them failures;
Maat is unchanging;
God is unchanging;
God is an unchanging part of you;
God is your Eternal Consciousness.
The culture provides the wisdom;
Wisdom provides awareness;
Awareness provides consciousness;

It is ultimately the village's responsibility to provide Maat, so that you can achieve your highest level of humanism;
You are the village; you must destroy all obstacles that obstruct Maat;
You are a self-defining value of Maat;
You are original matter;
You evolve from God.
God is, therefore you are;
You are, because God is;
God is, therefore I am;
I am because God is;
I am a unity with God;
Therefore I am;
I

BLACK FOLKS AND THOUGHTS

PERSONALITY AND THOUGHT

Level of Thought	Personality Type	Thought Process (This Personality thinks as below)
1.	Stone	I am everything
2.	Resistance	I don't want to understand
3.	Indifference	I don't have to understand
4.	Hopelessness	I am a puppet in 'their hands'
5.	Interest	Maybe I could understand
6.	Self-Satisfaction	I understand everything
7.	Seeker	I wonder whether that's right
8.	Awareness	I understand that I can't understand everything

LEVELS OF CONSCIOUS AWARENESS

Ancient African (Egyptian) Cosmology (Worldview) Construct and Levels of Thought

Contemporary Name	Ancient African Name	Level of Thought
The place we cannot think of	The One	0
The last Human Level	Judgment of Osiris	2
The Variable Levels	Maat	3
Level 5	Level of Fire	4
Cultural Domain Guidance		5
Cultural Domain Residence	Seknet Aaru	6
Level 4	Level of Hapi	7
Here-Now Guidance		8
Here-Now Residence	The Tuat	9
Level 1	Male/Female Paths	10
Mundane World	African (Kemet	11

Correlation between African and Contemporary Levels of Thought

BLACK CULTURAL ELEMENTS

Appearance - Skin complexion, hairstyle and facial features based upon the White Race as being ideal.

Dress - Bright colors, colors are combined for spiritual and visual reasons, flashy designs.

Food - Slave Food – "Soul Food", spicy, fried foods, starch centered diet, pork, adopts Caucasian scavenger food diet.

Knowledge - Lacks Military Logic, lacks understanding of White Supremacy, Slavery Trauma and Capitalism, tends to be emotionally attached to knowledge or feels knowledge spiritually.

Learning Right and Left Brain harmony, rhythm learning, rational, group

Style - Learning oriented.

Language - Ebonics "Rappin", slang, oral and written tradition, melodious and syncopated speech.

Music African harmonies and scales, soul, blues, jazz, gospel, rap; uses polyrythms.

WHITE SUPREMACY AND PARENTING

White Supremacy and White Racism has an impact on the parent and child. It exists in all areas of Caucasian society and a basic understanding of it is necessary in order to be an enlightened parent. White Supremacy is a Caucasian group behavior and a conscious or subconscious belief that their White race is superior to all colored races. When Caucasian culture is in charge, rule, dominate or control directly (overtly) or indirectly (covertly) the banks, militaries, medical industry, goods and services, news, fashion, human and material resources, grants, television, movie and music industry, sports, weapons, currency, farms, diet, politics of governments and industries, it is called White Supremacy.

Black people are victims of White Supremacy when they are socially or politically forced to use Caucasian civilization's education curriculums, certifications, licenses, diplomas, jobs, careers and professions or seek Caucasian awards and recognition, celebrate Caucasian holidays, use Caucasian rituals and ceremonies, use Caucasian religious books (i.e. Bible, Koran) or in some way work for or serve the interest of Caucasian civilization. When Caucasian society uses its police and/or military to manipulate, threaten or force Black people and/or Black governments or countries to follow Caucasian policies, standards, rules or decisions of what is a terrorist or act of war, it is White Supremacy. White Racism is used to exploit, criminalize, inferiorize and oppress Black people in order to maintain, protect and create White Supremacy (white power). Black people that cannot practice their culture at all times and in all situations are not free and are victims of White Supremacy.

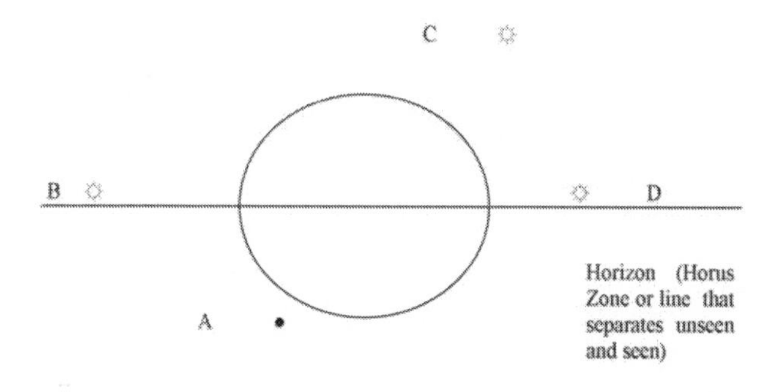

A =<u>Black Dot (Melanin),</u> Genetic code of Maat and ancestral wisdom, spirit world

B =Birth, The birth of the child symbolized by the sunrise

C =Maturity, Bonding to Culture. Culture gives Maat wisdom, wisdom gives awareness and Awareness gives consciousness

D =Death, Completion of life's purpose, a complete cycle occurs when the spirit leaves the Body and returns to the Spirit World. The cycle is a never ending eternity of God.

During prenatal (fetus) growth, the child begins to learn language and thought by what it hears, sees, touches and tastes. The baby feels the pregnant mother's emotions and spirituality. The baby reacts physically (has movements) and mentally to each emotion, thought and spiritual response of the mother. This is the baby's first learning process. The mother's pregnancy and the birthing process shape the baby's emotions. Breastfeeding is a continuation of language and thought development of the baby. The Prenatal, Fetus, Pregnancy, Birthing and Breastfeeding experiences are holistic rites of passage for the baby's emotions, thoughts, behaviors and spirituality development.

ROUTINES (RITUALS AND CEREMONIES)

Telling a child that they are to use African rituals and ceremonies will produce a reaction such as: "They are boring, old fashioned and useless." Children require rituals that have predictable behavioral patterns and monologues that are consistent in emotions, responses and behaviors. The Caucasians call rituals and ceremonies routine. Routines are rituals and ceremonies that are expected by the child. They help the child feel secure and in control.

A ritual is a set way of performing a task or activity while a ceremony is the dress, music and words used during the ritual. A ritual and ceremony acculturate the activity. For example, reading a story to a child before bedtime or in between activities can be a ritual. This ritual helps the child to make emotional transitions from one activity to another. The reading ritual can include reciting the principles of Maat before the story is read. Rituals eliminate a lot of time-consuming planning. Once a ritual is established, it helps to schedule activities. Rituals reduce the need for last minute planning. Prepare a miniature ceremony before free time, sing a song and recite Kwanzaa principles. This will reduce the stress caused from a chaotic or irregular schedule.

Bedtime rituals and ceremonies: Review an activity that occurred and talk about ways to improve it or the behavior. Recite a riddle, poem or tell a short story and then say a prayer together.

Mealtime rituals: Prepare a meal plan for the week. It takes the stress out of cooking and shopping. Make a weekend meal schedule, listen to music, meditate, do yoga, play games, take turns talking about the day's activities or some special event or occurrence and then say grace.

Leisure-time rituals: Recite Kwanzaa or Maat principles and then go for a walk, make pancakes or sing songs together. Saturday can be a day to do an activity with the Father while Sunday can be a day for an activity with the Mother. A relative or another parent may allow your child to do an activity with them or vice versa.

Going to daycare/preschool rituals: Before leaving the home, do an activity. For example, sing, "This is the way we go to school." Always walk or drive the same route, play name-those kids in the class or name something distinctive about each child in the class. This improves memory. Sing, chant or do a positive rap song. This makes the transition from school to home easier. Once you establish a ritual, stick to it as closely as possible, even when vacations, visitors and other extenuating circumstances may alter the daily activities. Toddlers are easily unsettled by change, particularly the last-minute variety. If a ritual has to be improvised, inform the child that you are modifying the ritual. Then be patient with the child as they adjust to the change in their daily activities and in the ritual. Make improvisation a joint activity and fun.

Good-morning rituals: Start the day off right – with a prayer, meditation and say, "Good Morning." Set a time to do the ritual – when it's light outside, when the clock radio alarms, etc. Start the morning with a positive rap, chant, jingle or prayer and then a hug and kiss. In age appropriate children, you can point to the clouds in the sky and say what time it is and then greet the child.

Welcome-home rituals: If your child comes home with you or is transported, they can be welcomed home. Greet them when they arrive or if you arrive together, say, "We are blessed to arrive home safe." Sing or rap, read a book together or allow them to watch an educational video or TV show or just review their day. Then give them an age appropriate chore such as getting the mail, setting the table, sweeping the floor, meditating, reading, etc.

Hygiene rituals: Some Toddlers would rather play or resist – hygiene activities. It is best to establish a ritual of brushing the teeth, singing a song, then hand washing. Say a rap before bathing or shampooing. When the toddler expects a ritual, it makes hygiene less troublesome.

Leaving rituals: Leaving a relative's house or a playmate's or the playground can be emotionally difficult for a child. A departure ritual such as singing a good-bye song or saying a Kwanzaa or Maat principle before saying good-bye helps to ease the transition from leaving one place and going to another.

Off-to-work rituals: When a parent leaves for work, a special wave, hug or saying, and then saying, "I love you or my love stays with you." This makes the farewell easier.

Clean-up rituals: Clean-up time should have a special phrase, song; rap or Kwanzaa or Maat principle sang or recited before clean up begins. This helps the child to emotionally detach themselves from the "play or toys." The toys can be put away after they are used or at the end of a play session. Clean up can be timed with a cooking timer, hourglass or by you counting. You can also challenge the child to complete the clean up before a song is finished.

REPEAT IT, DON'T CHANGE IT – RITUALS

Toddlers like rituals and ceremonies to stay unchanged. Any change in these activities can be upsetting. Toddlers find emotional comfort in the rhythm of a ritual as well as the rhythm of their mother's heartbeat when they were in the womb. Rituals and ceremonies establish an emotional rhythm that is nurturing.

Toddlers seem rigidly stuck in rituals and become irritated, insecure, frustrated and unstable if a ritual is changed. Rituals allow them to feel in control. Toddlers are more uncomfortable about an abrupt change in rituals than babies or older children. Toddlers do not feel comfortable or flexible about "abrupt changes" in rituals until they are at least a year old.

Conform to the rituals (routines) as much as possible. Toddlers can get upset by change and retaliate to change with negative behavior. Changing the color of their room, sheets, carpet or getting a new stroller or different car seat can cause a crisis in the toddler's world. If a change has to be made, use songs, special phases, chants or positive raps to prepare the child for change. Do not react to the child's irritation to change by becoming upset or angry. This will further irritate the child. They need you to be in control, relaxed, calm and an anchor of emotional stability. You have to stay in rhythm. Remember, the child spent nine months in the womb listening to a steady rhythm (i.e. heartbeat) and getting the amniotic fluid changed on a schedule (rhythm). Rituals help the child to schedule feelings. Rituals help the child to repeat the secure and safe feeling. This is why a child can listen to the same story, CD, tape over and over or have you read and reread the same story. They are enjoying the emotional safety of the ritual. Children like commercials because they are miniature rituals and ceremonies centered on a product. Commercials make them feel secure not because of the product advertised but because of the ritual.

Toddlers tend to like objects or things associated with rituals such as a favorite book, food, toy, song or blanket. Objects or things associated with a ritual help the toddler feel connected to the "spirit" of the ritual. An adult may feel bored with the monotonous repeating of a story or song. However, repetition helps the child to build retention, comprehension and vocabulary. The child feels good when they know every word or sound. Knowing helps the child to organize their feelings, anticipated feelings and enjoy the feeling of a feeling. The toddler through rituals develops an emotional vocabulary. They explore emotions as if they are toys. They play with them and rearrange them. Repetitive stories help the child to touch their fears in the secure emotional environment of a story. A familiar story, rhyme, rap, song or rhythm causes contentment in the child and boredom in the adult who rereads and rereads or watches and rewatches a story. The child will eventually out grow the favorite story and get another favorite story. Do not try to forcefully change stories. Let the new favorite story be the child's idea. Remember, the ritual helps the child to learn and be emotionally content.

Make the rereading of a story fun for you:

- Use body language and different voices for the story characters
- Tell the story with missing phrases (blanks). Let the child fill in the blanks
- Ask the child to identify the objects and colors in the illustrations
- Let the child tell part of the story with you
- Say things backwards and let the child say it correctly
- Ask the child to find unnoticed or hidden objects
- Change your clothes or wear a hat or say silly phrases when reading
- Read the story as if you were a frog, goat, mosquito, etc.
- Read a little from a new story at the end of the favorite story (it helps the child to switch to a new story)
- Read books that have sequels

If the child continues to be stuck on their favorite story, take them to the library or bookstore, let them select a story or have a friend or relative give them a new story, or let another toddler talk about their favorite story or give a new story as a birthday or Kwanzaa present.

CHAPTER 2
INFANT TO TODLERHOOD LEARNING

"If it (life) is not about the children then what the hell is it about?"
Malcolm X

Young toddlers may use side-by-side playing (parallel play) instead of playing with each other. Interactive play develops with time. With experience they begin to jointly-built block structures.

THE PROCESS OF LEARNING

In order to learn a process, order must be followed. The process of understanding a word such as Imani (Faith), the child has to:

1) Discriminate the "M" from "N" in the word Imani
2) Follow sequence (tracking of letters) "I" before "M"
3) Make a holistic picture that includes intellectual meaning, optical (visual) value, spiritual meaning, have an action associated with the word, sense the feeling of the word in the mouth and the sound of the word (phonetic) and feeling of the word sound in the ear.
4) See the word as a holistic symbol (word picture)

INFANT LEARNING AND PROBLEM SOLVING ABILITY

- Cultural influences, thoughts, emotions and spirituality develop in the womb. The growth and learning, fetus life during pregnancy and the birth process shape emotions, thoughts and spirituality of the adult.

- The fetus has a specific movement and feeling for each movement that the Mother makes. Human learning starts when the fetus has a physical movement for each of the Mother's words, feelings, spoken words, physical reactions, actions, etc. The fetus begins to learn thoughts, emotions and culture. The prenatal child learns from hearing sounds, taste of amniotic fluid, touch of the fluid and placenta, smell in the fluid and sight.

- The eating schedule and time between meals starts with the fetus amniotic fluid drinking schedule. The fluid is changed at 6 a.m., 10 a.m. (light amniotic feeding similar to a snack), 12 noon, 3 p.m. (light snack) and 6 p.m.

- Mother's mood influences the infant's feelings and behavior and taste of amniotic fluid.

- The infant can match sounds with objects (by 4 months)

- Turn their head to source of sound at birth

- Understand sign language in infancy (up to 6 to 7 months)

- Memory has developed (from 2 to 6 weeks)

- Long term memory (infant does imitation to different actions)
- Infants can choose between sounds and taste (from 2 to 4 days)
- Can plan (from 3 to 5 months)
- Self concept is developed before they are 1 ½ years old
- Has coordination and combining senses (i.e. sight with sound, taste with smell)
- Knows cause and effect relationship (by 6 months)
- Knows differences in sounds ("pah" and "bah")
- Has linguistic abilities
- Can follow instructions and understand words (at 6 to 8 months)
- Can compare objects (by 8 months)
- Knows Mother's voice
- Knows the smell of the Mother and father
- Knows the difference between living things and objects (non-living)

STAGES OF INFANCY/TODDLERHOOD LEARNING ACTIVITIES

BIRTH TO 6 – 8 WEEKS
(The imprint period, fundamental maternal infant bonding)

♥ Be aware of the infant's abilities and limitations and do not over stimulate or prematurely "teach" or force the infant to behavior or learn.

♥ Let the infant establish it's own rhythm for learning and interest. Encourage quiet alertness by stimulating and being aware of their senses.

♥ Engage the infant in contingency play by consistently exposing the infant to learning stimulation (e.g., twirling or mobile by kicking or waving their arms); interactive play (e.g., peek-a-boo)making friendly faces (smiling, etc.); observation play providing the infant with interesting sights, sounds and aroma.

♥ Play visual, touch, hearing, smell and movement games.

♥ Express nurturing behavior (e.g., gentle rocking) and soothing behaviors that will encourage the child's sense of trust, self-esteem and competence.

---

8 –13 WEEKS
(Increased social behavior, dialogue visual and hand activity)

♥ The above-named stimulation games, bonding and body toning activity continues.

♥ The infant's attention is increasingly focused on the hands and they respond readily to activities, which stimulate the exercising of their hands functions.

♥ Their desire for conversations can be encouraged by drum music, vocal imitation, alternating or reciprocal vocal games, facial expressions, stimulative eye contacts, gazing, modulating your voice, etc.

♥ They should be encouraged to give attention to objects and events.

- Contingent games encourage baby's eye-hand coordination.

- Encourage baby's awareness of their body as a whole, of their body parts and their body as separate from and part of the whole.

---

4 –7 MONTHS

- Encourage infant's interest in space, spatial relations and movement in space. Help the infant to learn about people and things in the spatial environment (i.e. light and shadows reflecting on objects, air and water movements, rock throwing in a pond, etc.).

- Continue enhancing the infant's eye-hand coordination and visual ability by using various toys, musical instruments, games, social interactions and by using stacking and nesting toys.

- Encourage the infant's attention by having colorful patterns, shapes and sounds in their room and/or play area.

- Engage in verbal patterning of imitative games.

- During these months, infants take pride in their ability, power to influence and change their environment.

- Their memory expands rapidly.

- Opportunities for interaction, solitary and some structured and free play provide listening opportunities and vocalizing opportunities.

- A variety of "category games" (categorization by shape, size, color, etc.). Games for building abstract thinking ability, naming ability as well as age-appropriate visual and sensory stimulation games will satisfy the infant's curiosity.

- Toys and instruments that they can manipulate helps them to indirectly influence, change and expand their expression of intentionality.

- The infant uses words as if they are toys during this period. They use words logically and manipulate and play with words similar to playing with toys. They have an interest in words and expanding their learning and understanding of words.

- Their ability to use and understand words will increase during the following stages: if appropriately stimulated by conversations during the prior stages, the infant may be able to repeat two-syllable sounds, recognize the names of some objects, imitate the sound of some words or say some real words. Their word usage follows their individualize ability and learning style.

- Their interest in words can be enhanced by; labeling and naming objects, encouraging them to talk about how they feel as well as talking about shapes, musical instruments, art, pictures, colors, sizes, etc.

- Encourage them to talk about the things they are experiencing.

- The reading of illustrated storybooks, reciting rhymes, engaging in finger plays, drumming and clapping games with infants will improve their vocabulary.

<u>8 –13 MONTHS</u>

- This is the period of expanded motor skills development as well as increased activity and creative exploration.

- Toys, musical instruments, African Yoga and dance, African Art, fabrics and artifacts, drums and symbols of Maat can stimulate.

- Read African American and African stories, talk about Maat and Cultural Virtues. Use call and response songs, raps and rhymes to help expand their vocabulary.

- Talking about African Art, Maat, Cultural Virtues and Kwanzaa symbols enhances the infant's vocabulary and encourages their efforts to speak words. (Do not worry; push or force talking. Speaking is based upon Learning Style. Some babies may not speak until they are two years old.)

- Imitating the baby's words can help them learn language.

<u>14 MONTHS – 2 YEARS</u>

- The infant may start to talk and engage in two-way conversations.

- The learning of different words and phrases are indicated by facial expressions, accurate use of language, by their ability to understand simple direct instructions and their response to questions.

- Talk about the activity and explain the activity as you are doing it. This is called experiential learning – learning while doing.

- The infant's improvisational and creative abilities continue to expand during this period.

- They will improvise and use variations while doing make believe or pretend games and play.

- Their improvisational and problem solving ability is expanded by musical instruments, drums, toys, objects, social interactive and relationships with others. Learning aids (i.e. music) and social relationships help them to express or act out improvised situations (play, games, etc.).

- Concept words and concepts about Maat and Kwanzaa should be emphasized. Concept words may include such terms as: more-less, long-tall, right-wrong, junk food natural food, up-down, cold-hot, truth-lie, etc.

SECOND YEAR

- Imagination, improvisation, vocabulary and speaking ability expands.

- Manipulative, coordinative exercises and activity become complex.

- Their improvisational, imaginative, linguistic, manipulative and coordinative abilities increase. Provide imaginative materials and activity (people, drums, imaginative figures, toy vehicles, play kits, etc.), language development materials (storybooks, picture books, African proverbs, alphabet books, paper and pencil, rhymes, etc.), manipulative toys (sorting boxes, stacking toys, puzzles, etc.). Use science, agricultural, nutritional and mathematics aids (magnets, plants, pendulums, nature collections, junk foods, magnifying glass, etc.), and constructions materials (blocks, interlocking plastic or wood pieces, etc.). This will increase their cognitive abilities and skills

- Many toys and materials can be made as well as bought.

- Many books provide instructions on the construction of objects, materials and toys.

- Increase their outside activity and exposure to sunlight.

- Introduce them to written words, symbols, the concepts of color, size, shape, musical types, number, time and sequential relations.

- Allow and encourage quiet concentration.

- Use different voice inflections, body language and facial expressions while using different reading styles.

- Make effective use of story time for language development by:
  - Asking "what" questions
  - Provide them with feedback
  - Use expansions (different adjective verbs and adverbs)
  - Provide corrective modeling of language usage.

- "Word" and "sentence" play
  - Stress the usage of prepositions (e.g., "in", "behind", etc.)
  - Emphasize and contrast adjectives ("big", versus 'small" etc.)
  - Use improvisation, drumming, music, dramatic and manipulative play to demonstrate Language usage. This expands language comprehension.

THIRD YEAR

- The developmental process of the prior period continues. The attention focus an abilities will increase.

- Continue the appropriate supportive activity of the prior period.

- "Interactive" (caretaker and child jointly initiated activities) multi-sensory learning and multi-skill mastering (e.g., spatial perceptual, large and fine motor expressive and artistic language mastery) will expand. Maintain the infant's spiritual, intellectual, personal, social and emotional development.

- Use many types of reading and language arts activity such as:
  - Developmentally appropriate activities (scribbling, making symbols, Adinkra and

- Hieroglyphic letters, circles, zigzag lines, letters, etc).
- Help develop language usage by using games (puzzles, card matching games, and alphabet matchups, etc.)
- Use socio-dramas as well as acting the part of professionals in various fields or use dolls for doctors, herbalists, musicians, and others. Put together professional kits, used by people in various fields (doctors, mechanic, etc.).
- Do Math activities (counting games, phases of the Moon, number puzzles, recognizing written numbers, measuring instruments-measuring spoons-cups, clocks, etc.).
- Do Science experiments with water, seeds, plants, etc.
- Do Art, musical and plays as well as improvisational activities.
- Travel to museums, historical places, factories, places of interest and construction sites to stimulate learning.

MONTH BY MONTH BABY ACTIVITY AND PARENTING

(1st to 12th Month)

1ST MONTH

BABY'S ACTIVITY

- Can focus on an object or look at an object
- Reacts to and recognizes voices by making sounds or using body language (i.e. moving arms and/or legs)
- Can lift head up while lying on stomach
- Can firmly grasp objects
- Sucks hands and mouth
- Follows objects moving above head (6 inches above)
- Mimics parents facial expressions
- Squirms and kicks
- Smiles

PARENT

- Place African Art and colorful objects and fabrics around child
- Play African music (i.e. jazz, gospel, reggae, positive rap, drumming, blues, etc.)
- Talk to the baby, do not babble, say words correctly
- Have mobiles and moving colorful objects and toys

Note: Each month there is an increase in the child's activity and a need to increase in the interactive parenting skills.

2ND MONTH

BABY'S ACTIVITY

- Grasp and controls objects
- Raises head higher while on stomach
- Smiles in response to another person's smile
- Can turn from side to side
- Follows movement
- Associates people with various activities (sibling will tickle feet, father may lift up high, etc.)
- Can support self with one arm straight out to side while other arm is above head
- Communicates with a variety of sounds

PARENT

- Place objects in baby's hand to grasp and drop, this develop reflexes
- Give the baby various shaped and textured objects to hold
- Give rattles and hang mobiles over the crib
- Move various color objects 8 inches in front of baby's fact this helps to develop tracking

3RD MONTH

BABY'S ACTIVITY

- Looks towards sound
- Can raise self up on forearms while on stomach and hold head up
- Smiles at will
- Put fingers in month
- Grasp objects with both hands
- Uses rattles for long periods
- Sits with support

PARENT

- Place rattle in hand
- Comfort and nurture when responding to needs
- Dangle color objects or toys from right to left 8 inches away from baby
- Make eye contact several times daily

4TH MONTH

BABY'S ACTIVITY

- Can follow dangling objects 6 inches from face and move them 180º degrees
- Splashes in bath
- Can sit supported with head steady
- Can reach for, grasp, hold and release objects
- Laughs
- Looks at and plays with hands
- Lifts head 90 degrees while on stomach
- Rolls from stomach to side or back and or back to side
- Coordinates both eyes

- Responds with arm and/or leg movement and responds with sounds, laughing and/or smiling
- Deliberately places hand or fingers in mouth

PARENT

- Let child see self in mirror
- Hold the baby's wrist and pull baby up to sitting position
- Give flexible toys
- Exercise legs

5TH MONTH
BABY'S ACTIVITY

- Plays peek-a-boo and laughs
- Can hold head and body steady while sitting propped up
- Clutches and clings when being held
- Smiles at self in mirror
- Raises chest with arms while on stomach
- Rolls over
- Makes vowel sounds and connects consonants with vowels (babbles)
- Can explore and play for longer durations
- Whines when upset and squeals if enjoying self or activity
- Can reach precisely for objects and grasp them
- Can open eyes wide and opens hands to reach for a specific object

PARENT

- Let baby touch different shapes, textures and colors
- Respond to babble
- Give starter blocks to baby in order to help develop thumb and forefinger grasping

6TH MONTH
BABY'S ACTIVITY

- Can hold and drink from cup with handles
- Observes upside down objects

- Sits without support
- Responds to likes and dislikes
- Can follow fast moving objects
- May bite nipple
- Plays for a longer duration which develops attention
- Switches objects from one hand to the other
- Creeps on stomach, can have early crawling motions with arms and feet
- Covers eyes with hands while playing peek-a-boo
- Makes funny faces
- In some form, can say "Mama" or "Dada"

PARENT

- Encourage older children to interact with baby
- Hold bottle if bottle feeding
- Encourage baby to sing, sway or mimic music that is playing
- Support baby in standing position
- Do not babble to child, use clear words
- Give paper (non-toxic) to play with

7TH MONTH

BABY'S ACTIVITY

- Begins crawling by using arms and shoulder
- Associates sounds with feelings
- Can feed self soft foods
- Can get to a standing position

PARENT

- Give child two different objects to hold
- Tell child when you are leaving the room and when you will return
- Place toys or objects out of reach to encourage creeping, rolling, crawling, etc
- Give various sizes and shapes of colorful block
- Hold a conversation with child

8TH MONTH

BABY'S ACTIVITY

- Will look for object that they have dropped
- Likes to touch and feel your face

- Sits with support
- Will step forward when standing
- Crawls forwards and backwards
- Turns in direction of voices
- Climbs
- Passes object from one hand to the other
- Holds two different toys, one in each hand

PARENT

- Encourage child to get toys
- Encourage child to turn pictures upside down and right side up. Let child know which is the right side with sounds, words and/or facial expressions
- Touch your nose and child's nose and say, "nose". Explore and touch other facial parts and name them
- Give child cause and effect interactive toys
- Encourage child to put things in and take things out of a plastic jar or container

9TH MONTH

BABY'S ACTIVITY

- Will point to things they want
- Crawls quickly
- Will try to get toys out of their reach
- Will grasp small objects such as marbles with thumb and finger
- Pulls self up to standing position by using furniture
- Stacks blocks on top of each other
- Passes objects from one hand to the other
- Understands and reacts to a few words
- Points to things that they want

PARENT

- Praise the child when they interact with strangers
- Play games that require hand and finger dexterity
- When they point to things, say the name of the object a few times
- Enjoys picture books read books to child
- Read books to child
- Encourage child to play with other babies

10TH MONTH

BABY'S ACTIVITY

- Climbs stairs
- Enjoys music
- Favors one hand
- Says a few words plus "Mama" and "Dada"
- Can drink from a cup with a handle
- Waves bye-bye
- Can finger feed self
- Obeys instructions
- Remembers where objects are and will look for them and find them
- Will try to dress self
- Imitates your behavior and facial expressions
- From a sitting position, can pull self to a standing position
- Follows simple commands
- Walks side ways while holding onto furniture
- Repeats words "no" and may not understand it
- Walks while supported
- Pushes object from side to side

PARENT

- Give interactive toys
- Encourage the baby to nurture favorite stuff animals, bugs or dolls
- Give baby simple orders and see if they can follow them
- Point to baby's parts on self or doll and ask "What is this called?" or "Where are the dolls eyes?"

11TH MONTH

BABY'S ACTIVITY

- Climbs up the stairs easily and climbs down the stairs with much difficulty
- Stands without assistance
- Uses both hands to do different activities
- Can stoop and or squat
- Understands the word "no"
- Feels guilty for disobedience
- Holds onto furniture while walking
- Can use pincer grasp to pick up small objects
- Can get into a sitting position from lying on the stomach
- Understands "bye-bye", "Mama" and "Dada"

Parent

- Practice walking with child while holding both of their hands. Use soft sole shoes
- Use voice tone, body language and facial expression to help the baby understand complex
- commands (i.e. "Give this cup to Dada in the room")
- Talk the child through the dressing process (i.e. hold up your arms to put on the shirt)
- Give see through objects and/or toys so the child can understand dimensions

12TH Month

Baby's Activity

- Recognizes self in mirror
- Undresses self
- Imitate sounds of machines, cars, dogs, birds, drums, etc.
- Uses crayons and pencils
- Vocabulary expands to three or more words
- From a sitting position, maintain balance while reaching for objects in various directions
- Walks around crib while holding onto the rail

Parent

- Show child how to stack blocks high
- Let baby play in pool or bath tub – parent stays in room
- Give age appropriate puzzles to take apart Demonstrate how to put puzzles back together
- Read and talk to child
- Praise the child's walking ability

MOTHER'S PREGNANCY, THE CHILD AND HEALTH

A sensitive touchy baby will have difficulty socializing. They can be recognized early by any or all of the following problems:

SOCIAL OVER RESPONSE: Uncuddled, fear response to lights and noise, has difficulty relaxing and sleeping, very ticklish, in the second to third month will have problems sleeping through the night, becomes uncomfortable and/or upset in crowds, by six month when separated from the parent will develop early temper tantrums with a long duration and may start crying.

MOTOR DYSFUNCTION: Held up head late, the word "no" has no meaning to them, developed sitting skills late, did not crawl but pulled self to a standing position and walked within the six to seven months; walked after eighteen months; did not explore surroundings, bites objects within reach and accident prone.

Mild and/or severe problems in these categories can indicate developmental problems as well as future social and health problems.

PREGNANCY AND HEALTH

MOTHER'S HEALTH DISEASES/PROBLEMS	MOTHER'S AGE 18-32 YEARS OLD	MOTHER'S AGE 16-18 YEARS OLD	MOTHER'S AGE 16 YEARS AND YOUNGER
Anemia, High Blood Toxemia Convulsions	None	Problems	Severe Pressure, Problems
If Mother used Medications or had Drug, Alcohol and Narcotics usage Bleeding Threatened miscarriage	None	Problems	Very Severe Problems
If Mother had High Fever, Rubella, Infections, Herpes, Pneumonia	None	Mild Problems	Severe Problems

CHILD IN WOMB

FACTORS	PROBLEMS	PROBLEMS	PROBLEMS
If Mother smoked Tobacco or used Marijuana	Problems	Mild	Severe
If Mother had an Unbalanced Diet Junk Food	Problems	Mild	Severe
Mother's Weight Gain (pounds)	20-25 pounds	18-20 pounds 25-30 pounds	Less than 18 lbs More than 30 lbs
Length of Pregnancy (weeks)	38-42	36-38 42-44	Less than 36 More than 44
If Mother had an Accident or Injury	Problems	Mild	Almost abort baby
Baby very active in the uterus	No	Problems	Kicked Mother out of bed

BIRTH HISTORY

Baby's Weight (pounds)	6-8 pounds	4 ½ -6 pounds	Less than 4 ½ pounds
		8-10 pounds	More than 10 pounds
BIRTH'S ISSUES	MILD PROBLEMS	PROBLEMS	SEVERE PROBLEMS
Length of labor (hours)	6-12	10-20	More than 20
Anesthesia or local	None	Twilight semiconscious	Deep unconscious drug sleep)
Caesarean Section, Placenta Praevia, Abruption, Complications, Breech, Face or Transverse Presentation	No	Some	One or two
If baby's color was unhealthy or did not cry	OK	Slow	Bluish skin, Oxygen needed Feeble cry,

CHAPTER 3
DO'S AND DON'TS AND PARENTING

"Black folks just don't get it, the school system destroys our children."

Barbara Sizemore

PARENTAL TYPES

THE HOPELESS PARENT could have the belief that "there is no use, it's hopeless" and thinks the child is incapable of changing the behavior. this type of parent could have been in denial about the child's behavior and ignored the child's behavior instead of using punishments appropriate for the unacceptable behavior. with each episode of unacceptable behavior there should be increased negative consequences. this type parent failed to gain control of the child. this parental type usually used beatings, which fail to bring behavior changes. this type may have accepted the hopeless situation, which resulted in "learned hopelessness." this type parent does not seek skills to change the parent/child relationship and usually ends up saying "i am at a loss for things to do, nothing seems to work."

THE NON-CONFRONTING parent could have the belief that the child will not love them if they confront the behavior. Often this type parent is usually motivated by their conscious and/or unconscious feelings of being unloved or unappreciated in their own childhood.

THE STRESSED PARENT could have nutritional imbalances, a disease, hormonal imbalances and physical or emotional problems that drain them of energy. This type parent is preoccupied or shields themselves from the child with their own problems, with their own issues or do not have sufficient parenting skills to confront the child's misbehavior.

THE GUILTY PARENT usually blames themselves for the child's problems. This can decrease the parent's ability to respond with appropriate parenting skills. A parent that believes they are responsible for the child's misbehavior causes the problems to increase.

THE ANGRY PARENT usually uses fear to stop them from parenting. They fear that they may have a rage of anger that could cause them to hurt the child. This type parent lets their past control them. They hide behind the rationale that their parents severely beat them and they don't want to do that to their child. They usually use inadequate means of behavioral control such as hollering, screaming, cursing and shouting, which do little except give attention and reinforcement to the child's negative behavior.

THE KINDRED PARENT usually allows what they assume others may say about their parenting skills to rule them. They feel inadequate and lack confidence in their parenting skills. This type parent usually says that their spouse, friends or relatives often tell them that they let the child run all over them and that the child rules the relationship or the child is out of control and that they would never stand for that type behavior in a child.

THE TROUBLED PARENT usually has personal problems that impact their marital relationship, friendships or work to such a degree that they are unable to spend enough time on the child's behavioral problems. This parent is inconsistent in giving rewards and punishments for behavioral problems. This causes confusion and inadequate learning and confusion in the child. Most of the child's behavioral problems affect the marital relationship, friendships and the parent's job.

BASIC PARENTING FUNDAMENTALS

(Applies to young children and teenagers and can be used with adults)

- A Caucasian Parenting style destroys the child. You must be able to use Black Parenting techniques or use an independent cultural school or Rites of Passage program to teach your child or teen.

- Know your child's (includes teenagers) favorite food, color, musical instrument, vocalist/rapper, Zodiac sign, learning style, actor, athlete, book, song, family activity, words, subject, etc.

- When you know you do not have the Parenting Skill to change a behavior do not spend too much emotional energy on the issue, wait. Develop the skill or use another adult (Karate teacher, Coach, Art, Music or Dance instructor) to teach the behavior to your child.

- A child's emotional ability to understand you exceeds your intellectual ability to understand them.

- Some children think that many rules (rewards/punishments) mean strict Parenting while few rules (punishments) means weak Parents. This is Eurocentric and not correct.

- In an African-centered society, very strict Parents lack Parenting skills to help the child through discipline difficulties. Mildly strict Parents are stronger in their ability to control behavior.

- Your natural African-centered Parenting style is made negative, while your learned and court/school supported Caucasian Parenting style is made positive.

- Keep in mind that in African culture, it takes a village to raise a child, have a marriage, family and freedom. You are not a village; so do not punish yourself because you cannot do what a village can do.

- When Parents are not consistent and predictable with rules, the child becomes undisciplined.

- Look for emotional habits, patterns and styles. Good parenting means that you watch patterns. When the child acts disobedient, they are showing weakness and need your strength to help them.

- Assess the child's ability to change before demanding change. Start with changing simple activities then advance to changing other inappropriate behavior.

- Remember that it is emotional stubbornness that causes behavioral stubbornness.

- Seek behavior change before demanding situational change. For example, a prisoner cannot change his situation but can change the behavior or attitude they have in a situation.

- It is easier to change behavior than change children's mind (attitude, feelings, etc.).

- Children have the consciousness and intelligence but not the life experience or ability to support their consciousness.

- Always be prepared for disobedience, mood swings, defiance, stubbornness and challenges of authority. Your Strength is your Parenting Skills. Weakness is in the child.

- The child's intentions to do or say the correct thing is often greater than their ability to do or to say the correct thing. It takes life experience to develop ability equal to intentions.

- Never blame, denounce, put down or insult the child for what they are incapable of doing. Choose rewards/punishments according to the child's ability.

- Do not correct your past or over compensate for things that were lacking in your childhood through your child or any child.

- Children have confusion spasms and dull stupors and should be allowed to talk and act confused.

- Children are not born knowing how to be children any more than you were born knowing how to be a Skilled Parent.

- Technology and Computers do not improve communications or Parent/Child relationships. Only humans can improve humans. Technology is a convenience.

- When you have little emotional or intellectual strength; enforce household rules only. When your strength is increased; enforce discipline and supervise the discipline. Parenting takes energy and disciplining a child takes energy. If you over discipline, you get drained. This allows the child to manipulate you. Your punishment becomes the child's reward. Your monitoring of punishments drains you and in your weaken energy state the child manipulates you. The punishment again becomes the child's reward.

- If you design rewards/punishments and fail to monitor or supervise them, then your Parenting skills become weak.

REWARDS AND PUNISHMENTS

▲ Know that Parenting and Rewards and Punishments are one in the same. Each rule and desired type of behavior must have a Reward and Punishment or they are worthless.

▼ Before initiating a Reward /Punishment, assess:
♦The child's strengths and weaknesses
♦Choose a behavior that the child has the ability to change
♦Decide the various ways to change the weakness

▲ The Parent is attempting to control a type of Reward/Punishment, which they cannot completely control because:
♦The ultimate control (courts, jail, jobs, school, etc.) of Rewards/Punishments is White Society (White Supremacy).
♦The African Parent/Child relationship is a team that must cope with Caucasian culture's control of society.
♦Too many rules, regulations and punishments lose their effectiveness. They act like a fire that burns itself out.

▼ Before initiating Rewards/Punishments or saying something to the child, assess whether it will:
♦Create Maat
♦Brings more unity
♦Benefit you and the child
♦Reinforce your Rewards/Punishments
♦If there is doubt, don't do it

▲ Use strategy, nurturing, wisdom and the current situations to get the child to submit willingly to Discipline (Advice/Punishment).

▼ When a Parent designs Punishment, they must also design Rewards or else the Punishment has no value.

▲ Compare the Rewards/Punishments with the ability of the child to understand and follow them. Establish clearly that the Parent is the Reward/Punishment giver and the child is the receiver. You will always have Parenting strengths and weaknesses. You may feel superiority (Parent) and inferiority (child). This is a Slave (child) and Slave Master (adult) parenting mentality. The Slave and Slave Master mentality will allow you to stay in control in each Parenting situation. However, it conditions the child to seek a Slave Master (White Leadership, Boss, Job not in a Caucasian controlled business/institution).

▼ Too many Rewards/Punishments (Rules) are emotionally expensive for the Parent and child and break down the relationship.

▲ Know the advantages and disadvantages of Rules/ Punishment/ Arguments before you use them.

▼ When the child begins to be disobedient, discipline them at once. Do not promise punishment. Figure out the form and direction of the bad behavior and confront immediately.

▲ Before initiating a Reward/Punishment, assess:

- ♦ Whether you have enough ways and enough flexibility to allow the child to participate in formulating a plan.
- ♦ Whether you communicated your ideas free of anger
- ♦ Does the child have a good idea of the change needed. Does the child know how the punishment should be done and why it should be done. As well as the time schedule for completing it and the Punishment for failure to change and why they should change.
- ♦ Do not enforce punishment unless you can do it without anger, cursing, violence or using insulting words.
- ♦ The correct purpose of Punishment is to create change, character development, and better Parent/Child Relationship and create Maat.
- ♦ Unless you are free to practice your African culture in all situations and at all times and have the military ability to protect your culture and attack your enemies, then you do not have life, liberty and cannot pursue happiness. This makes you and your culture dysfunctional and influences parenting.
- ♦ You are an African controlled by a dysfunctional Caucasian culture that creates types of dysfunctions in your Culture, Family, Marriage, Divorce, Parent/Child Relationship and your attempts at Rewards/Punishments will be with some degree of dysfunctionality. Therefore, you must be compassionate with yourself and the child. Remember, you

cannot get straight wood (Black culture) from a crooked (Caucasian culture) twisted tree.

PARENTING METHODS

(These methods are used with Teenagers as well as Adults)

♀ Do not make promises. Do not promise Rewards/Punishments. Be consistent, reliable and keep your word.

♂ The Parent and Child serves Maat. It is better to promise nothing and give something.

♀ Never curse or use "name calling". Call the Child by their name. Name calling (stupid, nigger, etc.,) causes anger, insults, self-hatred, subconscious scarring, violence, emotional injury and conflict between the Child and the Parent.

♂ A Parent and Child (Teenager, Young Adult) goes through many changes. Inappropriate behavior can be appropriate at times. Appropriate behavior can be inappropriate at times. What is appropriate behavior for the Parent can be inappropriate for the Child. Appropriate and inappropriate is cyclic. The Child uses this to manipulate the Parent. Know that Maat defines behavior, not appropriate.

♀ Do not fuss and constantly lecture. Eventually, the Child will not hear it. They read the intensity of the emotions, not the length of sentences or the rational logic of your sentences.

♂ Do not battle the Child. Battles cause emotional pain. If you battle, the Child wins and you lose. Rearrange the Child's plans, peer socializing and schedule as a way to battle.

♀ If you cannot stop the behavior. Get rid of anything that supports the behavior.

♂ Constantly assess your Parenting skills and weaknesses and how the Child uses both your strengths and weaknesses against you.

♀ A Child's emotional confusion or breaks in logic causes behavioral problems. The behavior is not the problem. The use of emotions and or logic is the problem. Emotions and Logic are the foundation of behavior; they are the "cause" while behavior is the "effect." Behavior is the symptom and emotions and thoughts are the cause.

♂ Remember. Children are masters of politics (ability to manipulate and control). Manipulation is neither bad nor good. It is how it is used that makes its bad.

♀ The conflict is inside the Child and reflected in their behavior and words. Do not think that you and the Child have a conflict.

♂ Use various rooms, lighting, music, food and colors to set the tone for a discussion.

♀ Use different tones of voice, loudness and softness in confrontations and discussions.

♂ To be willing to talk means, to be willing to be insulted, angered, irritated, humiliated, worried, sad and or stressed.

♀ Remember to always keep the Parent and Child relationship. Be a Parent and not a peer or adult type Friend.

♂ Do not constantly brag or talk too highly of another Child. Bragging causes feelings of inadequacy, jealousy, animosity, envy and can emotionally batter the Child/Teen. The child feels the other child that you talk about is "ideal" and this can make your child feel inadequate and hurt.

♀ Parents without adequate Parenting Skills see Rewards/Punishments as a strict rigid way to control. They do not see the flexible variety of Rewards/Punishments that may need to be modified to maintain control. A Parent must constantly observe mild changes in the child's behavior in order to know what is getting ready to take place.

♂ Do not ask questions that you would not answer if the question were asked of you.

♀ Practice talking to Children by using a cassette recorder or writing what you would like to say. This is good for Parents that may holler, scream or are unaware of the abrasive tones they use.

♂ Words are Maat instruments that should be used to cause correct behavior, encourage or create and maintain control.

♀ Let the Child attempt to solve their own problems. Just monitor the process.

♂ If your advice and orders to the Child require a long conversation, they will be less effective and lose the control over the Child. Your words lose effect in a long conversation. Children know your "generic conversations" and ignore them.

♀ Too many rules cover up weak Parenting skills.

♂ Preserve the Child's dignity so that your dignity is preserved.

♀ Never call a Child a liar. Say that what was said was incorrect, untrue or inaccurate.

♂ When you talk to a Child about another Adult, state the specific behavior or words of the Adult you agree or disagree with. Never criticize the adult person, just the adult's specific behavior or words. This is proper modeling of behavior.

♀ Assist the child in solving conflicts they have with themselves. Too much assistance, restrictions and punishments causes weaknesses.

♂ A confused Child talks confused. They use immature logic.

♀ Use your "Will Power" to maintain control. Will Power comes from knowledge of justice and injustice, truth and untruth and an understanding that the Child seeks and likes correct Parenting (supervision).

♂ Children hide from difficulties with you or themselves with TV, videos, drugs, talking on the phone, hobbies, computer games, Internet and E-mail addiction, recreational activities and sex or peer groups.

♀ If the child is overly mannerly and obedient, then Reward them by acknowledging that the behavior is normal behavior and deserves no special reward.

♂ Wait for a lull in the Child's conversation or behavior to use nurturing or point out behavior adjustment.

♀ Analyze the Child's body language, words and behavior. Know what it means for the child and what it means to you. Ask yourself, does it serve Maat.

♂ If the Child is overly quiet and orderly, pretend to be unaware of it. Give them nurturing, ask about their feelings, what they think about an event or situation. Then ask is there is something they would like to discuss. Nurturing can ask a question of the child emotionally, while words ask a question mentally.

♀ If the Child is easily upset or angered, then their feelings and thoughts are unbalanced and behavior is undisciplined. Use calmness and nurturing techniques.

CONFRONTATION TOOLS

(These tools can be used with children of all ages as well as Adults)

- Know when to confront and when not to confront. Do not use all your discipline tactics at one time. Use a mixture of mild and severe punishments. The Parent must adapt their techniques in order to stay in control of the Child.

- In a confrontation, point out that solutions to behavioral problems require struggling to find answers (solution). Your Parenting skill is to keep focused on finding a solution.

- When the Child talks intellectually, you need to direct the conversation towards emotions. When the child talks emotionally redirect the conversation to an intellectual focus. This will wear the child out and make it easier to confront the child.

- Do not allow the child to Blame the Teacher, Place, Crowd, School, Friend, Time Mix-up, Circumstances, etc. for their behavior. Confront them about Blaming. It is possible for behavior to be influenced by a situation or issue, but only the Child is responsible for their behavior.

- If the Child constantly has behavior problems and/or talks inappropriately, wait for their moment of calmness or weakness, then nurture and state the Rules, Rewards and Punishment.

- Children have a style and predictable behavior and unpredictable routine behavior. Use each to stay in control. Confront them about their use of behavioral types.

- Confront the child about a peculiar behavior or conversation. Ask the Child how what they said or did:
  - Benefits you
  - Benefits them
  - Benefits the family and community and
  - How it serves Maat

- Avoid the use of slang words in Parent and Child communications and confrontations. Slang words can have multiple meanings and be mistranslated.

- When you design a confrontation, punishment or reward, always consider the talent and creativeness that the Child/Teen can use to manipulate the punishment/reward.

- Do not use a confrontation to prepare for a confrontation.

- Never confront a Child to criticize their behavior without giving a positive alternative behavior. Keep in mind that another way of doing something does not mean the initial way was wrong.

- If intimidation and punishment styles are not working, prepare a confrontation so that you can address the problem and emphasize the Child's strengths and weaknesses while talking about the problem as well as your need to improve your Parenting weaknesses and utilized strengths. Then reverse your logic. In other words, shift the blame or guilt, first blame the child then blame yourself. But, emphasize that Maat will solve your problem with them and their problem with you. Keep reversing the order. This tactic is used in basketball and computer games. The Child/Teen is already subconsciously conditioned by this tactic and sees it as a reaffirmation of your control. It neutralizes the Child's offense and disarms the child emotionally. It gives the Parent a chance to figure out another approach.

- Parents in control plan strategies and then have the confrontation with the child, while unskilled Parents have a confrontation then expect it to give them control.

- The principles of confrontation are not how many logical reasons you have for punishment or rules, but always having a standard issue and surprise issue to state as part of each confrontation. The Child cannot prepare an emotional defense with this structure. Their attentions get divided and they become easier to structure.

- These confrontation tools work with adults as most adults are grown up children suffering from dysfunctional personality side effects or childhood developmental issues.

PERSONALITIES

Personality Types are generally classified and put into categories. Within one personality there can be a mixture of types. For example, an Extrovert can be a Concrete Thinker and Random Thinker. Added to this a Personality Type has a Gender influence plus a Learning Style. In order to understand, communicate with, discipline and/or reward a child or adult, it is best to know their Personality Type, Learning Style and be aware of Gender.

PERSONALITY TYPES

TYPE	CHARACTERISTIC
Introvert	-does not like to socialize, tends to be a loner, thinks before they talk; likes to think things over before acting on them
Extrovert	- likes to socialize, talks before they think, talks to understand an idea, talks to understand why they are talking, tends to be physical
Concrete Thinker	- things are either black or white, if you tell them do not climb a tree, they will climb the tree to find out why you said do not climb the tree
Abstract Thinker	- thinks over things before acting, understands the connection between conflicting ideas, likes to figure things out
Sequential	- likes order, organizes thinking and behavior in a step-by-step manner, may complete one task before starting another, likes closure on issues, may seem slow, speed of finishing task is fast, may have a clean organize room or work area
Random	- tends to be called a scatter brain, does many task simultaneously (multitask) which slows down their pace of thinking, may seem to be fast while speed finishing one task, actually slow consumers of information, may keep a junkie room or work area

GENDER IN MALE/FEMALE COMMUNICATION

The communicating and receiving of feelings and thoughts follow a sequence. Males thinking and feeling takes on a unique pattern caused by the rise in testosterone levels around the second or third month of prenatal life. Males begin to process feelings and thoughts differently from females. A male's brain and language skills are processed in the parietal lobe of the brain and females' language skills are processed in the frontal lobe of the brain. Male and female brains process data differently. Females have a thicker bundle of connecting nerves in the corpus callosum which causes them to process information differently from males.

Females and males process energy differently. They have different mental programs. The child can learn, obey and understand if you follow their gender energy flow. When the Male is in the Thinking Stage, the Female is in the Feeling Stage.

In order to avoid conflicts, arguments or confusion in talking, translation is needed between the different stages.

Parent talking to the Male child should say:

1. What they Think first, then
2. What they Feel, second

Parent talking to the Female child should say:

1. What they Feel first, then
2. What they Think, second

The Male/Female communications connects at Maat. The Male and Female conversation is a complimentary communication. When the Male is in the Thinking Stage, the Female is in the Emotional Stage and when the Female is in the Emotional stage, the Male is in the Thinking stage. The Male and Female are able to keep each other in balance by being at different elements at stages 2 and 3. The Male is not allowed to be too rationale (Thinking Stage) as the Female is the Emotional Stage in order to keep him in balance as well as herself in balance. They are a complimentary pair and complimentary communicators and are complimentary sexually. The Male/Female are not an opposite sex, but a complimentary sex. Parents should talk to Females using the Female Principle and the Males using the Male Principle. Remember, the purpose of communication is to establish Maat in the relationship.

Females

Females tend to Feel then Think, see, touch, hear and act. They act and react with Feelings first and Thinking second.

Element Association	Interpretation
Step:	
1. Earth	Receives or gives information
2. Water (Feeling)	Feels it and/or emotionally labels it and responds
3. Air (Rationalizes)	Thinks about the feeling, emotion, idea and/or behavior
4. Fire	Evaluates and adapts the information according to spiritual belief, Maat and/or God

Males

Males tend to Think then Feel, see, touch, hear and act. They act and react with Thinking first and Feelings second.

Element Association	Interpretation
Step:	
1. Earth	Receives or gives information
2. Water (Feeling)	Thinks about the feeling, emotion, idea and/or behavior
3. Air (Rationalizes)	Feels it and/or emotionally labels it and responds
4. Fire	Evaluates information according to spiritual belief, Maat and/or God

Learning Types

Type	Characteristic
Visual	Form a picture in their mind of the task, if they see it done they can do it, follows written instructions easily, likes to read, doodle on paper.
Audio	Likes things explained to them, may talk to themselves out loud when processing thoughts, can work around a lot of noise.
Rhythm	Has to pace, walk, wiggle their legs, chew gum, constantly moving while learning or talking
Tactile (Touch)	May touch you while talking to you, may attempt to put thing together without reading the directions, likes hands on activities, rubs their hands, hair or face while talking

How to Talk to the Child

- Use games, play or activities that require cooperation, sharing, hands on activities and/or interaction with you or other children as an opportunity to talk about morals, ethics, etc.
- Model appropriate talking skills and behaviors.
- Negative behavior and/or talking can indicate that the child did not completely understand the information or appropriate behavior.
- Use one-step direction, short sentences, eye contact and gentle touch to guide listening skills and behaviors.
- Talk according to child's level of understanding.
- Talk in a home or environment should be physically safe, stable and non-abusive.
- Be patient and encourage the child to express themselves.
- Talk to redirect inappropriate emotions and behaviors in a positive direction.

- Read to your child.
- Respond verbally and non-verbally to your child's conversation.
- Do not talk for the child or say what you think the child means.
- When talking do not deny or explain away the child's expressed needs, feelings, desires, etc.
- When talking respect the child's ideas, feelings and desires.
- Give positive feedback by mirroring, summarizing or paraphrasing so that the child feels you understand.
- Encourage good listening skills (use games, music, activities, etc.).

PARENTING SKILLS

1. Monitor and supervise what CD's, rap music, DVD's, computer games, Internet surfing, web TV, movies and TV shows your child watches. Their exposure to racism, sex, cursing, dysfunctional relationships, violence or inappropriate material should be censored. If they are exposed to it they should be told that it is inappropriate.

2. Increase your parenting skills, practice appropriate social behaviors such as Maat, listening, sharing, working or playing and relationship skills when necessary. Utilize modeling to demonstrate these behaviors when necessary. Reinforce appropriate behavior with praise, positive feedback and touch, as well as using rewards (granting a privilege, points or tokens etc).

3. Find out the areas the child needs to improve such as, how to handle White Racism and social graces. Work on improving and/or developing those social skills in which the child is lacking. Use modeling with imitation initially, when necessary, followed by reinforcing positive behaviors and maintaining those appropriate behaviors through the reward system.

PARENTING SETBACKS

(Failure to do or say the right thing)

■ PREPARE FOR PARENTING SETBACKS. Expect them to occur. Accept that in some situations, you will lack the ability to control or improve the situation. Think about what you will do regarding a setback before it occurs. Use the situation to practice coping techniques and to strengthen your positive parenting skills.

■ PRACTICE FOR PARENTING SUCCESS Use a variety of positive responses to resolve a setback. This will help you develop a strategy for a setback when it occurs. It will allow you to use the setback as an opportunity to learn about your child and yourself and how you can cope with Parent/Child stressful issues. A positive approach makes setbacks easier to emotionally manage and reduces future setbacks.

■ STAY ACTIVE Do not allow a setback to stop your forward progress. Do not put off resolving setbacks because you are afraid of facing your emotions or your child's emotions. Allow yourself to experience feelings, emotions, awkward sensations and/or thoughts. Use the parenting coping skills that have worked in the past.

■ USE YOUR FRIENDS, FAMILY OR A THERAPIST FOR SUPPORT Share your feelings of parenting frustrations and disappointments with those who care or those who have special knowledge about the cyclic (ups and downs) nature of the Parent/Child relationship.

■ SETBACKS CAN BE OVERCOME Our history before, the Civil Rights movement, during and after Slavery, verifies that we can maintain successful parenting.

■ HAVE CONVERSATIONS WITH YOURSELF Accept that you're having a difficult parenting episode. Affirm to yourself that you've made progress and that a setback is a temporary problem. Talk to yourself in a loving, soothing, nurturing and comforting voice and say: "I may be overacting, What's really the issue?" "What kinds of unrealistic ideas am I having about the crisis?" The more you can identify your actions and feelings, the more you will be able to control the crisis.

■ DEFINE YOUR FEELINGS PROPERLY Other feelings such as anger, sadness or loneliness can cloud the parenting issue with the child. Perhaps something you are unaware of is bothering you. Parents tend to have setbacks during stressful periods, try to identify any life situation, which might be increasing your mistakes with your child. Keep in mind that a poor diet, disease, stress, lack of sleep or adult relationship problems can cause your parenting problem. Do not blame yourself for creating the feeling; focus on the social issues that may be causing you to feel this way towards your child.

- Problem Solving Identify what emotionally or socially happened before your parenting setback began. Perhaps your emotions were misdirected towards the child. Your problem solving will help you to recognize what caused the problems between you and your child and what led to the setback. You can develop positive strategies to counter setbacks. Remind yourself that using your parenting skills makes you a better parent.

- Assess your progress Your parenting behaviors and the child's positive behaviors are proof of your progress. When you have a setback, remind yourself that you made it through difficult times before and you can do it again.

MYTHS AND FACTS ABOUT SETBACKS
(Parenting Failures)

MYTH	FACT
Setbacks are a sign of weakness and failure at becoming a good parent.	Setbacks are not your creation or fault. They are normal and a part of the trial and error learning process of parenting.
Setbacks mean you have to start over	You have already learned parenting strategies. It will take less time and effort to start using them again.
Setbacks mean you are never going to get better at parenting.	Setbacks are signs of improvement. A setback comes only after positive efforts are made to change. It means you have made parenting progress.
Setbacks mean that failure will continue to repeat themselves.	Setbacks are a temporary episode. You can gain increasing control over parenting skill weaknesses.
There is nothing good about a setback	Setbacks are opportunities to learn to explore new ways to be an effective parent
Setbacks mean that you are abnormal	Setbacks are proof that you are normal and that it is not difficult to overcome dysfunctional parenting episodes. No parent can perfect new skills without temporary failures (setbacks)

PARENT/CHILD STRESSORS

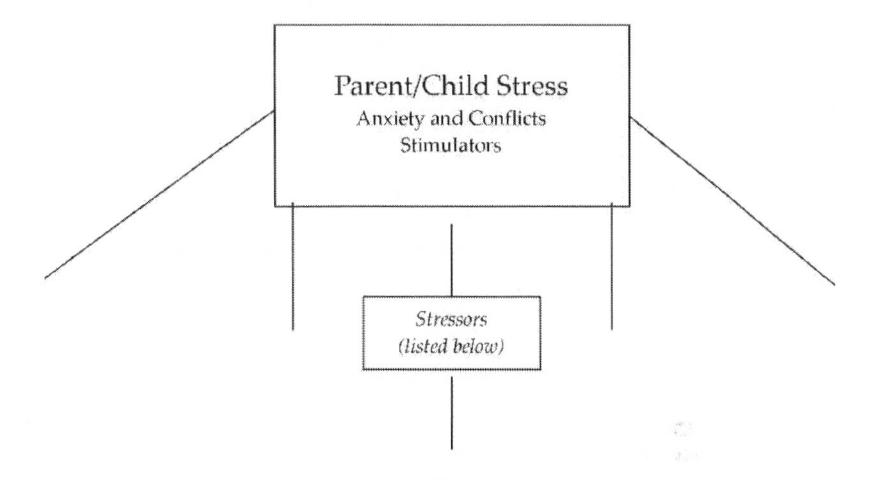

Parents Relationship (Mate of Non-existent)

STRESS WARNINGS

Many extremely Stressful Parent/Child Conflicts have physical warnings. During a stressful crisis, physical sensations can vary but the most common symptoms are:

- Heart palpitations
- Chest pain or discomfort
- Choking or smothering sensations
- Dizziness
- Cold and tingling feelings in your hands or feet
- Feelings of disillusion or disorientation
- Sweating
- Faintness
- Blurred vision
- Trembling
- Shortness of breath
- Stomach distress (i.e. rumblings, nervousness)
- Eye twitching or face twitching

TENSION AND RELAXATION FOR STRESS

Many negative emotions, stressors, bad feelings and dysfunctional behaviors can be controlled if Tension and Relaxation techniques are used.

- Tighten your neck and shoulders, bringing your shoulders up towards your ears. Relax your neck and shoulders as much as you can, letting your shoulders droop. Then relax your neck and shoulders more. Breathe deeply – inhale slowly and exhale slowly. This will help you to relax.

- Hold your arm out straight and make your entire arm as rigid as you can. Make a fist in front of you. Relax and lower your arm, allowing your hand to fall at your side. Feel the differences between your tensed arm and tight fist as compared to your limp arm and unclenched fist. Then, do the same for your other arm.

- Raise your leg. Turn your toes up and back and make the entire leg stiff. Slowly relax and lower your leg.

- Bring both of your hands in a fist position up high on your chest, pull both fists back and clench them as hard as you can. Slowly open your hands and let your arms fall limp. Feel the difference.

- Sit down in a chair; tighten as hard as you can all the muscles below your waist. You will notice that you rise off the chair a little. Feel the sensation of tension in the tops and bottoms of your thighs. Gently relax all of your leg muscles. Enjoy the relaxed sensation.

- Visualize your entire body. Tense each muscle group and then relax that muscle group. Feel the relaxation sensation in each set of muscles. If there is still tension, repeat the tension and relaxation exercise in that part of the body before continuing on to the next muscle group. When you turn your attention to each set of muscles, they will relax more. Enjoy the relaxation sensation for as long as you like before ending the practice. The longer you enjoy the sensation of relaxation, the more relaxed you will become.

- Wrinkle your forehead and bring your eyebrows up to your scalp. Feel the tension at the bridge of your nose and over each eyebrow. Relax your forehead and release the tension. Feel your face becoming more relaxed.

- Expand your nostrils and feel the tension around your nose and nostrils. If you feel tension in these areas, relax and feel the muscles relaxing.

- Close your eyes tightly. Relax your eyes and release the tension. Notice the difference in how your eyes feel.

- Smile as widely as you can. Make your lips and cheeks feel tense. Relax the muscles in your cheeks and feel the relaxed sensation. Pay attention to the sensation of relaxation and allow it to radiate all over your body.

- Clench your teeth together as hard as you can without causing pain. Push your tongue up against the roof of your mouth. Relax your jaw and tongue and enjoy the relaxation sensation. Let go of all tension and radiate the letting go feeling all over your body.

SOFTEN YOUR EYES Stop glaring, staring or squinting. Soften your eyes by letting the small muscles around your eyes relax. Each time you start to feel tension in your eyes, squint very hard and then relax the eyes.

BREATHE DEEPLY Count very slowly while taking ten deep and slow breaths.

TALK NORMALLY Control your voice. Find your normal tone, speed, loudness and pitch. If you talk at a low volume when you become tense or angry, speak at a normal volume. If you get loud, decrease the volume and talk softly.

TIGHTEN AND THEN RELAX A FEW MUSCLES Do this with the muscles that seem tensed. Breathe calmly and slowly.

THINK RELAXING THOUGHTS Repeat this positive affirmation to yourself, "I am relaxed right now" and "I can stay in control and relax." "I claim Maat as my guiding force." "There are no obstacles that can stop me from relaxing."

RELAXATION TECHNIQUES

The child can become overexcited which causes their energy level to escalate and this can overload the nervous system resulting in hyperactivity. When the child's energy reaches a hyper level, introduce soothing and calming relaxation activities such as follows:

◀A relaxing story
◀A warm bath which you can add Chamomile or Lavender tea (monitor the bathing)
◀Baking or cooking (with supervision)
◀Doodling, painting with a brush or fingers, drawing with crayons or chalk
◀Hugging or cuddling
◀Interaction with a calm parent or caregiver
◀Playing simple puzzles (only if the toddler does not get frustrated by them)
◀Soft music, with or without lyrics
◀Selected, low-key videotapes
◀Parent-child meditation
◀Egyptian yoga
◀Watching fish in a fish tank
◀Massage
◀Water play
◀Playing with clay

Once your child has calmed down, try to determine any underlying cause for the wild behavior and see if you can find a way to deal with it and prevent a repeat.

STRESS AND ENERGY OUTLETS

Children's energy reaches high levels and they do not know why or how to calm themselves. Their emotions accent their imagination, which collides with their feelings causing an energy traffic jam. The child starts to physically race pass the traffic jam with excess energy. Their excess energy stresses and irritates them causing them to speed into an energy frenzy. The energy has to be refocused, defused and given an outlet. When the child talks non-stop and goes from one toy or task to another non-stop, they need an energy outlet such as:

INDOORS	OUTDOORS
Bean-bag tossing (ditto, in a safe locale)	Ball kicking and throwing
Broad jumps ("How far can you jump?")	Free play: running, jumping, climbing
Dancing to lively music	Pulling a wagon
Drumming" on drums or pots	Pulling weeds in the garden or digging in the garden
Lively circle games and action songs	Playground play: swings, slide, etc.
Pillow fights (in an area free of lamps or fragile items)	Rolling" on an oversized ball
Punching a punching bag or a pillow	Splashing in a kiddy pool (or regular pool, for an older toddler)
Punching and kneading bread dough	On rainy days, splashing in puddles (wearing rubber boots)
Jumping up and down	
Running in place (for older toddlers)	
Splashing in the tub	
Pounding or hammering toys	
Aerobics (lead your toddler in "toe touches", "jumping jacks," and "head-shoulder-knee and toe touches")	
Pounding clay	
Tumbling (on a large mat or carpet in a safe area free from sharp corners and other hazards)	

SENSORY EXERCISE FOR STRESS

You and the child can avoid incorrect behavior and a negative Parent/Child episode by using this exercise. Negative sensations, thoughts, stress, feelings and emotions can be redirected (avoided) if you stop and do any combination of these sensory exercises.

- Hyperventilate (breathe rapidly)
- Spin in a chair
- Hold your breath
- Shake your head from side to side
- Run in place
- Bend quickly, then straighten up
- Rapidly run up and down the stairs or step on and off a box
- Put your head between your legs and raise your head quickly

CALMNESS GOAL

Stay calm. Claim calmness and affirm this with Maat (balance, harmony, justice, propriety, order, reciprocity and truth). Say, "I will use the Maat principle of control of action and thought."

Say, "I am..."

Calm	Peaceful	Relaxed
At ease	Composed	Patient
Quiet	Cool-headed	Steady
Serene	Tranquil	Poised
Focused	Centered	Balanced

There are two types of calm:

- Calm = almost never getting angry
- Calm = learning how to express yourself better, even when angry

TEACHING HOW TO LEARN A LEARNING TASK

- Consistent schedule of activities, eating, exercise, play, rest and reinforcements help the learning process

- Use child's learning type, visual, auditory, touch and rhythm. Right brain-tactile; Left brain-visual, mixed types.

- Encourage staying on tasks and using all learning styles.

- Be patient with efforts to perform a task or learn.

- Match the learning task with the child's level and learning skills. Provide clues, suggestions; clues and hints talk the child through the task. Let the child verbalize and/or visualize steps for tasks.

- Divide a task into small sections.

- Do not push the child too fast in learning.

- Allow transition time between tasks.

- Verbally introduce a new task and verbally make closure the new task.

- Encourage different problem solving methods for a task. The child's desire to learn or understand far exceeds their ability to learn and/or understand.

- The child is learning the process (steps) in learning and at the same time is learning

COMMUNICATING A TASK

- Establish eye-to-eye contact and/or move close to the child. You may gently hold the child's head or shoulders to do this, this depends on the child's age. If you give directions while the TV or loud music is playing, it may increase the likelihood that the child will not hear everything you said.

- Avoid using too much slang and speak clearly in a normal tone of voice. Most children with behavioral problems are quite sensitive audiologically. They are easily distracted by sounds that others ordinarily block or ignore. You do not need to curse or yell. Yelling can over stimulate and cause negative behaviors.

- Give your orders and/or commands or directives in a natural tone and use short sentences while emphasizing what you want the child "to do." For example: "Please pick up your CD's, books and clothes up off the floor and put them away." Avoid giving negative commands (i.e. what you do not want).

- Make sure that the child has heard what you have said by simply asking the child to repeat or paraphrase what you said. If the child is able to repeat or paraphrase it, say, "That's correct. Now please do it." If the child cannot repeat it, give the command again using the above steps, and again ask the child to repeat or paraphrase it. If the command is still too complex, you may break it down further into Part A (pick up your clothes) and Part B (put them away). Each action can be supervised. Thus, "Pick up your toys and clothes" (the child gets as many as possible), then "Put them away" (take the child to the toy box and hamper to put the items in). The two steps are repeated until the task is complete.

TEACHING TIME

A toddler mixes the past, present and future together as time. They cannot understand the concept of divisions of time. Tomorrow, this morning, tonight, later, yesterday, a minute, hour, second or day are abstract terms to a toddler. Do not expect a toddler to be patient when you say, "wait" or to rush when you say "hurry." Wait and rush are relative terms. Midway through the second year toddlers focuses on the moment, on "now". The past, present and future are beyond their rational thought process. Just before their second birthday, they begin to understand "later" or "soon" as something that is not done "now."

When they are three, they understand "today" as a long "now" and "yesterday" as before "now" and "tomorrow" as after "now". "Last night" is something that happen before "now". "Tomorrow" is not understood until they are one or two years older. The concept of time is not understood until they are six years old. When a toddler says "now", it means that "now" is a long moment or that they want something in the "now". When an adult says they will do something "sooner" or "later," "in a moment", "later on", or "in a little while," it makes "now" a complex thing (measure of time). It confuses the toddler's "now" understanding. When using a measure of time to talk to a toddler you can:

<u>BE A TWO OR THREE TIMER</u>
Use more than one physical activity to relate time to a toddler. You could say, "we will go to the store in the afternoon, after your nap" or "you can play this morning, after you eat breakfast." As the toddler gets older add a specific time. You could say "we will go to the playground this afternoon, after your nap, at 2 o'clock."

<u>DAYS OF THE WEEK</u>
Days are easier to learn if they are associated with an activity such as on "Sunday, we go to church", "Monday, you can go to the playground," "Tuesday, we will make juice, etc." If you discuss an event or activity, associate it with time, "Today, we will go for a walk," "Tomorrow, you will visit your friend," "Yesterday, we telephoned your grandmother, etc." Use a weekly calendar with pasted on pictures or other visual reminders.

<u>USE VISUALS</u>
Show pictures of yourself when you were young and little, then show pictures of your self when you were older and bigger. Show pictures of the toddler and say "Before you were this little" and "Now you are this

big." When reading a story show how times has past, by going to the beginning of the story and say "First, the frog jumped in the water, then the frog jumped out of the water, later the frog jumped on a leaf." This helps the toddler understand the passing of time and sequence. You can use a timer when you start a story. When the time rings, say, "You have been reading for five minutes." This helps the toddler learn the passing of time.

WORK ON SEQUENCE

Tell the toddler a planned sequence of activities in an order. "First, we will go to the playground, then we will sing a song and last, we will eat rice cakes." The toddler may not understand the specific differences in time, however, pointing out time helps them to track events and get introduced to sequence and order. Talk in reference too **soon, later, before and after**. "You will have to clean up your room **after** lunch," "**Soon**, it will be time to leave the playground," "**Later**, you can eat a snack" or "We will read a story **before** we leave."

READING IS TAUGHT

Teaching a child to recognize letters and to read words does not make reading fun nor does it teach the child to think. The child is trained to read with primers and a stack of flash cards with words or letters on them. Their mind is not challenged to think or enjoy thinking. A few reading suggestions are as follows:

BE SELECTIVE

Choose books that have cultural themes or ones that relate to Africans in America, Africans on the continent or Diaspora. The books should be realistic and have clear, large, bright and colorful illustrations with short sentences and age appropriate text. If the books have rhymes, then the rhymes should make sense. Toddlers like rhyming books. The stories should have a moral or something, which the parent can relate the Maat or Kwanzaa principles to.

Books ideally, should be sturdy, heavy board and with spiral binding. This allows the toddler to read alone without damaging the book. Books can be spiral bound or vinyl put on the pages at a photocopy store. Vinyl books are good for bathtub reading. They must be dried after use or they will mildew.

BE AN EXAMPLE

Keep reading materials such as books, magazines and newspapers in the home. Set aside time to read. Children of parents who read will be readers. Even if you do not like reading, make sure your child sees you reading. They learn to be readers by you setting an example. Families that watch less television, read more.

BE AN INTERACTIVE READER

Before your child is able to read allow them to participate while you are reading. Look for ideas, colors, objects, animals, environmental elements, weather and characters and point them out to the child. The next time you reread a story, ask the child about those things you pointed out. You can make the sound of the object (airplane, horse, etc.) and ask the child to point to the object that makes the sound or name the object. Older children can be asked to improvise a new ending to the story, ask them what will happen next in the story and about the feelings and emotions of the characters. You can ask them to pretend that they are reading the story to you and/or you can play fill in the blanks by omitting phrases, sounds or characters or ask the child to substitute the words or sounds in the story.

Be Emotional
Children do not like to be read to as if they are stupid. Make facial expressions and change the tone of your voice. Say some words louder and other words softer. Be theatrical, it makes listening fun for the child.

Improvise
Feel free to adjust, modify or change words in the story. Make long paragraphs short, make comments, point out the principles of Maat and/or Kwanzaa and explain the characters actions and reactions in relationship to Maat and Kwanzaa principles. If the story tends to be boring, focus the child's attention on the pictures, the size, shape and color of objects, animals, and people or you can pretend you know what's inside a cup, a closet or behind a close door.

Be Brief
The toddler's attention span and concept of time is emotionally influenced. Read short stories or make the time spent reading brief. Move from page to page and idea to idea. If the child is emotionally aroused or interested in a picture or idea, you can focus longer on it otherwise move quickly.

Be Nurturing
Children form emotional relationships with words and/or pictures. Reading becomes fun if the child is hugged, cuddled, kissed or touched affectionately while you are reading.

Be Patient
Toddlers tend to need time to get into a listening or reading state. They may be easily distracted. They may interrupt or talk about something emotionally related to a topic in the story or squirm. It may take time for the child to detach themselves from playing with a toy, climbing or making noise. If you are consistent with your reading time, persistent with reading and patient, the child will come to expect you to read to them. Do not force the child to pay attention or spank or holler at the child to get them to listen. This will make reading time a battle and a conflict instead of being a joy.

Be Ritualistic
Toddlers enjoy a story, read and reread over and over. They enjoy your undivided attention paid to them and feel emotionally comfortable and secure with the ceremony of reading. Reading takes on a ceremonial atmosphere, if you sit in a particular chair or in a particular position, play soft music, adjust the lighting or burn incense. Repetition helps the child to memorize some or the entire story aside from giving the child an emotional escape.

SHOPPING IS TAUGHT

- Reduce your shopping time by carefully reading labels when you shop alone and avoid comparing items and coupon clipping when shopping with the child.

- Avoid displays of candy, toy sections, glass, crystal and china displays.

- Give the child learning activities such as counting out three items that you will purchase, have them to point out letters, vowels, colors or shapes.

- Let the child help push the cart, put unbreakable items (i.e. box of cereal) in the cart as well as place items on the cashier check out counter. Some stores provide mini-shopping carts so that children can help shop for unbreakable items.

- If you only need to purchase a few items, shop at a convenience store. It may save you from being stressed. The prices are higher and the stress is low.

- Try to avoid shopping, if you are tired, hungry or in a bad mood and/or the child is restless, over stimulated, hungry and cranky. If you must shop, only purchase items that you absolutely need. If you do extensive shopping when either you or the child is not in a good mood, you will be setting yourself up for behavioral conflicts with the child and/or tantrums.

- Take the babysitter or a preteen to the store with you to monitor your child while you shop. This is sometimes necessary if the child has not developed good shopping behavior or if you are in a rush.

SHOPPING

It is best to take the child to the store when you do not have to shop in order to teach the child the do's and don'ts of behavior while in a store. Tell the child why you are reading labels and why items should not be touched. Before you take the child to the store to learn shopping behavior, you and the child should eat a snack. If you or the child are hungry or have a food craving attack while shopping, it will make you very easy to anger, cause mood swings and make you easy to get upset. Do not drink many fluids before traveling to the store as this may cause the need for many toilet visits while in the store.

When teaching the child shopping etiquette, take the child to the grocery store as well as a department store when you do not have to shop so they can walk thru the store and ask questions about items and satisfy their curiosity. Shopping behavior must be learned before you actually go shopping. Shop for one or a few items on your first shopping outing with the child. This will help the child to practice their shopping behavior skills. After a few practice runs, the child will have developed enough shopping skills to endure a long shopping episode.

- It may be to your advantage to do long shopping episodes without the child. The child is absolutely necessary if you are shopping for their shoes. If you are shopping for their clothes, they do no have to accompany you. If it is convenient for you, you can order their clothes via your computer, mail order catalogues or directly from the company. You may have someone to baby sit while you shop or you can shop during your lunch or on the way home.

- If you are taking the child shopping have a ritual (routine) to prepare the child for shopping (i.e. sing a song, chant or rap about good behavior). Tell the child the items you will be buying (i.e. food, household goods) and prepare a shopping list. Tell them you are not shopping for toys or items that they demand or wish for. Ask the child to help you find the items. Praise the child for following the shopping rules.

- Have a shopping list for groceries, clothing, household items, school supplies, etc. Arrange items to be purchased that are found in the same section or grouped together in the store and leave blank space for specialty items. Do an inventory. A shopping list and inventory reduces your shopping time and avoids making unnecessary shopping trips or forgetting an item or picking up last minute items at the check out counters.

TEACHING SELF-DRESSING

The child does not have the ability to dress themselves until they are around three years old. However, their desire to do so exceeds their ability to do. They will attempt to dress themselves at a much earlier age and fail to do it. This may cause frustration. Tell them that they are practicing getting dress and when you practice you make mistakes. Have them to recite or sing or rap a song such as "I am learning to get dress," "I can do it," "Dressing can be fun." Remember undressing is easier than dressing.

MAKE DRESSING EASY

Buy clothes that have velcro, elastic waistbands, easy on jumpers, easy to pull on pants, dresses that do not get stuck halfway, clothing with snaps and zippers and shoes with velcro instead of shoe laces. Despite, the easiness of dressing, some toddlers are not interested in it. Some children like your undivided attention and enjoy being dressed because they feel nurtured. Others like to attempt to dress themselves but are not concerned as to whether the clothes are clean, wrinkled or color coordinated. The act of dressing is in their imagination more than in reality. Dressing is more of a feeling than a reality to the child. They may dress themselves with wrinkled or dirty clothes and because they put the clothes on by themselves, they feel properly dressed.

BE PATIENT

Around the age of two begin encouraging the child to dress themselves. Let them start with one item; a skirt, socks, pants, shirt, etc. When they are around three years old, they should be able to dress themselves except for small buttons, etc. Let them start self-dressing for the playground before letting them dress for preschool or trips. If they refuse or delay getting dressed appropriately, let them be late or miss the activity or event they were dressing for.

INDEPENDENCE

Give the child a chance to practice dressing or undressing himself, make mistakes, take items off and on before they dress themselves correctly. Lay out the clothes. It may help to let them practice dressing and undressing a doll. This may make dressing and undressing themselves easier. Prepare the child for dressing or undressing with a rap, rhyme, song or a handclap rhythm. Give the child a reasonable time to self-dress before you offer to help.

Half Dressing

If you are helping the child to get dress or preparing them to self-dress do not completely dress them. Put the shoe, shirt or pants half way on then say, "That does not look right. What do you think you need to do to make it right?" The child may offer to complete the dressing. If they do not, then complete it yourself and do not fuss or say negative remarks to the child. If the child tries, always praise them for their effort no matter how small (zipping up, giving you the socks, pulling up one side of the pants, etc.).

Give Instructions

Putting on a skirt, shirt, socks or pants is a complex task. The toddler does not know the sequence, hand coordination, how to position the clothes or how to begin the process.

Criticize the Clothes

When the child has difficulty dressing, it may be due to their imagination or emotions distracting them. Talk to the clothes and say, "These pants are being lazy or silly, they just don't know how to act. Let's see if we can help them do the right thing." If the child puts both legs into the same pants leg, puts something on backwards, or puts the shoe on wrong foot, help them by partially putting the item on correctly and letting them complete the task. Do not insult, belittle, scream, holler or threaten the child. Do not say, "You are too old to dress like a baby" or "If you dress wrong, you will go outside and people will laugh at you." Help the child to dress. They want to dress themselves and enjoy the satisfaction that comes from doing-it-for-yourself.

TEACHING CHORES

Chores build a child's confidence. They enjoy the feeling of independently starting and finishing a work task. Chores let them feel that they have responsibilities like adults do. Young children have the ability to do simple chores such as putting fruit in a bowl, stacking newspapers, placing napkins on the table, etc. The chores should be age appropriate and not limited to gender. Girls can put tools away or help you repair or put together an item. A child helping you is actually helping themselves to build confidence and self-reliance.

START EARLY

Children learn by imitating. While you are cleaning, dusting or throwing away trash, let the child throw away wrappings, wastepaper, dust a table, etc. Keep their chores safe and easy to do. While cleaning, sing or talk about the Maat or Kwanzaa principles. You can say, "We have Nia a purpose for cleaning" or "We are working together – Ujima."

DO NOT COMPLAIN

Do not say negative remarks while doing chores such as "It makes me sick to see how messy this room is," "I get tire of picking up things" or "They must think I am the maid." Do not moan and groan while you wash dishes, vacuum, put away CD's, search for the remote or get easily irritated while cleaning. The child will learn from your negative attitude and behavior that chores are a type of punishment.

HAVE FUN

Decorate the trashcan, dirty clothes hamper or toy box with symbols, African art or a favorite character. You can ask the child to "Put your dirty clothes with Big Bird." Remember use a ritual before doing a chore such as saying a prayer, rhyme or rap, sing a song or play the drum.

LIMIT THE CHORES

The child may be happy and have fun while doing chores. Do not add another chore or push the child to do more. The child may get tire, resentful, upset or overloaded resulting in associating unpleasantness with chores.

FAMILY CHORES

Get everyone involved in the household chores. Assign chores that are age appropriate and be sure to be fair with labor distribution. Encourage conversation, singing, chanting, or saying the principles of Maat and or Kwanzaa while doing chores or say part of the Cultural Virtues.

COMPLETION OF CHORES

What a child sees as clean is usually different from the adult's evaluation of clean. The child judges the completeness of a chore emotionally. If the chore made them happy or was fun, then the chore ends when the fun ends. A messy room or area will be seen by the child as room filled with enjoyable things; therefore, when they partially clean a room they are leaving symbols of joy in the room. A joyful room feels like a clean room to a child.

TYPES OF CHORES FOR TODDLERS

A child between two or three years old can be given various types of chores. You can put up a list with a descriptive picture beside each chore. The child wants to have the feeling and attitude of "I did it all by myself." Try not to interfere with their chore assignment. Remember that most chores need adult monitoring, supervision and assistance.

CHORES FOR TODDLERS

- ▲ Clear the table of unbreakable items
- ▲ Cut sandwiches with a cookie cutter
- ▲ Take mail from the mailbox
- ▲ Dry unbreakable dishes, spoons, plastic cups, pans, etc
- ▲ Dust. Provide a dust cloth and give a demonstration before you let the child do it. Be sure there are no breakables in the area to be dusted.
- ▲ Help sort colored and white laundry.
- ▲ Set the table with placemats, napkins, unbreakable dishes and cups and flatware (no knives).
- ▲ Sweep the floor with a small broom and dustpan (a dustpan that has a long handle makes the task easier).
- ▲ Tear Romaine or Iceberg lettuce or Spinach leaves for a salad.
- ▲ Toss a small salad in a large bowl.
- ▲ Pull weeds from the garden (under close supervision).
- ▲ Put dirty clothes in the hamper.
- ▲ Pick up and put away toys.
- ▲ Mix or stir salad dressing, pancake batter, cake batter and uncooked pudding.
- ▲ Unpack and put away unbreakable groceries (toilet tissue, potatoes, paper towels, bread, beans, cereal boxes, nuts, pasta) in accessible cabinets.
- ▲ Wash, scrub and rinse fruit and vegetables in the kitchen sink (standing on a sturdy and steady stepstool).
- ▲ Water plants (use a small watering container).
- ▲ Wipe water-safe surfaces with a cloth or a damp sponge.
- ▲ Snap string beans, snow peas, shell peas, break broccoli or cauliflower into florets, husk corn or rinse sprouts.

CONVERSATION SKILLS

Open-ended questions allow more than a "yes" or "no" answer. These questions encourage the child to share their emotions, feelings and idea.

- Active listening which includes:
  - Using silence – so that the child can fill in the silent space
  - Restating (paraphrase) the child's sentences – allows the parent to assure the child that they are listening; gives the child's ideas in a short form; checks the parent's understanding of the child. The parent paraphrases what the child said.
  - Comment on feelings – the parent comments on the child's feelings expressed.
  - Summarizing content – similar to restating (paraphrasing) but with added words and/or feelings.
  - Summarizing feelings – synthesis of the individual's effective response. Summaries connect the child's feelings in a more effective way. This allows the child to respond with more ideas and feelings.

- Interpretation of the child's non-verbal behaviors – for example, say, "You seem worried." This helps the child to be aware of or express emotions. The parent has to recognize that the child's non-verbal behaviors and expressions are influenced by computer games, movies, TV, peers, rap music, fear, anger, other parents and children as well as the parent's emotions at the time.

- Parent/Child problem solving skills – the parent/child openly discuss ways to resolve problems between them and explore other options. The parent must keep in mind that the purpose of their relationship and problem resolution is Maat.

IMPROVE THE CHILD'S INTELLIGENCE

- Read to the child.
- Make reading and writing fun and a playtime activity.
- Touching and the labeling of different colors, sounds, rhythms, shapes and textures that are within the child's reach or vision.
- Use puzzles, indoor and outdoor play, interactive toys, stackable toys, form-fitting interlocking toys and/or objects, drawing supplies, mazes and rhythm exercises.
- Allow the child to lead or make-up play (improvise).
- Model verbal, non-verbal listening and visual behaviors.
- Encourage interactive play and group activities.
- Improve muscle and coordination activities with dance, crawling, jumping, Egyptian yoga, climbing, throwing and martial arts.
- Use nature walks, tours, visits to different places and observation of skilled craftsmen.
- Monitor television shows, music videos, the Internet and web surfing.
- Beware of violent, sexual oriented video games and structure the child towards cultural games and non-sexual, satanic and/or male/female abusive games, etc.
- Never holler at the child or curse or say negative remarks about their Mother/Father or about them as a person. Only comment on specific behaviors as being negative and not the child.

FORGIVING

Forgiving is for you, not the child you forgive. Not forgiving hampers your parenting ability. Being constantly upset with the child may be destroying your relationship with your child. Meanwhile, the child you are upset with may not know or care. Forgiving is a gift to yourself. You forgive your child so that you can be a more effective parent.

Forgiving takes time. It's usually a slow process. It is an on-going process. But you must decide that it is something you want to have the ability to do for yourself and your child. Holding onto resentment, frustration, upset feelings or anger towards the child holds back your development as a parent.

Forgiving means letting go of the past. The past cannot change. It is over. Remaining upset is a way of clinging to the child's past negative words and deeds. Forgiving does not mean forgetting. You need to remember what happened so you can know what parenting skill is most effective for your child's personality and learning style.

You may have to forgive yourself. Sometimes you cannot forgive the child until you forgive yourself. All the time you spend being easily upset with the child is time and energy you can use to love them. Your wasted energy and resentment of the child's behaviors are usually added onto the newest episode of your child's bad behavior. The new episode locks you into more unforgiveness. Children do stupid things and have a right to do stupid things in their search for balance (i.e. Maat). If you choose to weigh and measure all their childish behaviors on an adult scale, you will stay in a constant state of unforgiveness. This will isolate you from the child which means, you are isolated from a part of yourself. This distorts your reality, parenting skills and ability to give and receive love from your child. When you do not forgive, you lose a part of yourself and most of all you lose your child.

The inability to forgive can serve negative purposes. For example:

- The parent can be getting pleasure from being upset and resenting the child's inability to be perfect.

- The parent may maintain an upset attitude towards the child in order to emotionally blame the child for faults and failures that they have as a parent.

- The parent may be using their upset attitude towards the child as an excuse to be violent, abusive or angry.
- The Parent maybe clinging to an upset attitude out of habit.

- The parent's inadequate parenting skills are hidden by an upset attitude. Holding onto a negative attitude towards the child allows the parent to have an excuse for not expressing love or devoting time to the child.

COPING WITH DEATH STYLES

Children coping with the death of an adult, friend or significant other (rap star, actor, athlete, etc) caused by diseases (Cancer, AIDS) suicide, terrorists, drugs, shooting, war and/or accidents respond in various ways such as:

- RISING ABOVE THE DEATH – the child focuses on meaningless activities and other issues as a way to ignore death or the possibility of death. Early in the death process, they focus on task completion. Later in the death process, they concentrate on computer games, drugs, sex, religious and spiritual activities and peer group activities.

- ACCEPTANCE OF DEATH – they accept a deadly illness, death and reality. They need to have grieving explained, how to cope with grieving feelings, the grief process and how to live with grief.

- DEFY DEATH – the child fights accepting a deadly illness. Often, the child will have episodes of crying, laughter, anger, rage and sadness as a way to fight the death and experience the death trauma feeling.

- DENIAL OF DEATH – the child copes with illness by denying it's reality and it's emotional gravity. They believe the dying person will survive. Denial is used to hide from their lack of emotional vocabulary. Emotionally death has to be defined, lived and experienced. The child may lack the ability to climb into and out of emotional states – emotional vocabulary.

- HIDING FROM DEATH – the child does risky death defying type counterproductive behaviors. The child becomes disorganized. They seem to invite death by doing risky acts that create a false sense of giving their life value.

- BEWILDERMENT OF DEATH – the child turns themselves off through depression, moodiness or apathy or by having excessive crying spells to the life threatening illness and possible death. Feeling helpless and doomed, they make no effort to disconnect their own feelings or share the joy of home going to the Ancestors.

SUICIDE

Unresolved negative words and deeds can be used by the child as an excuse for suicide. For example, feeling guilt about not being perfect or normal. The child may feel guilty about behaviors they committed or failed to commit in the past. The child feels that getting rid of themselves (suicide) will get rid of the problem. The child may feel that in order to hurt someone else or their parents, they can hurt themselves (suicide) to hurt them. The child may blame themselves or feel morally the blame for their parent's divorce, drug addiction, adultery, homosexuality or fights. The parent should help the child to understand that the parent's failures are different from the child's failures and the parent's guilt belongs to the parent. Talking about the child's feelings with the child helps to defuse (resolve) suicide. Talking with the child about guilt may help them to understand that death by suicide is a way to punish themselves for issues and problems which were not their responsibility or creation.

Suicide can be avoided if the child's emotions and feelings are defined by them correctly. For example:

The comment "I do not want to live" frequently means, "I do not want to live like this." The child's feelings should be attached to the specific situation that they feel is destroying them. Often the child allows a negative feeling or situation to define their entire life as worthless. Therefore, the child should say, "I do not want to live like" instead of "I do not want to live."

The parent can defuse the child's emotion that is causing the suicidal feeling. Have the child to agree to a contract by which they promise to contact the parent before a suicide attempt or agree to perform some other specified preventive (write, sing a song, talk, exercise, etc.) action prior to any suicidal act.

The parent and family members may seek to "suicide proof" the home by removing ropes, household cleaners, poisonous chemicals, sharp implements, limiting the presence of medication and monitoring the child's behavior.

The suicide has to be assessed by the child's values:

IMMEDIATE How soon does the child want to attempt suicide? Is it a future thought or a present plan? Is it used to make the parent give attention or punish the parent? Is the suicide procrastination? Is the child copying a movie character?

CAUSATIVE FACTOR What has occurred to cause the suicide? Is the child experiencing a current crisis, new failure or inadequately dealing with an ill defined negative feeling?

PLAN Does the child have a plan? Is it an organized or unorganized plan?

MEANS Are the means to do a suicide available? Can the child physically do it?

TEEN SUICIDE

(The U.S.A is the #1 country in the world)

1. Mental and emotional status and hormone levels are critically affected by a teen's.

2. Teens in general suffer from under-nutrition and eat no foods with any adequate Vitamin B content.

3. They constantly consume sodas, junk foods and alcohol, all of which have been proven to bio-chemically reduce the already critically levels of Vitamin B in the body.

4. The early signs of Vitamin B deficiency are characterized by delusions, disorientation and depression. These symptoms are consistent with early Beriberi, Thiamine and Vitamin B deficiency disease.

5. Biochemistry textbooks list the major symptoms of Vitamin B deficiency as anxiety, mood swings, depression, hostility, rage, vague fears, forgetfulness, instability, sweets cravings, mental confusion, irritability and a constant feeling that something dreadful is about to happen.

Suggested Reference

[1]Kleiner and Orten, Textbook of Biochemistry
[2]White, Handler, Smith and Stetton, Principles of Biochemistry

SHAME AND SUICIDE

Shame means the child feels bad about their total personality and not just a specific behavior, situation or statement. When a child feels ashamed it is as if there is something bad about their entire life that will not go away. In African culture, shame was directed at a specific behavior and not the person.

A Shamed child tells themselves:

- I'm nobody
- I'm not good
- I'm not good enough
- I'm not loved or loveable
- I do not belong
- I should not be alive

Shame can distort the child's thinking and behavior. Shame can cause the child to use an outer personality that hides the shame. The "I am tough," "I say what I mean," "I am real," and "Don't mess with me," on stage performance and behavior of rap singers can be used to hide shame. Shame may be caused by living in poverty, a homosexual parent, having to take Ritalin, low grades in school, living in a one parent household, being in Special Education, being Black, the lack of an ideal family or special talent, etc. Shame can cause hypoactivity, hyperactivity, as well as suicide. The parent must be aware of the child's shame, emotions and behaviors and help the child to discuss their shame. This will help defuse shame.

DAILY AFFIRMATIONS

The uses of positive affirmations are useful for parents. These affirmations should use Maat and or Kwanzaa principles and reaffirm your desire to change the way you respond to your child. See Cultural Virtues and use phrases from that section as affirmations. Listed below are a few suggestions:

"I am blessed with skills and my Ancestors wisdom to guide me to solve my child's behavioral problems."

"I am striving to be purified and holistically healed and possess the ability to heal my child's behavior."

"I am empowered with the knowledge and the strength to deal with my child's difficult behavior."

"In the past, I have been inadequate and harsh with my child's behavior. I can use other parenting techniques that would be less abusive and emotionally upsetting for my child and myself."

"I will heal my child's behavior problems and will control my anger, yelling, cursing, temper and dysfunctions in order to serve God.

"I made a mistake and did something wrong, next time I make a mistake I will do something right.

DON'TS FOR CHILD RAISING

DON'T:

♦ Ignore attention getting behaviors, words, songs, etc. (may lead to tantrums)

♦ Spoil the child (using gifts, food, money and clothes to win the child's love)

♦ Confine the child to a room or in the home for excessively long periods of time

♦ Let them look to you to solve all of their problems

♦ Force toilet training

♦ Be over protective (mistakes are a part of learning)

♦ Bore your child

♦ Lecture. A lecture becomes generic words that are ignored. Lectures are a scratched CD that is irritating and ignored.

♦ In all arguments (especially during Negativism Period = Terrible Two's) do not be afraid to say," No." When you say, "No," mean it and stick to your decision

♦ Try to force your child to follow the growth and development schedule of a book (Eurocentric, Caucasian)

♦ Holler at the child, curse or say negative remarks about their personality or Mother or Father

DO'S FOR MOTHER/CHILD INTERACTIONS

DO:

♥ Direct your attention to the infant/child and stimulate them with sounds, facial expression, words, songs and objects

♥ Imitate the infant's sound

♥ "Quiet alertness" – Mother's ability to keep the child quiet with sensory and visual stimuli

♥ Look at the infant/child with pleasure

♥ Name objects, colors, music, parts of the body

♥ Encourage the child to pay attention to dreams, events and objects (improves Attention Deficit)

♥ Allow the infant/child freedom to choose play

Parent's Do's and Don'ts Behaviors

DO'S	DON'TS
DO tell the child exactly what behavior and what verbal response you want	DON'T tell the child what you want. This is negative reinforcement.
DO name the specific behaviors that are liked	DON'T use "good boy/girl."
DO model behavior you desire the child to establish and develop.	DON'T wait for important behavior to appear. It must be developed.
DO provide a punishment as a consequence for inappropriate behavior	DON'T threaten to use punishment as a consequence for wrong behavior.
Use punishment for wrong behavior	
DO provide a reward as a consequence for appropriate behavior.	DON'T punish appropriate behavior.
DO match the degree of punishment to the degree of inappropriate behavior.	DON'T use verbal abuse and physical punishment for aggressive behavior. A spanking is appropriate while beating is not.
DO punish inappropriate behavior.	DON'T reward inappropriate behavior.
Do reward immediately.	DON'T ignore appropriate behavior.
Do punish immediately	DON'T ignore or fail to respond or delay punishment for inappropriate behavior.
Do reward with social praise and touch.	DON'T use physical punishment and verbal abuse (hollering, cursing, screaming, yelling and name-calling) for behavioral problems .
Do work on small changes.	DON'T expect immediate major changes in behavior.
Do name the behaviors you like.	DON'T focus on the child (i.e. You are hardheaded. You are always doing wrong. You are stupid). Focus on specific behavior.
Do withdraw attention to some	DON'T attend to behavior undergoing

inappropriate behavior.	extinction.
Do a time out discipline and have the child recite or draw principles of MAAT or Kwanzaa.	DON'T shake the toddler as it can damage the brain and/or eyes.

TALKING ABOUT FATHERS DO'S AND DON'TS

DO'S	DON'T'S
Increase the amount of information you give about their absentee father.	When children get older, it is unnecessary to answer all of their questions or come up with solutions for their problems. You cannot have all the solutions or fix the problems. It is better to be able to discuss their feelings about problems and what they have experienced. Help them to interpret and explore their observations, emotions and understanding of their father. Their world becomes more complex and things are less black and white. Children grow in their understanding so you will do more listening and less explaining and comforting
Tell them that their father's negative behavior does not mean that they will have the same behavior or be a less desirable person.	The positive and negative comments you make about your child's father becomes a part of how your child sees themselves. Be truthful and try not to have an attitude. Saying insulting things or putting down their father causes serious consequences for your child. Positive statements about their father can help them to have good self-esteem. The key is to share your feelings without negative judgments. For example, "Your father is with one of his girlfriends instead of seeing about you." Try, "Your father was unable to be a good parent and husband." If your child ask why, say, "I just know that's how our relationship was."
Tell them that they do not have to copy their father's negative behavior. If he broke the law, he would not want them	Do not say that their father does not pay child support because he does not care. These words will hurt your child

doing the same thing. Even if he was a lifelong woman, drug or child abuser, criminal, liar or thief, you still can be a nice and honest person.

and will not solve the money problems. It is better to explain gently, he is not behaving like a good parent and may have other issues. Children are aware when fathers do not pay child support, because money problems and finances become a critical issue.

If the father's lack of financial support is due to sickness or unemployment, poor parenting skills or neglect, tell your child the truth.

Lying to your child about the father will not work because you will not be able to sustain the lies. When children get older they eventually find out the truth. Sometimes they wait until after they become adults to find out the truth. Tell the child the truth instead of letting them live a lie by holding an ideal image in their minds and hearts. Lying can jeopardize your future relationship and risk losing their respect. Be as open as possible and tell them the truth.

Do point out that their father's lack of parenting skills may be due to issues or anger he is unaware of. However, let the child know that not paying child support cannot be excused because of issues or anger.

QUESTIONS

"WILL DAD EVER COME BACK?"

The child wants their life to have a happy ending and to be like a fairytale. However, if their father has no intention of coming back or if you have no plans of having a marriage/relationship with the father, it is best to tell them the truth. It's better to say, "I hope that you and your father will have a good relationship but he and I will not get together." It is best for the child to have fond memories of their father and keep him in their heart than live a dream that will not come true.

"CAN I LIVE WITH DAD?"

This question indicates a dream the child has of having a normal life. They feel that they are incomplete without their father. Older children probably are thinking about living with their father when they are older or as a way to be free from your rule. Sometimes, the child may ask the question to make you feel bad or because they feel bad. Tell your child that it's okay for them to think about living with their

father. Remember that this may not happen. It is alright for the child to have childish dreams and hopes. Keep in mind that it is good for an adult to develop a friendship with a long gone father. If this happens, your strength and loving spirit has enabled the child to forgive the father's past and you have helped make their father a part of their lives. Children want their dream of
their father to become a reality and living with him makes him real and makes them feel like a real, normal child.

"WHY DID YOU AND MY FATHER SPLIT?
Avoid saying, "You stopped loving each other." The child may think that it is possible for you to stop loving them. Tell the child you will never stop loving them. Tell your child that you love their father as a friend. Assure your child that a mother is always a mother and that you will always be there for them.

MOTHERING DAUGHTER DO'S AND DON'TS

♦ Teach your daughter to fix (repair) items. Teach her the names of tools and how to use them. Let her watch you repair household items, check the oil in your car, tighten loose nuts and bolts. Do let her take self-defense classes.

♦ Do not focus on her looks, clothes and jewelry. Try to emphasize that her ability to use Maat, Kwanzaa Principles and Cultural Virtues and a good relationship with God makes her attractive. Talk about her strengths, good personality traits and talents. Talk less about her dysfunctionality, weak or inadequate characteristics or behaviors.

♦ Do participate in outdoor activities with your daughter such as hunting, camping, nature trails, looking for herbs, bike riding in the park, mountain climbing and health retreats.

♦ Do not give her contradicting statements and mixed messages. For example, telling her "She looks attractive in a dress and that she has a good figure and then tell her that her looks are not important." Beware of emphasizing studying to be an engineer and then criticize her for wanting to be a hairdresser.

Parenting Boys Do's and Don'ts

Do's

Do teach your son to respect all females the same as they would respect their sister, mother, aunt and grandmother

Do believe in yourself and encourage your child to believe in themselves. Let your child know that you are confident as a parent.

Do engage in activities with healthy other males he comes in contact with

Do censor or limit the amount of violence and pornographic videos, music and movies. Let him - know that what is in the videos and on television is not Maat and does not show the healthy behavior men should have.

Talk about positive thoughts and behaviors that your son has that are similar to his father. Talk about men who have Maat behavior – male heroes that have/had good behavior.

Do teach your son values and let him understand and express them in his own masculine way. This can mean that he sometimes does not show or express his feelings.

Do understand that most boys grow and develop slower than girls, so be patient about your son's emotional maturity. Boys do not practice relationship skills with dolls, girls do. Boys practice manipulation and

Don'ts

Do not make your son the "man of the house." He should have responsibilities and chores but a - boy should be allowed to be a child, he is not a grown man.

Do not worry that he will learn how to be a man without his father not living with him. Half the population is male and he will get the male attributes and social skills from male models. Point out the positive moral and ethical qualities in men he sees on a day-to-day basis, including the store clerks, the friendly barber or the talkative senior citizen.

Do not avoid talking about his father even if you do not like him or know he is dysfunctional.

.

control of objects such as trucks, airplanes, cars, etc. They usually lack the emotional vocabulary needed for a relationship.

Parenting Teens Do's And Don'ts

♦ Do spend time talking with the child about issues in society and their feelings and understanding of them. Share information about your challenges, obstacles, mistakes, triumphs and your feelings about things. Let the children respond in their own way. Do not give lectures during conversations. Make the communication a two-way street. Always reassure the child that you will be there for them and always love them. Give plenty of hugs and kisses.

♦ Do be involved. Attend your child's after school activities, sporting events and community activities. Shared activities and experiences help you to bond with your child. It helps you to have conversations and share common interests. It is good to be in contact with other parents. Volunteer to help at school functions or at community functions that your child is in. This helps you to network with parents and provides a common interest with the child.

♦ Do not argue about hairstyles, diet, clothing or loud music. Teenagers tend to use them to express independence and individuality. Try to point to the value of Maat behavior and the need for moderation. Let them know that every trend or fad is created and promoted by businesses to make money. Point to the health hazards of tattoos, birth control pills, condoms, loud music and body piercing. Rings can be pulled out of the skin and infections can be caused. If the teen's room tends to have an odor, place an air deodorizer in the room.

♦ Do be alert to emotional changes in your child. Watch for mood swings, sugar cravings, eating disorders, excessive E-mail and Web surfing usage, depression or violent tantrums. Being a teenager is difficult for children and you need to let them know that you are there to help them understand and cope with the challenges in their life. The child does not know how to be a teenager. A teenager is a pre-adult phase and between being a child and an adult. Their are sex hormones are stimulated and they do not know or understand how to understand themselves or why they are themselves. At any given moment, they may do something stupid, which is usually caused by a clash between their rationale thoughts and their sex hormone created thoughts.

Public School Do's

♦ Remember that it is the principal of the school who is accountable and responsible for problems at the school. Hold the principal accountable by meeting with them to discuss any problems or concerns. The principal will make time to meet with you about your concerns.

♦ Remember that you have a right to confront teachers and the principal because you are an equal. Do not feel intimidated. The teachers and principal are parents. Do not feel like a victim and be defensive, apologize for your life circumstances, have a negative attitude and holler or talk loud when discussing your child's problems. The school may use your behavior as an excuse to defend the inability to meet the demands of educating your child. Remember schools are under police control and/or state control and any behavior that they define as inappropriate can cause a criminal charge or file to be created on you as well as the child.

♦ Seek out supportive people at the school such as the psychologist, guidance counselor or a teacher your child may have had a positive experience with. Use the resources the school has to offer.

♦ Do be mindful that public schools have an unofficial "3 strikes and you are out or a point system." Once your child has reached their allotted points or strikes, they may be placed in an alternative school or special education. Your behavior or harsh words to school officials can contribute to your child's points or strikes.

♦ Do talk to friends, other parents or adults that have the same values and standards as yourself. They can be supportive in your efforts to manage you child's education and help you through parental issues.

♦ Stay in contact with other parents at the school. They can relay information to you when you are unable to attend the Parent Teachers Association (PTA). Most schools have E-mail and Web pages that they use for information dissemination. However, talking with another parent is the best resource.

♦ Remember you are not the only parents who has a work schedule that does not allow you to visit the school or attend school meetings or events. Despite your conflicting work schedule, you are still a parent and still have the right to get the best education for your child. If your school district or school board is not helping you, then contact your state or congressional representative office to find out about advocacy groups that can help you.

♦ Do not feel bad because you cannot help your child with their schoolwork or computer problems. The school and your community have resources that can provide help free of charge.

Child Home Alone Do's

♦ Make Rules Clear
Rules should be based upon the child's safety, maturity, neighborhood and home circumstances and the child's capabilities. Keep in mind that children will do childish things. The rules should be clear and in some cases written. The rules should include appliance use, phone and E-mail use, friends that can or cannot visit, homework and study, leaving the home, television viewing, how to answer the phone or door and their chores.

♦ Cellular Phone
Cellular phone usage has to be based upon the level of responsibility the child can maintain. Determine if the child's safety requires a cellular phone that has 911 or other emergency services numbers.

♦ Caller ID
Tell the child to only answer calls from callers that you have approved. This can prevent the child from telling unwanted or unexpected callers that you are not at home and that they are alone.

♦ The Law
It is a crime in many states to leave a juvenile home alone. It is considered child abuse and abandonment. Therefore, you can be convicted of a crime.

♦ Seek Back Up
It may be difficult to get a reliable parent to act as an emergency backup. Most mothers and/or fathers are usually at work. Consider using an older neighbor to watch your child when an emergency arises.

♦ Beeper
The child can beep you when they arrive home or when an emergency arises. Some jobs do not like your children calling about non-emergency matters. Use numerical codes or special phrases to deliver messages. If the child is mature enough to go out without you being present, then a

beeper can keep you in contact. If your beeper pages and you do not get a response in a reasonable amount of time, find out why.

♦ WHAT IS AN EMERGENCY

Clearly tell the child what are emergencies (i.e. accidents, sexual advances, fire, sickness, violence). Have a beeper numerical code for different types of emergencies. If you are beeped, the emergencies should require immediate voice contact with you or your designated backup.

♦ HUNGER

Children may need a prepared food or meal or easy to prepare foods for an after school snack. Warn them not to eat artificial sweeteners and white sugary snacks, stress eating more fruits and avoid drinking sodas.

♦ KNOW THE CHILD

You must evaluate whether the child feels comfortable to be home alone. Have them do relaxation exercises or meditate or listen to calming music/movies. The movies or videos should not be violent because they can cause the child to be fearful, scared or nervous. Some children if left home alone too long will imagine and create fear in themselves. They may need a baby sitter, an after school program or an adult to check on them periodically in order to handle their emotional unsteadiness and fears.

SINGLE PARENT FAMILIES DO'S

A family is a cultural unit. The culture creates a family that is centered around Cultural Virtues, Maat and Kwanzaa principles. Family is a community (village) of people with common ethics, interests and values. Family can consist of extended family (aunts, uncles) or a network of male and female friends. A family can be headed by a male (patriarchal) or a female (matriarchal) or headed by both (unilateral) or a grandparent. The purpose of family is Maat and Cultural Virtues not necessarily who heads it or how it is constructed. The Caucasian influence on family can cause problems. A book such as ": The Hite Report on the Family Growing Up Under Patriarchy" by Shere Hite (Grove/Atlantic) can expose some of the problems of the Caucasian culture's influence on family. The following can be helpful for a single parent:

- The parenting skill of the adult whether they are single or in a marriage is the primary factor in creating a home atmosphere that is nurturing. Single parent homes should emphasize behavior and roles that are not gender confined.

- Daughters in such families can see the independence, strength and gentleness needed to develop feminine attributes. They confide more to their mother.

- Sons in a "mother only" family do not feel the need to be aggressive or suppress emotions to be a man.

- Mothers tend to share more female issues and societal pressures dealing with Black females with their male and female children.

- Boys feel less forced to prove themselves as men and feel their character makes them a good and strong male.

- Men raised by positive cultural single mothers tend to develop a better emotional vocabulary and have better relationships with women.

- Two parent homes tend to force children to see one parent as the boss and the other parent as weaker or easier to manipulate. The child duplicates this in their relationships.

- Boys usually have a significant male to relate to or have a male support group of friends.

- When visiting his father. Boys have to be told that some feelings between his separated or divorced father are not good. He has to be warned that his father's negative words about his mother is a problem within his father. He must understand that problems between his parents is not his problem. Reassure him that both parents love him despite their separation. Tell him to say, "I love you daddy and I love momma. I wish you would not talk that way about my mother."

- When visiting her father. Girls have to be warned about negative words her father may say about her mother. She has to be told that her father has problems with his feelings towards her mother. Reassure her that his words are about his hurt and not intended to hurt her. Tell her that both parents love her despite the emotional problems the father has about the mother. Tell her that her father has his own problems and hurts. When he talks about them it is not meant to hurt her. Tell her to say, "I love you daddy and I love momma. I wish you would not talk that way about my mother."

- The child should be told that they should not pick sides. They should not feel one parent is right and the other one is wrong. Tell the child that both parents helped to make the relationship good and helped to make it bad. Tell the child it is not good to say bad things about one parent in order to please another parent. Single parents need to accept that using the child as a teammate to bash the other parent damages the child and their relationship with their child.

- Boys and girls learn how to be adults and how to behave in a relationship by observing the way their parents behave and talk with the opposite sex. "Opposite sex" is a Caucasian cultural term. In African culture, we say, "Complimentary sex." There is no battle between the sexes or opposite sex, there is Maat between the sexes, which makes them complimentary sexes.

- If you have a boy, he should learn house cleaning, ironing and cooking. Girls should learn how to repair and put together equipment, furniture, etc.

Parent Dating Do's And Don'ts

- Do keep in mind that your social and sexual needs may force you to date people that do not fit into your children's life.

- Do remember that children do need to be taught how to deal with their emotions concerning you dating. Dating is a learning experience for you and the child. It sometimes will take awhile for your child to accept it.

- Do remember that your date can be considered an invader and someone that is taking you emotionally away from the child.

- Do not stop having a private life and socializing because of your children. They have not given up being a child because of you and you should not give up being an adult with adult needs because of them.

- Do not discuss adult issues with your child. They are not to be used as an adult confidant. The child should not be used as your solution for loneliness.

- Do not refer to a male sexual partner that spends the night with you as "Cousin" or "Uncle." This sends a confusing message about adult sexual practices. If a male guest spends the night, it is best that they sleep where overnight guests do or else make other arrangements for your sexual encounters.

- Do not make your date assume fatherly responsibility when they visit. They can use their parenting skills but only as a friend not as a substitute father.

- Do not allow the child to use your guest as their company or allow them to occupy their time.

- Do encourage the child to be polite to the male guest.

- Do not argue with your guest around your child.

- Do not let your guest ignore or disrespect your household rules (i.e. wash hands before getting something out of the refrigerator, take off shoes while in the house, no loud music, no cursing, etc.).

Dating A Single Parent Do's And Don'ts

- Do meet your dates children and spend time with them before introducing them to your children. Do not force the children to be friends or like each other.

- Do not force the oldest child to be the baby sitter. This could cause the oldest child to resent and dislike you and your date. Avoid this until the children are able to get along with each other. It may be better to see if you and your date will have a lasting relationship before bonding the children together. If you and your date decide to end the relationship or have a negative relationship, the bonding between the children will force you to see each other.

- Do explain to the children that they cannot come along on your dates. Tell them that you and your date need time together similar to them spending time with their friends.

- Do not take both sets of children on outings, lunches or places to travel until they are comfortable with each other.

- Do not get upset or worry if the children don't get along or have conflicts. Children forgive each other easily and are flexible. It may take awhile before they get along.

- Do not expect the children to immediately share their feelings about your date or your date's children. Keep in mind that the children's attitudes may be their attempts to selfishly keep you to themselves or punish you for not staying in a relationship with their father.

- Do have family dates such as going to the movies, a festival, park, museum, roller skating, bowling, etc.

- Do prepare the children for your overnight date by having a slumber party (rent movies) have sleeping bags or a sleeping space and spend the night together in the same room. This makes the children feel comfortable about your future overnight dates.

Remarriage, Partner And Children Do's And Don'ts

- Do not try to make your children accept your spouse or like their personality. They may not agree with the new spouse's opinion or decisions involving the family. Your children can have their own opinion and have a dream about how a family should live. All you can demand is that the children respect your spouse and your marriage. Children require time to experience the new spouse, and to adjust and develop a one-on-one relationship.

- Do ask your children to politely talk about their feelings, likes and dislikes with you. The children have a right to have feelings of resentment, betrayal, anger, confusion, an attitude and emotions that they cannot explain. Do not try to rationalize or explain away a feeling. Expect feelings, recognize them and let the child know that you love them and need time to adjust to their feelings. The child may be feeling guilty because you did not marry or stay in a marriage with their biological parent. They may feel that the spouse does not have the rights of their real parents.

- Do have consistent punishment, rules, rewards and discipline styles. Children may try to take advantage of the honeymoon period of the marriage. They may wait for marriage difficulties or arguments and bend the rules to their advantage. Children must know that the parenting rules will not change.

- Do observe your child's behavior and emotions. If the child is reacting with inappropriate behaviors, mood swings or overly sensitive and irritated, you may have to seek a therapist or family friend for them to confide in. It is rare in Black families, however heterosexual and/or homosexual molestation can be an issue.

- There are support groups for children.

- Do constantly communicate with your children. Let them know when, where and how certain changes will take place.

- Do let the child know that the non-custodial parent is not a referee, judge or rescuer to save them from the new marriage.

Rough Children Do's

Rough children that behave by pushing, poking, squeezing, jabbing, twisting and shoving do not mean to be harmful. They experience this environment by touch and prodding and pushing others to see how they will react. They are treating others as if they are toys or an inanimate object without considering the physical damage and hurt feelings that they cause.

If the child has developmental problems such as a limited vocabulary, they may have limited ability to learn through sound (verbal), sight (visual) and or rhythm and will tend to be rough with others. Instead of saying, "Hello, how are you," "What are you doing," "Let's play" or "Goodbye," they will push or be physically rough as a form of communication. The rough child will drag a child into their room when they want to play and/or push a child out of their room when they are finish playing. The rough child is use to being around others with verbal skills but has not learned to know when to be physical and when to be verbal. They have to be encouraged to understand that their behavior is considered violent and painful. Try the following:

- Do let the child know that their physical contact is painful. If they poke you, yank your ear or hit your arm, tell them you do not like it even if it does not hurt.

- Do not let them play rough at home and demand that they be gentle with others outside the home. Let them know that rough play hurts and upsets people.

- Do use good manners at all times say, "Good morning." "It is nice to see you." Let them know that handshakes, hugs and high-fives are good manners and hitting, pushing and being rough is bad manners.

- Do not promote rough behavior by yanking their arm, pulling their ears, pinching or pushing the child when they misbehave or refuse to do something. They imitate their parents. You have to be gentle and not rough at all times.

Naked Parents Do's

Parents' nudity in front of their children can present problems for the child in this heterosexual and homosexual, hypersexual society. If the child is less than two years, you probably will not have problems with cross gender nudity. Once the child is near two years old, parental nudity should stop. When the child becomes curious about your sex organs and or breast, it is time to stop. Toddlers tend to be unaware of the sexual activities attached to your genitals. They may ask questions, touch or pull at your genitals. If they do, keep your composure and answer their questions.

- Do tell the child that other people's sexual organs are not to be touched.

- Do stop bathing or showering with a child that is nearing two years old.

- Do explain that you need privacy when you are nude. Say, "You are older and when you are older, privacy is needed by adults."

- Mothers do continue to dress and undress in front of your daughter, if you and her are comfortable with it. Do not bath or shower together. Be aware if an older daughter is looking at your nude body with sexual pleasure or in a homosexual or manly type manner.

- Fathers do continue to dress and undress in front of your son. If you notice the child staring at your penis or buttocks or smiling a lot or always wanting to come in the room when you are nude, stop nudity in front of them. This may be indirectly stimulating homosexual issues in the child. Do not shower or bath with your son.

- Do avoid nudity in front of the children if you are not comfortable with it or lack the parenting skills to handle heterosexual and homosexual questions.

- Do let the child know that the naked body or clothed body has to be respected.

NAKED CHILD DO'S

The child is not conscious of their nudity being related to sex until they are over two years old. Their awareness of the genitals is usually associated with the responses adults give when they show or touch their genitals. Children will take off their clothes a lot between the ages of two and four years old. They could be practicing their undressing skills or find it relaxing to be naked or could be using nudity to protest your authority, to get attention or they can be tired of wearing diapers and or training pants.

- Do not over react, holler, scream, yell or spank the child, touch their sex organs or be nude at inappropriate times. This may cause the child to feel ashamed of their body and or sex organs later in life.

- Do let the child practice dressing and undressing on a doll or stuffed animal. Use clothes that are easy to put on and take off. Monitor the activity as their little fingers may have difficulty dressing and undressing objects. This can cause frustration, tantrums and instill in their mind that life is easier if you are nude.

- Do not respond to their nudity with laughter or cute remarks. This will encourage the child to strip off their clothes more.

- Do let the child play naked in sunlight coming in through the window or in the house if it is warm enough. If the child is not toilet trained, protect your furniture and or carpet as much as possible. Place a blanket or sheet on the play areas. However, you must let the child know it is not good behavior to be naked around visitors.

- Do try to dress the child in clothes that are difficult to remove. Clothing with buttons, belts, overalls or suspenders are difficult to remove and can reduce the nudity episodes.

Seen Having Sex Do's And Don'ts

If the child wanders into your room or accidentally catches you having sexual intercourse handle it with good parenting skills.

- Do not get upset, angry, holler or scream at the child to get out of the room. Do not push the child out of the room.

- Do calmly ask the child to leave the room please. Immediately put on your clothes and walk with your child back to their room or go to the child's room.
- Do answer questions only when asked about your sexual activity.

- Do understand that some children do have a concept or know about sexual intercourse or have misconceptions and may think the sexual positions and sounds are reactions to pain, aggression and violence.

- Do not use long complex answers to respond to their sexual intercourse questions. Explain that adults have special ways of being together and the positions and sounds are pleasurable.

- Do get a lock for your bedroom door or lock the door when you are having sexual activity.

- Do plan appropriate times to have sex (i.e. when the child is not home or when your are sure the child is asleep).

- Do remember that most sleepy children forget witnessing a sexual act. They remember if you make them feel guilty or ashamed. If they catch you, tell them they did nothing wrong and you did nothing wrong. Tell them that you love them.

Children And Genitals Do's

Children begin to pay attention to their genitals once they are out of diapers, wearing training pants or being toilet trained. Their genital areas are the focus of adult attention due to urinary and bowel incontinence. A toddler explores and touches their genitals with the same innocence as their toes, fingers, ears and navel. They discover that touching their genitals is pleasurable. It is not a sexual sensation. Little boys who touch their erect penis do not have the sex hormones to feel adult sexual pleasure or an adult sexual imagination needed for masturbation.

- Do give the child another activity that requires working with their hands.

- Do take their hand(s) away from their genitals and say, "It is not okay." Do not use a harsh tone or handle the child roughly.

- Do remove and gently squeeze their hands. Shake your head to indicate "no".
- Do try to ignore the behavior. You do not want to draw attention to the behavior.

- Do consider that it maybe a fear, stress, anxiety or an attention getting reaction.

- Do consider that the child may have worms crawling out of the anus which can be stimulating and irritating their genitals.

- Do remember that a child may hold their genitals to urinate or to avoid a potty accident.

- Do tell age appropriate children that "We do not touch ourselves around people." It may trigger pedophile arousal in an adult who is watching this behavior.

- Do give the child a substitute toy to use whenever they want to touch.

- Do be aware of the possibility of heterosexual or homosexual molestation.

Talented Children Do's And Don'ts

Children always have a uniqueness and special quality about them that is their character logic and not a special talent. The child may have an above average skill and not a talent. Talent can be indicated by the ability to excel in an area without much effort or making an ordinary story, event, and artwork, object or thing into something unique.

- Do not make the talented child perform or demonstrate their talent to entertain visitors.

- Do encourage and support the child's talent.

- Do not think it is an advantage to have the school psychologist or a professional, label or recognize the child as "gifted."

- Do not push and force the child to concentrate most of their time towards their talent. This can cause the talent to suffocate them and hamper growth in other areas.

- Do accept that the child may switch from one talent to another.

- Do understand that some children's talent is not recognized until they are older.

- Do understand that a child can be stressed, unhappy and burnt out by their talent. They may stop using their talent or hide their talent so that they can feel normal.

- Do accept that the child may like the talent but not the attention and the discipline and social skills that the talent demands. They may hide their inadequate emotional and social development by causing others to focus on their talent.

- Do realize that traditional evaluations may not detect your child's talent.

- Do not love the talented child more than your other children or practice favoritism. The talented child and the other children will suffer.

CHAPTER 4
BEHAVIOR AND CONSEQUENCE

"I seen some slaves sold off dat auction. De little chillum sho would be cryin when dey sol deir mothers away, we be cryin wen dey Whites sex de mother or dey don whip dey mother til mos dead. I never see my fatha. I don't know freedom in my head. I twas happee all in all and b'long to mama's marster"

Unknown Slave Woman

BEHAVIORAL TRAITS

AGES	TRAITS LEARNED
8	- begins to socialize with small groups - begins to learn self-defense (video games influenced) - begins to learn how to signify and play the dozens and mimic slave behavior - knows the meaning of the curse words "P____" and "F____" and knows how to rap - has a fair understanding of poverty, ownership of power and riches and calls it "The Man (white society)". - begins to develop inferiority feelings about the Black race, African culture and Africa - begins to have negative feelings and attitudes about their community - begins to develop a negative attitude towards school and places low values on the purpose of education
9	- learns to use violence in a detached manner and participates in reckless behavior - begins to identify with a gang, social group, sports celebrity, rappers and singers - begins occasional truancy from classes and/or school - becomes familiar with ghetto life styles (via music videos) - begins to challenge authority or things that represent authority (teachers, police, rules, etc.) - realizes the need to develop "coping skills", denial of slave trauma, low self-esteem and anger - begins to spend more time with peers (horizontal relationships)
10	- becomes more curious about sex (pornographic type music videos, music, TV, movies, etc.) - becomes more acquainted with weapons - becomes more active with peer groups - begins to establish street personality and image - is able to see certain contradictions in society - develops fluid street language - is aware of community's police traps, drug areas, sex prostitution areas - begins to experiment with cigarettes, marijuana, drugs, and alcohol
11	- begins to associate with older boys and girls - begins to use the curse word "MF" (Motherf___) - creates sex drive – hyper sexed - is able to distinguish undercover school police, probation officers, truant officer and undercover police agents - signifies and plays the dozen and exhibit other slave behaviors - avoids school work and spends most of their leisure time hanging

out in the street
- surfing the Web or E-mail
- may have engaged in petty crimes, shop lifting, rape, theft and first demeanor activities

12 - is ready for street gang activities
- has awareness of street culture
- becomes interested in more computer games, materialism, gadgets, fashions and jewelry
- knows the life styles of a drug dealer, pimp, prostitutes, homosexual activities, hustler, rap, sports and movies stars, street man, militant, etc.
- can talk with adults
- may begin having a series of sexual relations
- has formed an image of themselves – becomes skeptical of social institutions, white supremacy, and the powerlessness of black leaders and black adults

BEHAVIORS

YOUTH PEER GROUP	ADULT PEER GROUP
Gangs, Dealers, Sports Teams, Clubs, Computer Games, E-mail and Phone chats	Adult peer groups meet at clubs, gyms, churches or call themselves Parents, Teachers, Concerned Community Citizens, Friends from the Job, Old School Friends, Fraternities, Sororities, Shoot basketball together, Buddies, etc.
Gang member socialize daily 2 to 8 hours together. As age increase, involvement increases	Parent allocates 5 to 30 minutes with the child – as age increases, involvement decreases
Gang members listens to each other Two-way communication	Parents talk at the child not to or with the child - one-way communication
Media emphasizes immediate Rewards and Gratification	Parents emphasize long term Rewards and Gratification
Caucasian culture emphasizes materialism, cars, body mutilation (ear, nose, navel, lip, eyebrow, tongue and genital rings, tattoos), designer	African culture emphasizes moral integrity, honesty, spirituality and Maat Parents emphasize getting money by serving white folks (good

clothing and society advocates getting large sums of money via drugs, sports, music, crime and the lottery	job, good education and working hard)

BEHAVIOR AND CONSEQUENCES

The child's awareness, attitude, feelings and judgments (cognitive behavior) can be shaped and developed by Rewards and Punishments. If the child knows (cognition) that each behavior will produce a consequence (Reward/Punishment) then their social and emotional health will be realistic and more Maat. The following steps can guide the process:

STEPS

■ Encourage decision making, independent activities, allow space for spontaneous activities (improvisation).

■ Allow the child to express their feelings by using games, dance, dolls/toys, play, conversation, books, music (develops control of a broad range or emotions/feelings).

■ Interact with the child, respond holistically to their feelings, spiritual and physical needs, etc.

■ Gently rock or massage the child, hum, sing, dance and drum with them, smile and establish eye contact and mutually touch each other.

■ Allow the child to express their needs, wants and desires. Let them learn the consequences of their actions. The child maybe free to choose a behavior but they cannot chose the consequences of a behavior. For example, they may freely choose to touch fire. The consequences of being burnt by the fire cannot be changed.

■ Respond to fragmented, mixed and or confused feelings, emotions and actions by providing and demonstrating appropriate responses.

■ Encourage the child to label their feelings, words, and actions.

■ Give verbal and non-verbal responses.

■ Encourage the child to observe and label others' emotions, spirituality, words and behaviors.

REINFORCEMENTS AND BEHAVIORS

1. How to give Positive Consequence: Reward

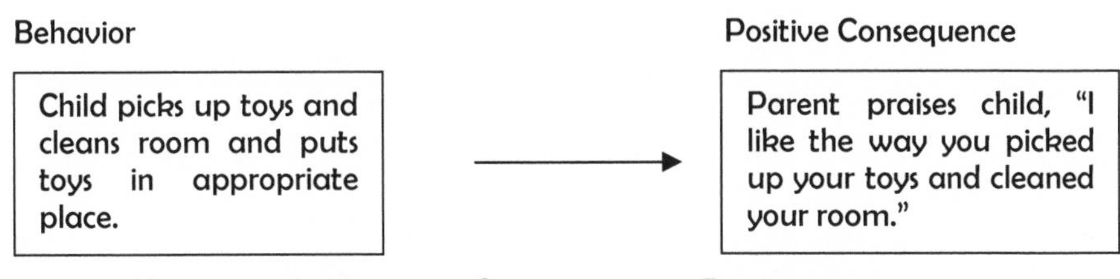

2. How to give Negative Consequence: Punishment

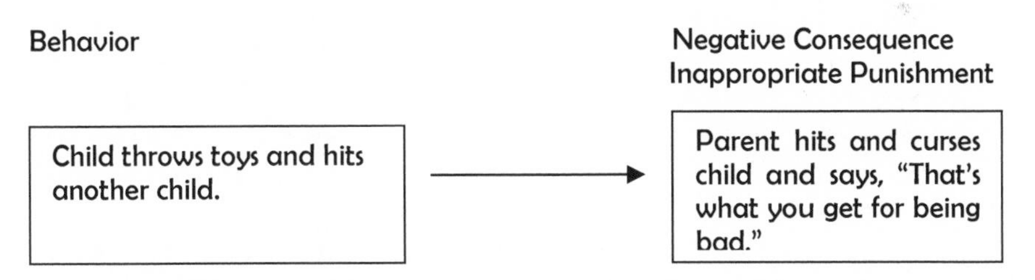

The child feels hurt, abused and emotional pain and will develop their own interpretation of the situation:

- ▲ The child thinks that they should not hit their siblings; another child or throw toys because they will get hit.
- ▲ Adults are bigger and do what they want. They will hit you, curse you and give you painful beatings.
- ▲ Confusion – parent tells me not to hit but it is all right for them to hit.
- ▲ I cannot do this and cannot do that. What can I do?

3. How to take away a Positive Consequence: Punishment

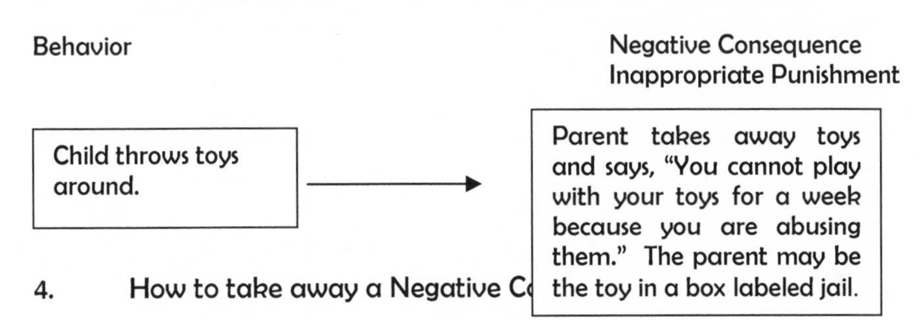

4. How to take away a Negative C

Behavior		Consequence (Negative Reinforcer Withdrawn)
Child stubbornly refuses to do a task. Parent monitors (stands over) child until task is completed.	→	Parent leaves the room. Negative Parenting behavior is avoided.

POSITIVE SELF-BEHAVIORS OF CHILDREN

- Identifies self with African cultural views, people, social movements, economics, etc.
- Wears African clothes. Has an African name.
- Views White Supremacy government and civilization as destructive to Black folks and culturally abrasive. Seeks solution and activities to solve problem.
- Actively changes feelings and behaviors in order to make self personally responsible to solving individual and group problems.
- Uses Maat to define self, nature, God, truth, science, diet and solves problems based upon Maat.
- Self-examining, self-determined and self-actualizing.
- Seeks to be actively productive and contributive to the Black community (local, national, and international community).
- Does not doubt Black people's ability to free themselves of Racism.
- Does not belittle their people, culture and legacy.
- Uses scholarship, left mind and right mind, universal knowledge and Maat to continually improve self (evolve to highest level of humanism).
- Understands that an organized people can end Racism.

NEGATIVE SELF-BEHAVIORS OF CHILDREN

- Accepts negative stereotype of Black people. For example, believes Black people are weak, non-supportive of each other, unable to get along with each other, genetically criminal, hypersexed, violent, lazy, etc.

- Self-worth is based upon materialism (clothes, car, job, sex, popularity, friends, gadgets, gang, etc.).

- Medicates self with movies, sex, gossip, games, music, television and food in order to relieve the symptoms of racial problems instead of seeking to eliminate the cause of the problem.

- Does not base self-knowledge or personality on African heritage or culture.

- Assumes European identity, universal personality, multi-cultural identity.

- Seeks recognition or status from society (i.e. job, education, social status).

- Does not feel that they are culturally advanced compared to other ethnic groups.

- Has superficial limited responsibility to African people and businesses and global interests.

- Condemns inhumane behavior and attitudes towards Africans while completely accepting non-African values and behaviors that create disharmony.

- Blames Black people for causing the negative problems (crimes, drug abuse, underemployment, poverty, ghettos, violence, etc.).

CHILDREN'S BEHAVIORS

Behavior Problem	Inappropriate Behaviors	Appropriate Behaviors
Aggressiveness	Acts out, angry, disrespectful	Controls anger,
Oppositional behavior	to authority, says, "No!"	respectful of authority Says, "Yes, sir," "Yes, ma'am."
Attention problems	Short attention span	rapidly sustained attention
distractibility	shifting attention, (multi-task), gets off task, forgets to do task	focuses on one thing, stays on task,
Hyperactivity	Overactive, constantly moves around, exhibits excessive vocal motor activity	Sits still
Impulsive	Acts too quickly, acts before thinking	Delays response(s), thinks before acting
Social problems	Ignores peers and siblings, exhibits anger towards siblings, peers and siblings, selfish	Greets peers and plays appropriately with peers, with toys siblings, shares toys

Desirable Behaviors	Undesirable Behaviors
Says "Good Morning"	Snubs others (lacks social manners)
Listens to parents	Talks back to parents
Carries out tasks	Ignores commands
Waits turn to talk	Interrupts others
Helps siblings with tasks	Fights with siblings
Cares for toys	Destroys toys

Behavior Action/Reaction

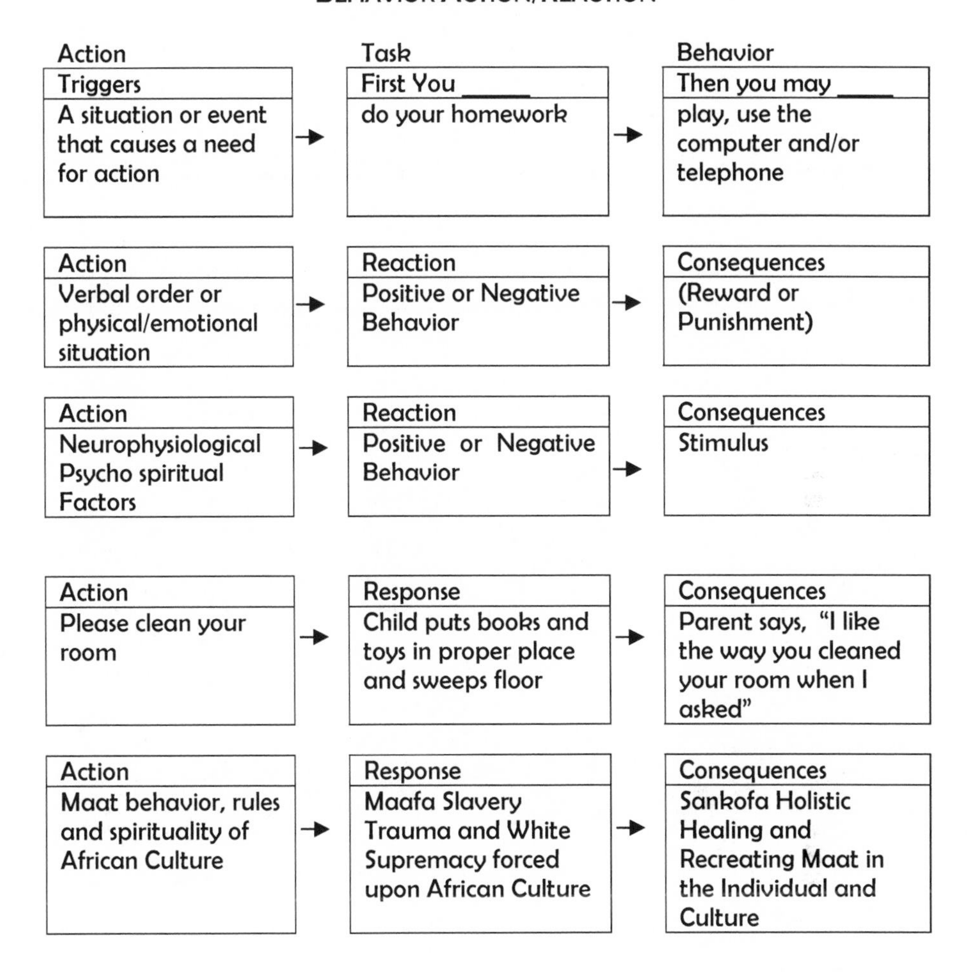

BEHAVIOR IDENTIFIER CHART

Symptom KEY: AP = Actively Present
PP = Probably Present
NP = Not Present

Behavioral Symptoms	Attention Deficit	Anxiety Disorder	Depression	Conduct Disorder
Aggressive	PP	NP	PP	AP
Crying	PP	PP	AP	NP
Day Dreams	AP	NP	AP	AP
Difficulty Focusing on Task	AP	PP	PP	PP
Fails to Complete Tasks	AP	NP	AP	AP
Fearful/ Avoidance	PP	AP	PP	NP
Guilt over Behavior	NP	AP	AP	NP
Impulsive	AP	NP	NP	AP
Memory Problems	AP	AP	AP	NP
Mood Disturbance	AP	AP	AP	AP
Poor	AP	AP	AP	AP
Concentration Low Self-Esteem	AP	NP	AP	AP
Inadequate Sleep	AP	AP	AP	AP
Poor Social Skill	AP	NP	NP	AP
Quiet and Withdrawn	PP	NP	AP	NP
Restless	AP	AP	PP	PP
Sensation Seeking (Does many risky activities)	AP	NP	PP	AP
Stealing/Lying	NP	NP	NP	AP

This chart is designed to help you identify behaviors. The child may have other symptoms to a lesser degree.

BEHAVIORAL PROBLEMS AND DIET

Diet of Child with Criminal Behavior

The Diet of a Typical child prisoner with behavioral problems: The child maintained a junk food and high sugar consumption diet prior to criminal behavior. The behavior is drastically changed and improved by eliminating the harmful foods. The following is an example of a typical child prisoner's diet:

MALE:	14 years, 2 months
GRADE:	7th
CHARGE:	Vandalism
PREVIOUS OFFENSES:	2 prior 2nd degree burglaries in 2 years
BREAKFAST:	5 cups of Sugar Smacks with ½ teaspoon added sugar 1 glazed doughnut 2 glasses of milk (20 ounces)
SNACKS:	1-foot long rope of red licorice candy 3 six-inch beef jerky sticks
LUNCH:	2 hamburgers French Fries 2-foot long ropes of red licorice candy Small serving of canned green beans Little or no toss salad

TAHOMA COUNTY PROBATION PROGRAM

Tahoma County Probation Department (California), observed in 1977 that children detained at the Tahoma County Juvenile Hall (prison) were hyperactive and had aberrant, inappropriate behaviors. The administration decided to change the eating habits of children in the institution.

The junk foods at the prison had to be used before starting the new dietary regime. As the junk foods were consumed, they were either not reordered or substitutions were provided.

FOOD ELIMINATED	SUBSTITUTION
Sugar (granulated and powdered)	Honey
Syrup	Honey
Sugarcoated cereals	Plain cereals
Ham	Other meats
Jell-O desserts	Knox gelatin with fruit chunks and juices

Packaged foods	Foods prepared at the facility
Kool-Aid, coffee, tea, carbonated sodas	Milk, water, fruit juice (unsweetened/natural)
Bread with preservatives	Bread without preservatives
Jelly and Fruit preserves	Honey and fresh fruit
Flavor enhancers	None
Syrup packed fruits	Water packed fruits
Chocolate	Carob
Foods containing dyes	Foods without dyes
Candy	Fruit
Animal fat shortening	Vegetable shortening
White flour	Whole Wheat flour

With the substitute diet, there was over a 70% decrease in hyperactivity and criminal behavior.

DIET AND BEHAVIOR

The hyperactivity and criminal behavior decreased when children substance abusers changed their diets. Basic diet changes were:

1. At least three evenly spaced well-balanced meals per day were prepared.
2. Consumed adequate protein daily (Rule for protein determination: is desired body weight divided by 2 grams of protein daily). Protein may be of animal or vegetable origin.
3. Consumed vegetable, fruit and/or protein in between meals and for bedtime snacks.
4. Used only whole grains.
5. Consumed fresh vegetables and fruits daily.
6. Decreased consumption of salt, dried fruit, coffee, tea or tobacco.
7. Legumes (beans), nuts and seeds were included in the diet.

Common Sense suggestions for the criminal and hyperactive drug abused children were:

1. Overweight? Follow basic rules but limit fat intake and portion size.
2. Balance meals with whole grains (unrefined), protein foods, vegetables and fruits.
3. Observe how you feel. Do not eat anything that will cause you to feel bad.

The Children's Correctional institution completely eliminated the following foods:

Sugar (white, brown, turbinado, raw)
Honey, Molasses
Corn syrup
White flour
White bread
All soft drinks
Ice cream
Canned fruit
Canned vegetables
Processed or pre-packaged food
Cakes, cookies, and pies
Pastries, candy and doughnuts
Breakfast cereals
Commercially made granola
Fruit flavored drinks
Flavored yogurt
Coffee
Tea
Alcohol

The Children's prison authorities found that alcohol and drug abusing clients usually had under nutritional symptoms related to their poor diet as follows:

Anxiety
Nervousness, Blurred vision
Sweet cravings
Alcohol cravings
Dizziness, faintness
Depression
Feelings of doom
Headaches
Insomnia, nightmares
Rages
Tiredness, weakness
Morning nausea
Transient muscles ache
Transient joint pain
Weight problems
Irritability

The Correction facility found that these same criminal behavior children's typical diets consisted of the following:

Alcohol consumption
Sugary breakfast
Skipped meals
Light eating during the day
Heavy eating at night
Refined carbohydrate snacks
Skipping breakfast or a high sugared one
Pre-packaged food
Heavy consumption of
Sugar
White flour
Caffeine
Salt
Tobacco
Junk food

BEHAVIORAL PROBLEMS, LEAD AND CRIMINALITY

Environmental polluting products as well as the pollution has caused an over 500 times increase in lead compared to the 16th century. Symptoms of lead toxicity and blood sugar problems tend to be the same. For example:

1. Headaches
2. Nervousness
3. Dizziness, weak spells, cold sweats or fainting
4. Drowsy
5. Depression
6. Sleeplessness during the day
7. Forgetfulness
8. Mood swings
9. Digestion problems (upset stomach)
10. Fatigue or exhaustion

In the 18th century in the Kingdom of Kongo, the Bakongo men wore jewelry (amulets, bracelets, etc.) made of copper, tin and lead. The Bakongo designed the metals to represent cultural ideas. Some of the Bakongo developed lead poisoning from wearing the lead amulets and bracelets. They were so toxic from the metal poisoning that they became manic, drowsy, irritable and or aggressive. To treat the lead poisoning, the Bakongo used herbal pharmacological preventive and curative herbs (i.e. paw paw and palm oil) and physical therapy. The preventive, curative and physical therapy methods became the tribe's traditional way of using knowledge to keep one step ahead of technology. It is difficult to stay one step ahead of toxicity, poisonous foods and radiation caused by computer technology. Too much lead has and is still being released into our environment. Dr. Herbert Needleman et al, reported in the New England Journal of Medicine (1979), that evidence existed of a lead-behavior learning triad after 2,146 school children's shed teeth were examined. Boston's Children's Hospital Medical Center and Harvard Medical School study revealed the following:

1. Children with high lead levels had developed learning problems in the areas of verbal performance and auditory processing.
2. The children had developed Attention Deficit Disorder.
3. Teachers' reports of classroom behavior indicated that learning disorders were due to high levels of lead. The common behavioral problems exhibited were:
    a. Impulsiveness
    b. Easily became frustrated

c. Lacking in persistence
d. Dependent on structuring and clingy
e. Daydreaming
f. Failed to follow simple directions
g. Tracking problems
h. Easily distracted (could not follow sequence)

4. Children with high lead levels performed significantly poorer on the Weschler Intelligence Scale for Children (WISC-Revised), particularly on verbal items and three measures of auditory and verbal processing.

CHAPTER 5
SCHOOL

"I nurture myself through the nurturing of others (children)."
Queen Afua

Toddlers find security with the accumulation of possessions – the more possessions they have the more secure and comforted.

KWANZAA PRINCIPLES IN THE CLASSROOM
NGUZO SABA

- Umoja – Unity; working together in such a way that if one person has a different goal they will still participate in the total Maat of the group. The group will help the individual with a different goal achieve success and happiness.

- Kujichagulia – Self-Determination; pursuing a goal in the spirit of Maat.

- Ujima – Collective Work and Responsibility; in the activities and programs, no one will be allowed to leave until the area is cleaned and each person participates in the activity and cleaning.

- Ujamaa – Cooperative Economy; as a group, they should save, bank and utilize all resources together and purchase items.

- Nia – Purpose; each person in the Rites of Passage group has to state a career goal. They must develop a plan for achieving the goal and tell how their goal serves Maat.

- Kuumba – Creativity; in drumming, cultural dancing, jewelry making, tie dyeing cloth, sculpturing, making positive messages and designs on T-shirts, caps, jackets, school bags, etc.

- Imani – Faith; believing in God, demonstrated by understanding the principles of Maat and the 42 Declarations of Innocence.

CLASSROOM EDUCATION VS. TRAINING

The Eurocentric schools have different effects on Black children. The non-African (i.e. Caucasian) children are taught to control (Slave Master mentality) and the Black child are taught to be subservient (Slave mentality). Listed below is an example of the effects of schooling:

NON-AFRICAN CHILDREN ARE:	BLACK CHILDREN ARE:
Abstract Thinkers	Concrete Thinkers
Educated	Trained (Indoctrinated)
Employer	Employee
Thinkers	Memorizers
Opportunistic	Job seekers
Entrepreneurs	Consumers
Leaders	Servers (trained to serve and/or work

for others)

LEARNING CONCEPT

NON-AFRICAN	AFRICAN
American Contemporary Culture (European)	African Traditional Maat Culture
I (Individual Centered)	We (Group Centered)
Competition based upon Ownership	Cooperation based on Maat
External (highly values material things)	Internal (highly values spiritual things)

NON-AFRICAN AND AFRICAN CULTURAL CLASSROOM

In the Eurocentric classroom, learning takes on the linear slave and slave master style.

Non-African Culture's Class (vertical communication)

- Teacher (Slave Master)
- Student (Slave)

African Culture's Class (horizontal and circular communication)

- Circular Communal (Family) Cognitive

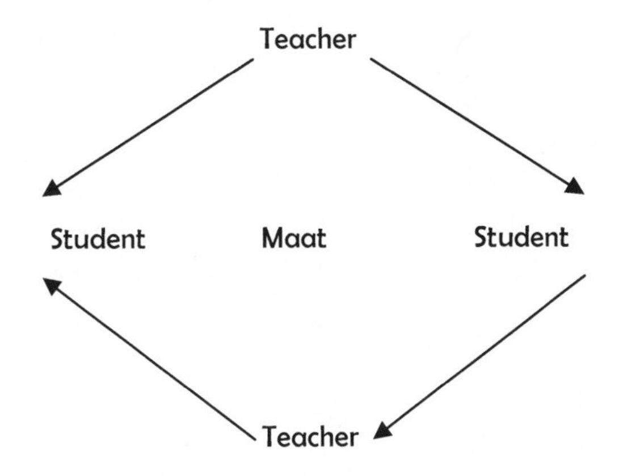

Maat Guided Classroom Purpose and Mission

The child should be taught in order to help them define their Maat guided purpose and mission in life.

PURPOSE: The child should be taught their reason (purpose) for being on the Earth (mission).

MISSION: A (spiritual) strong desire to take a course of action that makes you feel (spiritually) bound or connected to God and/or your culture.

Classroom Activities

The child's classroom activities are actually Rites of Passage. The foundation of the Rites of Passage is Maat. The key elements to develop in the educational Rites of Passage should not only teach the child how to think but also heal the effects of Slavery Trauma, Racism and Oppression.

AFRICANS AND AFRICANS IN AMERICAN HISTORY ACTIVITIES

- The development of Africans in America and the African family tree.
- Design an African time line from 4 million years B.C. thru 2000 A.D. and place indicators on the time line regarding social significance occurrences.
- Read lessons from History: The United Independent Compensatory Code/System/Concept, The Destruction of Black Civilization, Marcus Garvey Philosophy, The Autobiography of Malcolm X, Man child in the Promised Land, Native Son, Kaffir Boy, Abdul and the Designer Tennis Shoes, The Art of War, African Holistic Health, The Isis Papers, The Black Women in Antiquity, Egypt Revisited, etc.
- Utilize raps, plays and debates to teach about men and women of importance to Africans in America as well as the Diaspora and Africa.
- It is essential that the parents develop a list of Rewards/Punishments, House Rules, Family Goals and Principles, chores and a sign in sheet that confirms the completion of tasks and provides an understanding of the Rewards/Punishments.
- Develop African cultural classes in Holistic sex education and the difference between breeding a baby and taking care of a baby (parenting skills).
- Provide activities that allow boys to do natural food preparation, cooking, ironing, sewing, washing dishes and house cleaning. This can be done in an in-house session or at a campsite.
- Provide the opportunity for girls to learn about cars, electrical wiring, plumbing, carpentry, small motor repair etc.
- Develop activities so that the boys can baby sit and teach infants and toddlers.
- Provide firearm target practicing and self-defense training.

Career Development

- Have the child develop self-employment occupations.
- Invite guest speakers to talk about subjects or about their careers.
- Provide tutorial services and awards ceremonies in recognition of academic achievement.
- Review the study course in order to make sure that career goals can be accomplished.

Spirituality

- Teach the children the Principles of Maat

Truth Righteousness Harmony Justice Propriety
Order Reciprocity Balance

- Provide the opportunity for the children to meditate.

Community Involvement

♦ Encourage the children to participate in African centered groups and lectures, community activities, neighbor clean up drives, car washes, can recycling, etc.

♦ The child should volunteer a minimal number of hours in African centered (social, political, etc.,) and community organizations

♦ Allocate time for the elderly, nursing homes, child abuse or rape centers, homeless shelters, food distribution centers, alcohol and or narcotic anonymous groups, etc.

Physical Development

♦ Incorporate physical fitness exercises (sit-ups, push-ups, jump rope, running, etc.,) into a weekly schedule.

♦ Create sports contest and Junior Olympics along with participation in Egyptian Yoga, martial arts training, drill performances and African boot dance. Additionally teach health, nutrition, herbal and supplements usage and self-diagnosis.

- Study anatomy, physiology, melanin, and biochemical racial differences.

Economics

- Teach the child about Capitalism, African and European Economics and the Global Market.

- Develop a family and individual budget.

- Review the techniques for buying and selling livestock (slaves) during the Wall Street Slave Market (1600 – 1800) and how the concept has been carried over to contemporary times (Wall Street Stock Market).

- Teach how to read and interpret stock market information, newspaper, television and news, etc.

- Review examples of purchased stock/mutual fund investment and how it was monitored over a certain period of time.

- Teach about the private corporation known as the Federal Reserve and other exclusive (secret) societies.

- Observe, analyze and write about the types of businesses and business activity in ancient African and African American communities under European economic control.

- Develop production thinking by making a product or providing a service and selling it to the larger community (i.e. T-shirts, sweatshirts, African artifacts, jewelry, incense, flutes, healthy snack foods, aromatherapy soaps and candles, etc.).

- Develop a business plan (business forecast/projection).

Politics

- Provide information on the ancient African political systems and European-American politics.

- Create an election, campaign speeches and debates.

- Arrange field trips to African centered schools, Kemetic villages, Yorba village, nature trails, city, state, national and international offices, jails and courts.

- Participate with voter registration drives.

FUNERAL

- Create an African centered mock funeral and burial.

- Review the Last Rites Ceremony.

- Explain the role of the family, colors, stool, fast, gifts, spiritual bath, ancestors and food.

- Explain the grieving process, how to grieve and the emotional, spiritual and Maat purpose for grieving.

HIGH AND LOW ACHIEVERS

Successful Student	Unsuccessful Student
High Achievers	Low Achievers
Child has some stimulating and stimulating and supportive supportive schoolteachers	Child lacks schoolteachers
Students accepts African centered norms as legitimate	Students have less long-term acceptance of African centered norms and are in conflict with Euro centered norms
Frequent school contact by parents	Infrequent school contact by parents
Parents want to play a major role in their child's schooling	Parents do not have the time or the desire to play a role
Parents are psychologically and emotionally calm with the child	Parents are psychological and emotional abusive with the child
Parents have clear achievement centered rules and norms	Parents have unclear achievement centered rules and norms
Child is psychologically and emotionally calm with parents	Child is not psychologically and emotionally calm with parents
Parents wants child to go to college or a technical school	Parents do not expect the child to go to college or a technical school
Parents wants child to be positive about schooling	Parents have lower expectations of their child's schooling
Parents allow the child to use parents' knowledge in intellectual manners	Parents do not allow the child to utilize their knowledge in intellectual matters
Parents participate in implicit achievement training activities with	Parents participate less frequently in achievement training activities with

their child	their child
Parents give nurturance and support	Parents provide less nurturance and support
Parents are consistent with monitoring, rules, rewards and punishments	Parents are inconsistent with rewards and punishments and exercise less monitoring of the child's time and activities
Child's brother/sisters interact as organized sub-group	Brothers/Sisters socializing skills are less structured and they are not inter-active as a sub-group
Parents participate in deliberate achievement training activities with their child	Parents seldom participate in deliberate achievement training activities with their child
Conflict between family members is infrequent	Conflict between some family members is frequent
Parents establish clear and specific boundaries and status structure with parents as the dominant authority	Parents establish unclear roles between parent/child and unclear rewards and punishments

SCHOOL MODELS COMPARISON

Caucasian SCHOOL	African SCHOOL
Rote Learning	Conceptual Learning
Abstract rules	Maat rules
Standardization	Variation
Memorize facts	Understands facts
Conform in rigid order	Utilizes variety of ways to conform
"Normality"	Uniqueness
Superior/Inferior Differences/Equal Deficits	Differences serve Maat
Preconceive	Improvise
Logical (without spirituality)	Logic and Creativity (with spirituality)
European centered	African centered
Convergent	Sociocentric
Controlled	Divergent
Meanings are European culture centered	Meanings serve Maat
Cognitive	Indirect
European Linear	African Linear (Maat)
Mechanical	Cyclic
Unison	Humanistic
Hierarchical	Individual in Group
Isolation	Democratic
Deductive	Reductive
Scheduled	Inductive
Materially focused	People focused
Constant	Cyclic with nature
Sign oriented	Meanings oriented

PRESCHOOL GUIDELINES

- Requires parental involvement
- Staff should be knowledgeable about African-centered education and have an ongoing in-service training program.
- Facility should be child proof (covers over electrical outlets, no sharp table edges, etc.) clean, roomy, age-level and gender focused. The Preschool should provide culturally related educational materials, toys, games, play activity and equipment. There should be an appropriate childcare giver and child/ giver ratio.
- Curriculum should have structured interaction activities, incorporate stimulating colors, instructional play and social activities for the children.
- The facility should be well lit and the building temperature should be regulated. The noise level should be minimal, the floors, walls and the restroom (toilet) should be clean and (pleasant smelling). Age appropriate furniture should be provided.
- Caregivers and staff must be conscious of their gestures, language and conversation (no sexual oriented dancing, slang, songs, should be allowed).
- The facility should provide meals consisting of natural foods (no white sugar, junk foods, white rice, white flour, etc.)
- Incorporates consistent discipline.
- Incorporates field trips to educational and cultural events, institutions and museums.
- The curriculum should emphasize attention skills along with learning and attitude skills.
- Caregivers and staff should be capable of using therapeutic skills for hyperactive, attention deficit, chemically altered and hypoactive children.
- The school must not use physical and emotional abuse.
- There should be transitional activities between primary activities for the children.
- The staff should be aware of behavioral and emotional clues.

CHAPTER 6
LEARNING

"It is the way we handle difficulties (with children), that is the mark of spiritual growth."

Elaine R. Ferguson, M.D.

Sharing is difficult for a child to learn.

LEARNING TYPES

TYPES OF LEARNERS	USES TYPE WORDS
Auditory – Speaks early	I **hear** what you are talking about
Visual – Acts before they speak	The answer is **clear.**
Touch (Tactile) – Touches constantly	I **feel** that I know the answer.
Rhythm (Cyclic) – Beats on objects with drum rhythms while reading, studying and paces (walks) or wriggles legs or feet. Taps pencil on table (drumming).	I am out of **step** with the class. I am **moved** by your words. It was **slammin.**

Note: Children's intentions "to do" "learn" and or "understand" exceeds their ability "to do," "learn" and or "understand." Children tend to feel that they can do something or have learned or understood something even though they cannot do it, learn it or understand it. They have extremely positive thinking without positive results. They are often frustrated, have mood swings, cry or have negative behavior because their positive thoughts do not bring about positive results. You should calm them and explain that they should keep trying, pause and try again later or another day.

HOW TO USE LEARNING TYPE CHARTS

A "yes" or "no" answer to the following Learning Types statements will identify the type of Learner you and your child are. If the majority of the "yeses" are in one type then you or your child are those types or favor that type of learning.

Once the type is identified, start using words that are associated with the type. For example, when talking to an Auditory Type, you could say, "That's a loud color," "If you stay angry you will explode," "What you said does not sound correct," "That's clear as a bell," etc. When talking to the Visual Type, you could say, "What you said is unclear," "You had a bright idea," "That answer is foggy" etc. The Touch Rhythm Type responds better to statements such as "That really touched me," "That moved me," "Did you run across the right answer yet," "Are you shook up" etc.

LEARNING TYPES IN TODDLERHOOD

(INFANT TO 13 MONTHS)

Visual Auditory Touch/Rhythm

Communication

When the baby wants to express themselves they...:

▲ like to observe activities
▲ are prone to tantrums rather than participate
▲ say their first word before
▲ point to what they want
▲ rarely babble
▲ try to imitate words spoken by others
▲ usually do not babble until late in their first year
▲ use gestures rather than words

▲ follow directions easily
▲ play quietly
▲ grab at objects and toys impulsively
▲ babble early and frequently
▲ respond with gestures not words
▲ shake their head to "No" or "Yes"
▲ use inflection when vocalizing

Favorite Toys and Activities

When the baby plays they

▲ are visually alert
▲ enjoy the swing, scooter/ bike rides
▲ like rattles and noisemakers
▲ like dangling toys, color and motion
▲ like to be rocked, cuddled and held
▲ "eavesdrop" on conversations

▲ babble to their toys
▲ enjoy a Busy Box
▲ like being bounced and tickled
▲ like rhymes, songs and plays finger
▲ look at picture books
▲ often kick at their crib's mobile

Motor Skills

When moving about they:

▲ like to examine small objects with their hands
▲ are very active
▲ spend more time talking not walking
▲ reach for objects before five months of age
▲ crawl before eight months and walk before age one
▲ were slow to sit up and more interested in babbling before ten months of age

▲ prefer riding and toys that make noise
▲ like to pick up and place small pieces and enjoy puzzles/shape sorters
▲ are quieted by being picked up
▲ use toys to create sounds
▲ watch their hands while playing
▲ use riding toys

Ways to Nurture

When the baby becomes fussy they are:

- ▲ calmed by a familiar toy
- ▲ calmed by music
- ▲ calmed by being nurtured, held and rocked
- ▲ distracted by a change of scenery
- ▲ easily distracted by music or drumming
- ▲ easily distracted by a massage or car ride
- ▲ quieted by the sight of a familiar face
- ▲ quieted by the sound of a familiar voice
- ▲ quieted by being picked up

LEARNING TYPE FOR TODDLERS

(13 MONTHS TO 3 YEARS OLD)

Visual Auditory Touch/Rhythm

Communication

When expressing themselves they...:

▲ put words in the wrong order in sentences

▲ combine words into sentences that are easily understood

▲ have unclear speech which is difficult to understand

▲ have a small vocabulary

▲ have a large vocabulary

▲ rely on body language and non-verbal communication

▲ speak in short sentences

▲ like to talk

▲ speak very little

Favorite Toys and Activities

When playing they

▲ choose to play with blocks

▲ learn rhymes and words to rap and songs easily

▲ pull things out of drawers and off shelves

▲ like crayons, paper and paints and tapes

▲ like music videos, CD's

▲ take toys apart

▲ like shape sorters and stacking rings

▲ enjoy being read to

▲ choose the playground, sandbox and outdoor activities

Motor Skills

When moving about they:

▲ look around while playing

▲ have limited coordination

▲ are well coordinated

▲ like to use their hands and fingers in play

▲ focus on language instead of full body movement activities

▲ enjoy climbing

Social Skills

When moving about they

▲ use facial expressions to indicate happiness, sadness

▲ change the volume of their speech according to their mood anger and other feelings

▲ like to touch and hug

▲ tend to avoid being touched

▲ like to be close, prefer talking to

▲ like to be rocked and held and

touching or holding

enjoys nurturing

Emotions

When it comes to their feelings they

▲ tend to be surprised by the outbursts of other children

▲ tend to have frequent outbursts of joy and anger

▲ use names for feelings, such as "happy" or "sad"

Memory

When the toddler learns they

▲ remember activities after seeing them

▲ remember activities after doing them

▲ remember a word or name after hearing it only once

LEARNING TYPES IN PRESCHOOL

(3 TO 5 YEARS OF AGE)

Visual Auditory Touch/Rhythm

Communication

When expressing themselves they...:

▲ are reasonably quiet

▲ use body language and facial expressions rather than talk

▲ are talkative and use complete sentences

▲ speak in short sentences, using simple language

▲ use brief sentences

▲ tell stories in details

▲ communicate through drawing and painting

▲ sometimes talk to inanimate objects

▲ enjoy conversation and searches for words

Favorite Toys and Activities

When playing alone they

▲ like beads, blocks, puzzles and crayons

▲ enjoy climbing

▲ like books, music and drumming

▲ like watching TV, videos and films

▲ tend to use tricycles, bicycles and other wheeled toys

▲ like being read to

▲ enjoy drawing, coloring and crafts

▲ like to play outside

▲ make up stories

Motor Skills

When moving about they

▲ are not particularly active

▲ do not draw or print anything recognizable

▲ enjoy talking about the work they produce

▲ cuts, colors and prints with ease

▲ prefer active play to sit-down activities

▲ talk and instruct themselves while drawing

▲ can draw a recognizable person

▲ run, jump and climb with coordination

▲ prefer talking to fine or gross motor activities

Social Skills

When socializing with other children they

▲ observe before joining in an activity of touching

▲ often avoid being touched

▲ are sometimes bossy

▲ take charge during pretend play

▲ talk to others with

▲ are very sociable playmates

▲ are often quiet
▲ enjoy their company
▲ make conversation easily

Structured Group Settings

When the preschooler is at day care, babysitters or school they

▲ need time to feel relax around other children
▲ fidget and squirm during sit-down activities
▲ prefer to play in groups rather than by themselves
▲ prefer to watch others play
▲ like active group games
▲ are attentive and follow directions well
▲ like working on activities alone and cutting and pasting
▲ sometimes use distractions or attention getting behavior
▲ like to talk in front of the group

Emotions

When it comes to their feelings they

▲ are surprised by the outbursts of others
▲ seem to need reassurance (hugs, smiles and praises)
▲ use names for their feelings, such as "happy" or "angry"
▲ use words to settle disputes
▲ find conflicts enjoyable to watch
▲ have mood swings which are extreme they can be angry one moment and laughing the next moment

Memory

When the preschooler learns they

▲ learn colors, numbers and letters quickly
▲ are more attentive when they can play an active part in the lesson or exercise
▲ memorize songs and rhymes
▲ remember activities after seeing them
▲ imitate the actions of others
▲ enjoy asking and answering questions
▲ recognize packaging of products and the logos
▲ remember activities easily best after trying them
▲ add new words to their vocabulary

LEARNING TYPES FOR KINDERGARTNERS

(5 TO 6 YEARS OLD)

Visual Auditory Touch/Rhythm

Communication

When the kindergartner expresses themselves they:

▲ mispronounce some words
▲ act out events and sounds instead of talking about them
▲ use adult like speech patterns
▲ use simple language
▲ are difficult to understand
▲ tell elaborate stories
▲ omit adverbs and prepositions
▲ speak in short, grammatically incorrect sentences
▲ use sentences that are structurally correct

Favorite Toys and Activities

When playing they

▲ enjoy computers and calculators
▲ find full-body uses for almost every toy
▲ like records, CD's and tapes
▲ like puzzles and board games
▲ like to play outdoors
▲ learn new things by listening to instructions
▲ learn new things by watching
▲ enjoy swinging, sliding and climbing
▲ like books and fantasy play

Fine Motor Skills

When using their hands they

▲ have neat, attractive artwork
▲ do artwork that is messy
▲ create acceptable artwork
▲ print neatly
▲ reverse many letters and numbers
▲ talk to themselves while working
▲ cut, color and paste easily
▲ find printing difficult
▲ have acceptable printing

Gross Motor Skills

When moving about they

▲ like games with set rules such as "Mother, May I?"
▲ never walk when they can run or climb
▲ do more talking than actual playing
▲ choose table games over outside play
▲ prefer outside play to table games
▲ talk themselves through activities
▲ choose games such as badminton which require eye-hand coordination
▲ are well coordinated
▲ choose games such as "Simon says,: which involves verbal interaction

Social Skills

When the kindergartner socializes with other children they

- ▲ become friendly to new people slowly
- ▲ like to be physically active with others uses mock fights, wrestle, etc.
- ▲ enjoy friendships during class time
- ▲ tend to be a loner within groups
- ▲ are sociable but not very talkative
- ▲ often answer for others and are somewhat bossy
- ▲ watch to see what's expected of them before taking part
- ▲ get into trouble for poking and hitting
- ▲ get into trouble for too much talking during class time

Emotions

When it comes to their feelings they

- ▲ have trouble understanding others emotional outbursts
- ▲ react with anger rather than shame or regret when disciplined
- ▲ talk freely about their emotions
- ▲ confront others about their feelings
- ▲ are not very emotional
- ▲ are emotionally needy and easily hurt

Memory

When the kindergartner learns they

- ▲ remember what they have been shown
- ▲ are easily distracted
- ▲ know their address and phone from memory
- ▲ know the sounds of the letters of the alphabet
- ▲ write letters and numbers
- ▲ have trouble number remembering

School

When in the classroom they

- ▲ keep their work area very neat
- ▲ are uneasy and squirm when seated
- ▲ lead most discussions and tend to report others misbehavior to the teacher
- ▲ dress neatly and likes to stay clean during play
- ▲ are active during free time
- ▲ have to be structured
- ▲ are attentive and agreeable
- ▲ warm up slowly to new situations
- ▲ are unconcerned with their appearance and appear sloppy
- ▲ have an appearance that is neither messy nor neat
- ▲ choose blocks, puzzles, or arts and crafts during free time
- ▲ work in an unorganized messy area and quickly clutter their work space

LEARNING TYPE FOR 1ST GRADERS
(6 to 7 Years Old)

Visual Auditory Touch/Rhythm
Communication
When expressing themselves they

▲ mispronounce some sounds and words
▲ tell stories out of sequence
▲ use the correct verb tense
▲ use simple language
▲ speak in short direct sentences
▲ enjoy conversing with adults
▲ are quiet and rarely volunteer an answer
▲ tend to mumble speech sounds
▲ enjoy creating and telling stories

Favorite Toys and Activities
When playing they

▲ like crafts and models
▲ like bicycling and scooter riding and outdoor activities
▲ like reading aloud and having others read to them
▲ enjoy calculators and computers
▲ enjoy pets
▲ like to invent stories for pretend play
▲ enjoy reading and watching others at play
▲ enjoy sports and outdoor play
▲ like the TV, CD's, radio and tapes

Fine Motor Skills
When using their hands they

▲ are particular about coloring and art projects
▲ confuse the order of worksheets
▲ instruct or read to themselves while working
▲ frequently ask for assistance with art projects in words
▲ make neat and complete
▲ presses hard with pencils, paint brushes and crayons

Gross Motor Skills
When moving about they

▲ would rather draw in the sand than use playground equipment
▲ have excellent coordination
▲ use playground toys and equipment to perform and increase their field of vision
▲ like board games more than races or tag
▲ swing and climb faster and higher than others
▲ have average coordination
▲ climb in order to see better
▲ enjoy being outdoors
▲ like talking games and pretend

Social Skills

When socializing with other children they

- ▲ seldom initiate conversation but answer when spoken to
- ▲ are a leader on the playground or doing play activities
- ▲ initiate most conversations
- ▲ are a loner within a group of children
- ▲ express themselves through movement rather than words
- ▲ are sometimes reprimanded for talking too much during class
- ▲ prefer individual projects to group activities
- ▲ are very sociable on the playground
- ▲ are very verbal

Emotions

When it comes to feelings they

- ▲ make facial expressions that reflect their feelings
- ▲ blush and cry easily
- ▲ do not hesitate to express their feelings in words
- ▲ are high strung but calm down quickly
- ▲ rarely express their feelings
- ▲ use their whole body to express their feelings

Memory

When the first grader learns they

- ▲ read words by memorizing
- ▲ require extra help
- ▲ learn math facts easily
- ▲ read words by sounding them out to learn to read
- ▲ remember what they see
- ▲ have problems recalling what they have seen and heard

School

When in the classroom they

- ▲ insist on keeping their work area neat
- ▲ are constantly out of their seat
- ▲ lead discussions and volunteer answers often
- ▲ dress neatly
- ▲ usually wrinkle their clothing
- ▲ are easily distracted by sounds and voices
- ▲ are distracted by the sight of colors or movement
- ▲ are active and are distracted by sights and sounds
- ▲ have an appearance that is not messy but is not neat either

LEARNING TYPE FOR 4TH GRADERS
(9 to 10 Years Old)

Visual Auditory Touch/Rhythm
Communication
When expressing themselves they

▲ prefer to communicate face-to-face
▲ avoid using the telephone whenever possible
▲ like to talk on the telephone and Email or join chat rooms
▲ make sentences that are short and unelaborated
▲ are quiet in but loud on the playground
▲ volunteer to answer questions in class
▲ have a large vocabulary
▲ use an average vocabulary
▲ have a limited vocabulary
▲ speak in long complex sentences
▲ rarely volunteer answers to questions in class
▲ speak in short sentences and tend to mispronounce words

Favorite Activities
When there is free time they

▲ enjoy board games and strictly follows the rules
▲ prefer outdoor play to indoor play, they seem to lose pieces to indoor games
▲ take charge when playing games
▲ spend much of their time at the computer
▲ excel at contact sports, basketball and baseball
▲ read books, surf the web Email, join chat rooms
▲ are often chosen for leading roles in school programs
▲ assemble puzzles, equipment and/or kits easily
▲ can act out a part in a play but are unable to memorize their lines
▲ memorize songs and raps from music video and radio
▲ excel at video games
▲ enjoy attending sporting events

Fine Motor Skills
When using their hands they

▲ make their school work neat
▲ write off the line and into the margin, their number columns tend to drift
▲ tolerate art class but may repeat a project from one year to the next
▲ turn in acceptable but not neat paperwork
▲ produce beautiful, creative art projects
▲ like the hands-on art but are messy in their use of materials

Gross Motor Skills

When moving about they

- ▲ prefer non-contact activities such as running and hiking
- ▲ prefer playground games that involve words
- ▲ are usually the game leader and team captain
- ▲ are best at eye-hand games
- ▲ need a lot of encouragement to participate
- ▲ are flexible and very coordinated, good with gross motor activities

Social Skills

When socializing with other children they

- ▲ prefer to work on individual rather than group projects
- ▲ prefer group projects to working alone
- ▲ do not work well independently or in a group, they need structuring (teacher assistance)
- ▲ tend to be a loner within the group
- ▲ are sociable and maintain interaction by talking
- ▲ seek out other children who enjoy noisy active play

Emotions

When it comes to their feelings they

- ▲ are uncomfortable
- ▲ are understanding and sympathetic to their friends' feelings
- ▲ seem to be moody, impatient and easily frustrated displaying their emotions
- ▲ do not readily express emotion
- ▲ expresses their feelings by talking about them
- ▲ express themselves non-verbally by shouting, hugging, jumping/dancing,i.e.

Memory

When they are learning they

- ▲ have a large vocabulary of words that refer to sight
- ▲ remember new vocabulary words after hearing them only once
- ▲ remember action and movements
- ▲ write and doodle to help themselves remember
- ▲ are good at memorizing poems, jingles, facts, raps, and dates
- ▲ have trouble remembering what they see and hear

School

When in the classroom they

- ▲ dress neatly
- ▲ excel in social studies and reading
- ▲ enjoy doing science projects, tend to need extra help in reading and math
- ▲ excel in math and spelling
- ▲ like to put together their own outfits, which may not match
- ▲ wear clothes that they often wrinkled, rumpled and stained
- ▲ have an organized desk
- ▲ sometimes get in trouble for talking and passing notes

▲ are often up and out of their seat
▲ are moderately organized

▲ conscientiously follow class rules
▲ have a work area that tends to be a mess

The fundamental learning styles do not change significantly from the 5th to the 7th Grades. Therefore, it has been omitted. The attention, moods and behaviors tend to be motivated and modified by sex hormone imbalances, stimulation and sex hormones in non-organic foods during puberty. The child is hormone driven.

LEARNING TYPES FOR 8TH GRADERS

(Ages 13 to 14 Years Old)

Visual Auditory Touch/Rhythm

Communication

When expressing themselves they

▲ participate in discussions when called upon but rarely volunteer to talk

▲ have a very large vocabulary

▲ have a small vocabulary

▲ have an average sized vocabulary

▲ listen and speak easily and effortlessly

▲ avoid eye contact with the teacher in order to avoid being called upon

▲ carefully watches their audience

▲ are uninhibited about speaking in class

▲ often unable to find and use the correct words in conversations

Favorite Activities

When there is free time they

▲ like computer and video games and TV sports

▲ enjoy socializing with friends Email, chat rooms and phone conversations

▲ play a variety of sports

▲ enjoy using the computer

▲ read a lot and often follow the works of a single author

▲ enjoy outdoors activities

Fine Motor Skill

When using their hands they

▲ have excellent hand writing and do precise artwork

▲ have penmanship and artistic efforts that are average

▲ have penmanship and artwork that tends to be sloppy

▲ show great dexterity and coordinates their eyes and hands easily

▲ tend to avoid fine motor tasks like typing and assembling models

▲ feel clumsy using their hands except when their large muscles come into play, as in sports

Motor Skills

When moving about they

▲ have average coordination and are aware of their athletic shortcomings

▲ avoid games and activities that might make them look deficient

▲ excel at every sport they attempt

▲ prefer non-contact activities like bicycling, riding or running

▲ prefer group activities to individual ones

▲ usually enjoy contact and competitive sports

Social Skills

When socializing with other teens they

▲ are self-motivated rather than socially motivated

▲ are more sociable during physical activities than at social gatherings

▲ are sociable and enjoy group activities

▲ are motivated by the opinions of friends

▲ tend to pair off with one or two people

▲ like physical closeness and tend to touch the person to whom they are speaking with

Emotions

When it comes to their feelings they

▲ are uncomfortable displaying their emotions

▲ tend to be impatient, moody and easily frustrated

▲ are sympathetic and understanding when it comes to their friends feelings

Memory

When learning they

▲ make frequent use of mental pictures when remembering

▲ are aware that they have problems memorizing and seek helpful ways to improve memory

▲ talk to themselves and listens to an inner voice for answers

School

When in the classroom they

▲ are happiest while working alone

▲ require support when studying

▲ tend to let their socializing activities get in the way of school work assignments

PARENT LEARNING TYPES

Visual Auditory Touch/Rhythm

Communication

When talking with others I

▲ speak in simple, clear language

▲ enjoy talking and I am very talkative

▲ have problems selecting the right words to say

▲ prefer to watch rather than talk and I tend to be quiet

▲ excel in verbal expression and I have a good vocabulary

▲ seem to express myself non-verbally, using gestures and body language

▲ observe the speaker carefully

▲ am a good listener

▲ tend to touch the person I'm speaking to

Activities and Hobbies

During leisure time I

▲ enjoy videos, CD's, movies and television

▲ watch music videos and listen to CD's, tapes and read novels or poetry

▲ prefer dancing, running, swimming, and physical activities

▲ express myself through painting, crafts and or artwork

▲ express myself by talking or writing to others

▲ like watching soccer, basketball, football, wrestling, races, track, etc.

▲ enjoy games like Scrabble, Monopoly and computer games like Password or Jeopardy

▲ like talking and listening games

▲ prefer to be active and enjoy participating in sports

Motor Skills

How I feel about my physical self

▲ I prefer watching sports and computer games

▲ I try to avoid sports and outdoors activities

▲ I enjoy outdoors activities

▲ my fine motor skills are better than my gross motor skills: I'm good with my hands

▲ I'm not well-coordinated

▲ I'm coordinated

Feelings

Emotionally I

▲ am embarrassed by others talking about their emotions

▲ am sympathetic to others feelings and problems and am a good listener

▲ cry and laugh easily and tend to have mood swings and emotionally fluctuate between highs and lows

Memory

When remembering I

- ▲ make visual pictures
- ▲ "act out" to help myself remember, I have problems understanding the real meaning of what's been read or said
- ▲ sometimes record material

Work

While at work I...

- ▲ need to follow an agenda at meetings
- ▲ avoid meetings and sitting and concentrating
- ▲ need social interaction and does not like to work alone
- ▲ need lots of space and do not like to sit or stand
- ▲ have problems completing work on time
- ▲ enjoy meetings and like to exchange views with others
- ▲ use outlines and notes to help me stay focused
- ▲ like the company of others but not necessarily to talk, I enjoy working with others
- ▲ talk to myself when working

CHAPTER 7
BEHAVIOR

"Each child comes with the message that God is not yet discouraged of man."

Egyptian Proverb

Toddlers Need For Independence And A Fear Of It. They Still Need A Sense Of Security That Comes From Clinging To A Parent. They Are In An Emotional Conflict.

BEHAVIOR DISORDERS
BEHAVIORAL DISORDER PROGRESSION

Holistic healing intervention can stop the following disease progression:

PRESCHOOL – ADHD (Attention Deficit Hyperactivity Disorder) children with behavioral problems can have mental, emotional, nutritional, food and environmental allergies problems that make them impulsive, non-compliant and their behavior may be described as "fearless in the face of danger." They often have a "tracking disorder" which is the inability to synchronize thoughts with response causing speech and language problems. Normal rewards and punishments tend to be ineffective.

MIDDLE CHILDHOOD – (ages 6 to 12 years old) behavioral and psychological disordered children have difficulty focusing; completing tasks and their schoolwork is inconsistent. They have attention lag and require two days to do a task. They have difficulty in social situations and tend to be emotionally immature. They are usually rejected by peers because of their inability to have self-control and deal with rules that govern behavior.

ADOLESCENCE – children with hyperactivity or hypo activity symptoms may be repressed, cyclic, diminished or subsided. However, the problems with attention and impulsivity tend to remain. At this age, the ADHD problem has caused emotional and mental scarring due to parental emotional battering and repeated failures academically and unsuccessful social relationships. These teenagers are socially branded and tend to associate with peers who have similar problems and they harbor the idea that there is something wrong with their brain. Their dysfunctional relationships accent the negative behaviors and reject the positive behaviors.

ADULTHOOD – in adulthood Behavioral-Disordered children grow to be dysfunctional in many areas. They have problems relating with themselves and problems relating to achievement. They have vocational/work, personal and social relationships problems. Psychological problems, marital and parenting difficulties are more frequent. Their problems become multiple because of their inability to cope with or heal Slavery Trauma and Racism. They distort, alter, and bend information and feelings that they receive and warp the thoughts and feelings they transmit. They may medicate their dysfunctional thoughts and behaviors with anger, violence, sex, drugs and workaholic habits or some other dysfunction.

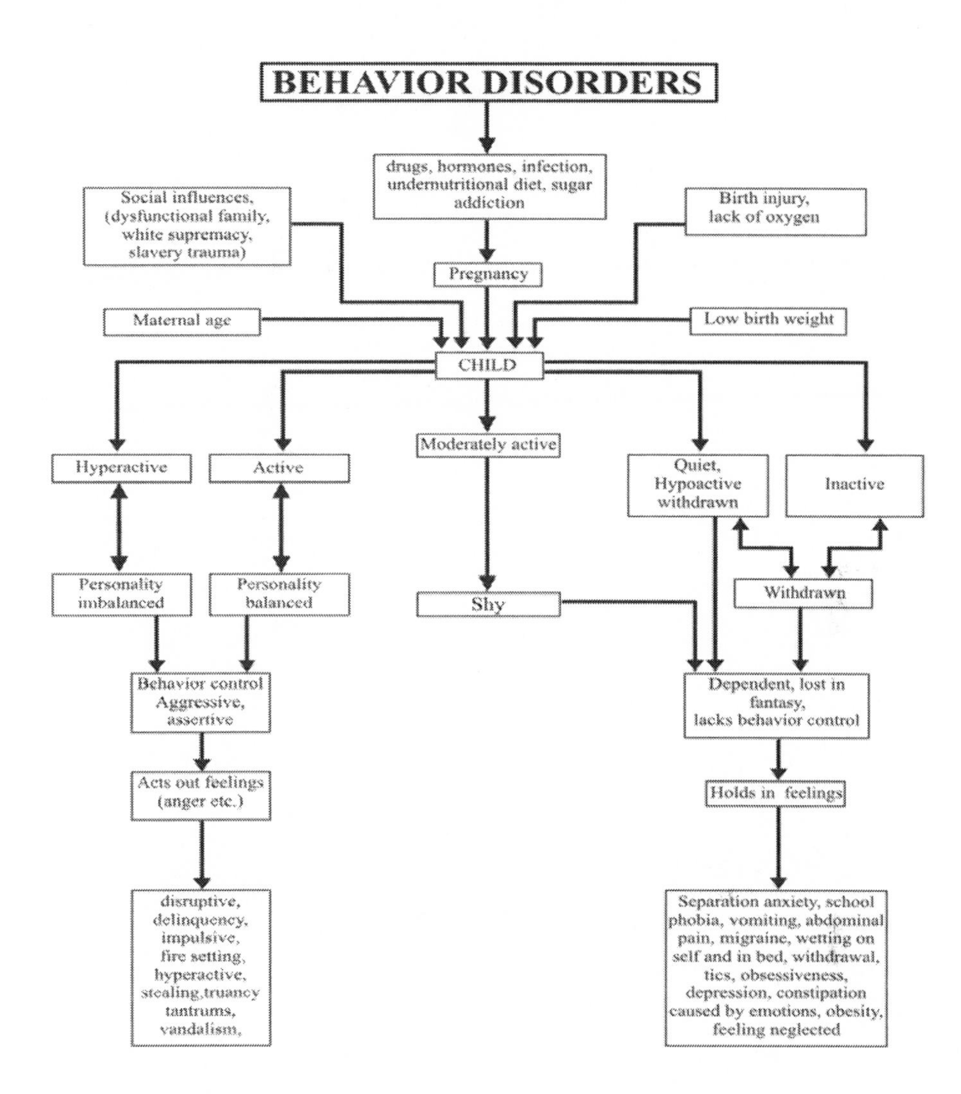
BEHAVIOR DISORDERS
drugs, hormones, infection, undernutritional diet, sugar addiction
Social influences, (dysfunctional family, white supremacy, slavery trauma)
Birth injury, lack of oxygen
Pregnancy
Maternal age
Low birth weight
CHILD
Hyperactive
Active
Moderately active
Quiet, Hypoactive withdrawn
Inactive
Personality imbalanced
Personality balanced
Shy
Withdrawn
Behavior control Aggressive, assertive
Dependent, lost in fantasy, lacks behavior control
Acts out feelings (anger etc.)
Holds in feelings
disruptive, delinquency, impulsive, fire setting, hyperactive, stealing,truancy tantrums, vandalism,
Separation anxiety, school phobia, vomiting, abdominal pain, migraine, wetting on self and in bed, withdrawal, tics, obsessiveness, depression, constipation caused by emotions, obesity, feeling neglected

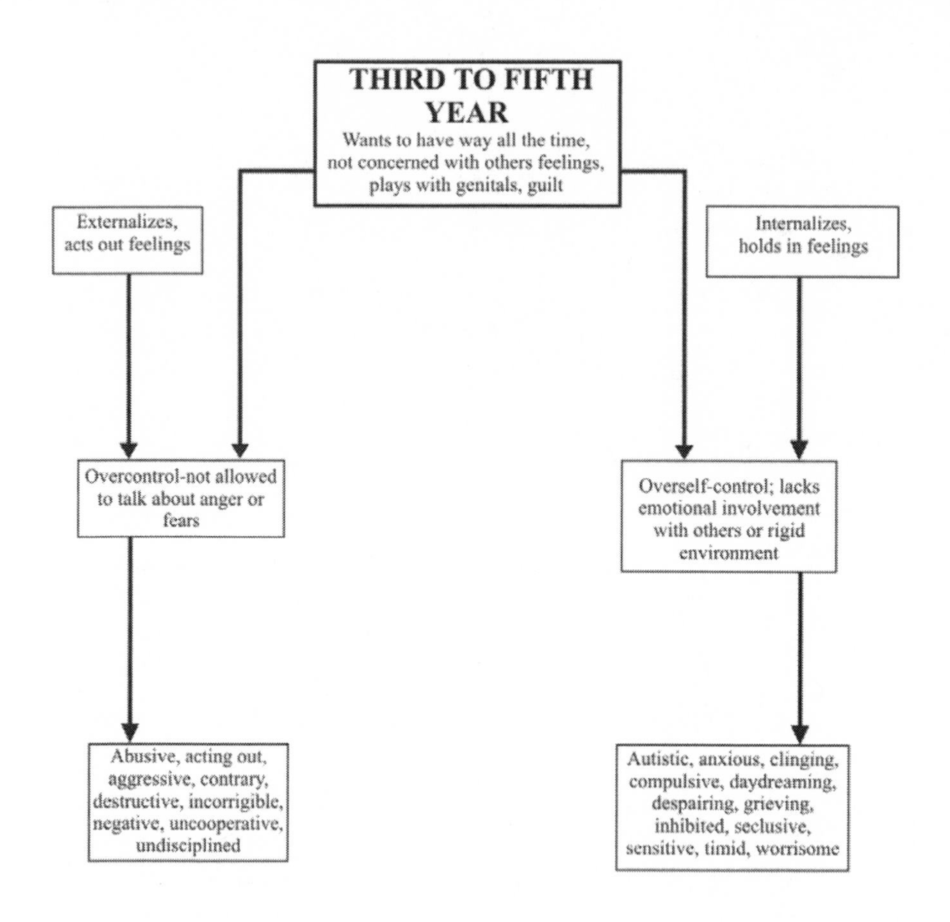
THIRD TO FIFTH YEAR
Wants to have way all the time, not concerned with others feelings, plays with genitals, guilt
Externalizes, acts out feelings
Overcontrol-not allowed to talk about anger or fears
Abusive, acting out, aggressive, contrary, destructive, incorrigible, negative, uncooperative, undisciplined
Internalizes, holds in feelings
Overself-control; lacks emotional involvement with others or rigid environment
Autistic, anxious, clinging, compulsive, daydreaming, despairing, grieving, inhibited, seclusive, sensitive, timid, worrisome

ADHD
(Attention Deficit Hyperactivity Disorder)

Children that are diagnosed as ADHD may be reacting to white sugar consumption, an education that is too slow for them or is not emotionally or intellectually challenging, family issues, lack of parenting skills or teacher skills, a culturally irrelevant and culturally abrasive education and/or they may have a high energy level (high-strung) and are super active. Most ADHD children calm down when their nervous system completes its development, which is around the time they begin puberty. ADHD is not related to intelligence or learning ability. Most of these children have average or above average intelligence. They have difficulty tracking (sequence) and lack the ability to focus on anything for a few minutes and can not ignore distractions. The distractions can be noise, others talking, colors, odors, touch as well as emotions and thoughts in their mind that are not related to the subject or task assigned. Therefore, they go from one thing to another and appear to be scattered.

IMMATURITY
Often they have slow development of emotional, fine motor coordination and impulse control.

BAD CHILDREN
The child cannot sit still or concentrate and this causes hyperactivity. Their inability to be focused causes the parent/teacher to think the child is deliberately being bad. The child did not create the ADHD; they are reacting to the condition. Unfortunately, their reaction is called a "bad child."

❖ Have the child wear bright colors or wear something that will help you locate them in a crowd. They are impulsive and tend to run away

❖ Keep in mind that allergic reactions to environmental pollutants, household chemicals, lead and/or aluminum in public drinking water, carbon monoxide from cars tailpipes, cleaning agents, fumes from carpets, radiation from computers, television, microwaves, noise pollution and foods can trigger hyperactivity.

❖ Be on alert constantly as the child may punch a strange cat or dog, run into the street, grab items in the store, grab hot coffee or food and will have emotional outbursts for no reason.

❖ Remember the child is afraid of their feelings and gets confused when two feelings collide. Give the child coping methods. Tell the child it is okay to be scared, frustrated, angry, sad, confused or feel that they don't know what to do. The child can alleviate these emotions by doing various activities such as using a punching bag, laying down to listen to music, dancing, running, climbing or jumping in a playground or play area.

❖ Learn first aid. Your best preventive methods will not cover all accidents.

❖ Evaluate whether an illness (mental and/or physical), stressor or a dysfunctional family member is contributing to the child's behavior.

❖ Try to avoid physical restraints (tethers-leashes) and physical punishments. An ADHD child lacks the ability to control itself or sit still for long periods. Allow for and anticipate plenty of physical activity. Punishing them is the same as punishing someone with a cold. The hyperactive child is afraid of themselves, and their out of control impulses. They often have a runaway impulse.

❖ Praise positive behavior and/or quiet play.

❖ Do give reprimands in a positive manner rather than a negative manner. For example, "Can you jump up and down on the floor?" Instead of saying "Don't jump on the bed" or "Stop jumping on the bed" or "Can you pretend the floor is the bed."

❖ Avoid taking the child to places where sitting still or keeping quiet are absolutely necessary. You will be creating a disaster and will be setting yourself and the child up for failure.

❖ Help the child improve basic skills such as riding a tricycle, dressing themselves, catching a ball and following directions. This will limit their frustration. Frustration leads to hyperactivity.

❖ When traveling, bring many play items or activities; take breaks just for the activities. Stopping for food does not provide enough interactive time for the child.

❖ You can use a timer for activities. Keep it fun. Tell the child that they have to do a task until the buzzer goes off. Have the child to draw a picture, read a book, put together a puzzle, color a picture, build something, jump up and down, do a matching problem, etc. Set the timer for two minutes for each task. Make sure there are no distractions such as the radio or television on, rap music playing, a window open, a favorite toy laying in the area, etc. You can start with two minutes for each task and gradually increase the time. You can offer a reward for the task. Do not use sweets (white sugar) as a reward.

❖ The child usually does not need as much sleep as an average child. Give them herbs at night such as catnip, kava, hops, etc. Develop a bedtime ritual and ceremony (routine), tell a story, talk about Maat or Kwanzaa principles, give a gentle massage, sing a song or a rap. This allows the child to unwind and relax. Avoid over stimulation, excessive noise or talking, a lot of physical activity or rough play late in the evening and near bedtime. Do not allow white sugar in the diet in any form.

❖ Do keep a schedule and consistent rituals and ceremonies (routines). Order helps the child to search for the emotion and/or thought they need for an activity. Sustaining an emotion or thought is not a skill they have, so a consistent time for a nap, bath, snack, playtime, meal or chores can be of help.

❖ Use relaxation techniques, affirmations, and exercise, give them relaxation (sedative) herbs or ADHD natural supplements. Parents with ADHD children usually are emotionally and physically exhausted especially if they are at home with the child all day. Get as much support as possible from your extended family, spouse, friends and use a baby-sitter.

❖ Give the child alternative play activities and tasks that you can allow to be messed up. It will be less stressful for you. Do not tell the child that you expect the worse from them. For example, do not say, "You will make a mess" or " I can not take you anywhere" instead say, "I know you will do your best" or "I know you will play nicely."

ADHD Drugs
(Attention Deficit Hyperactivity Disorder)

Ritalin (methylphenidate hydrochloride) and similar drugs such as Desoxyn (Methamphetamine hydrochloride) and Cylert (Pemoline) are harmful. They are usually given to children that have ADHD.

RITALIN (METHYLPHENIDATE)

Ritalin is a stimulant (speed) and similar to cocaine (crack).
It causes:

- Learning and memory problems
- Headaches
- Allergic reactions (synthetic coloring, additives)
- Rashes
- Epileptic twitching of the mouth, body and neck (Tourette's Syndrome)
- Drowsiness
- Abdominal pain
- Dizziness
- Cysts
- Cancer
- Alert stupor (pays attention but fails to understand)
- Wiggly legs
- Confusion
- Sleep problems
- Nervousness
- High suicidal tendencies
- Poor relationship skills (with self, others and job)
- Rage
- Liver damage
- Handwriting goes from large to small
- Retards growth
- Dull stare
- Weight loss
- Emotional problems
- Blood pressure problems
- Bedwetting
- Uncontrollable talking (Tourette's Syndrome)
- Tumors
- Puffy eyes
- Belligerence

- Nose rubbing
- Fever
- Nightmares
- Deadly drug interactions with other drugs
- Addiction
- Depression
- Crying spells
- Irritation

Ritalin causes the same problems it is supposed to solve such as nervousness, uncontrollable talking and/or movements (Tourette's Syndrome). It should not be used if there is a history of anxiety, hypertension/hyperactivity, tension, agitation and hyperexcitability – these are ADHD symptoms. Ritalin should not be used if the child plans to do an activity, which requires alertness and coordination such as learning. It is addicting. Ritalin, Cocaine and Crack are Schedule II drugs. The following is a list of a few of the drugs given for ADHD.

DESOXYN causes ADHD symptoms such as talkativeness, hyperactivity, hyperexcitability, irritability and nervousness. It causes blurred vision (reading problems), fast heartbeats, palpitations and irregular heart beats, diarrhea, tremors, constipation, insomnia, dizziness, headaches, weight loss, problems with sugar craving (diabetes), hives and itching. It should not be used for activities that require alertness and coordination such as learning. Desoxyn is used to treat ADHD.

CYLERT causes ADHD symptoms such as irritability, nervousness and uncontrollable behavior. It causes psychosis (learning problems), seizures, rashes, depression (concentration problems), dizziness (reading problems), heart and liver problems, stomach pain, diarrhea, nausea, hallucinations and sleeplessness. Cylert is used to treat ADHD.

WHITE SUGAR, Brown Sugar, Corn Syrup, Dextrose, Sucrose, Maltose, Maple Syrup, Honey and Aspartame can cause ADHD. White Sugar causes the child to become hyperactive and lowers the blood sugar resulting in attention deficit (hypoactive). Food additives, dyes, flavoring, preservatives, artificial colors, salicylate (preservative and flavoring) non-organic foods, chocolate, sodas (high in phosphates), non-organic milk, mustard, cheese (dairy), tomatoes, oranges as well as commercial toothpaste, perfumes, deodorants, cough drops, throat lozenges, antacids, soy sauce, wheat, pork and luncheon meats can cause ADHD.

ANAFRANIL (Clomipramine).
It is addictive and used as an antidepressant; it causes dizziness, difficulty urinating, seizures, dry mouth and sedation.

DILANTIN (Phenytoin).
Anticonvulsant and causes slurred speech, tremors, diarrhea, headaches, confusion, depression, twitches and nervousness.

CLONIDINE.
It causes heart disease, dizziness, nausea, rashes, sedation, eye problems, dry mouth and affects hearing.

ELAVIL (Amitriptyline).
Antidepressant, used for sleep and sexual problems, and causes weight gain, constipation; sensitivity to the sun and sluggishness.

PAXIL (Paraxetine), PROZAC (Fluoxetine) and ZOLOFT (Sertraline).
Stops serotonin, blocks brain function.

KLONOPIN (Clonazepam).
It is used as an antianxiety, it is addictive and causes muscles to relax, as well as constipation, colds and sleep.

XANAX (Alprazolam).
It is addictive and causes sedation, rage, hostility and decreases memory and learning.

TOFRANIL (Imipramine).
It is used as an antidepressant and causes dry mouth, anxiety, sweating, weight gain and drowsiness.

Medically recommended ADHD drugs should not be used if you are expected to do an activity that requires alertness and/or coordination. This obviously includes learning activities (i.e. schoolwork). They cause an educational problem to become a medical problem.

Warning!!!

There is **NO** biochemical test and **NO** biopsy that can justify the use of drugs for Learning Disorders. ADHD is a non-scientific subjective diagnosis. The diagnosis is made based upon the feelings, prejudice and cultural bias of the teacher, counselor, social worker, nurse, doctor etc. **NO** scientific test can confirm a Subjective Diagnosis and/or pinpoint a drug to prescribe.

ADHD NATURAL SUPPLEMENTS

GABA (Gamma Amino Butyric Acid) = Anxiety, stress, pain, depression

Natrol **Cravex** or Nature's Secret **Crave-Less** or NOW **Awe Slim** = Reduces desire for sugar, salt, fats, etc.

TAURINE = Anticonvulsant, antianxiety, eye problems

TYROSINE = Stress, anxiety, depression

PHENYLALANINE = Turns into tyrosine and Dopamine

GLYCINE = reduces aggression, manic depression, sugar substitute

MAGNESIUM = Irritability, confusion, nervousness, jerking muscles, noise sensitivity, constant eye twitching, muscle spasms, tremors, pain

CALCIUM = Nervous stomach, tingling arms and legs, cramps, inattentive, irritability, anger, sleep disturbance

ZINC = Fatigue, tastelessness, alertness, decreased appetite, healing

B VITAMINS = Nervousness, stress, mood swings, fear, depression, anxiety, concentration, tantrums

NIACINAMIDE (B3) = Calmative, improves circulation

PYRIDOXINE (B6) = Calmative, irritated nerves (Carpal Tunnel)

VITAMIN E = Slowly enhances learning

GLUTAMINE = Memory, concentration, cravings

GINGKO OR GOTU KOLA = Memory, concentration

Hyperactivity Herbs

The following herbal extracts should have a vegetable glycerin base without alcohol or vinegar. The extracts should be combined into one formula. They can be used in capsule form or as a tea.

- Chamomile or Catnip or Kava or Hops (relaxers, calmatives)
- Valerian (strongest calmative, taste may be unpleasant)
- Feverfew (stress, tension, headaches)
- St. John's Wort (mood swings, depression)

Attention Deficit Herbs

- Gingko and/or Gotu Kola (memory, brain fuel)
- Damiana and/or Astralagus (energy)
- Feverfew
- St. John's Wort

Hyperactivity Hormone Supplement

- Liquid Melatonin

Attention Deficit Hormone Supplement

- Liquid Serotonin

Attention Deficit Games
(Increases Attention)

Game	Visual Training	Auditory Type Training
1. Focuses Attention	Make mark each time Black card appears	Make mark each time word "Black" is heard
2. Sustained Attention	Make mark each time Black card follows a Green card	Make mark each time word "Black" is heard following word "Green"
3. Selective Attention	Place an array of 3 X 5 cards on the table – make a mark every time a Black card follows a Green card as the cards are placed randomly on the 3 X 5 card array	Make mark each time "Black" follows "Green" on tape recorder as second tape is played with random but different sequence of Black and Green. Must attend to one tape Distraction tape Name cards, e.g. Black three
Alternating Attention	Make mark each time a Black card comes after a Green then change to mark Green coming after Black then change back to Black coming after Green	Make mark each time word "Black" is heard to come after Green then change to Green after Black then change to Black after Green
Divided Attention	Visual auditory is presented at the same time. The child must Mark on the left for Visual and the right for Auditory. When (a) a Black Card is seen to come after a Green one, mark LEFT and (b) when the word "Black" is heard to come after Green, mark RIGHT	

For Visual Training, cut many pieces of Black and Green paper the size of playing cards or color 3 x 5 inch cards. The child makes a mark (✓, o, x, +) on a score sheet each time a flashed card appears in a specific sequence.

For Auditory Training, the child makes a mark on a score sheet each time the word Black and/or Green is said in a specific sequence or when the word is heard in a sentence or story. The exercise can be recorded so that the child can practice alone.

OTHER GAMES

❑ Dot-to Dot Drawings – These drawings help to increase "stay on task" as well as sustained attention along with sequencing and work completion

❑ Crossword Puzzles – Can be used to increase attention to words and sequencing

❑ "Flinch" – This is a two person game in which the players face each other with their palms touching (one's palms face up, the other's palms are down). The one with the palms up (on bottom) must try to slap the other's palm. If the palms up player slaps the other's hand then positions are reversed. "Flinch" allows a behavioral problem child to become more sensitive to body movement and non-verbal movement cues (body language). An adult or parent has to supervise this game because the slaps may become violent. If behavior or slaps become inappropriate, then the game must be stopped.

ATTENTION DEFICIT HYPERACTIVE REPORT CARD (PAID ATTENTION, STAY ON TASK GRADE)

Date	Name of Story or Activity	Length of Story or Activity Minutes, Seconds	Paid Attention on Task Before Training	Paid Attention on Task After Training	Did Not Pay Attention Off Task	Number of Questions Answered	Your Parenting Skill was Good, Fair, Poor

The Report Card measures the progress of the child and the parent's grade indicates how well the parent is utilizing parenting techniques. The stories can be read or can be a video or audio story. The activity can be creative, physical or mental. Computer learning aids can be used. It is necessary to write the minutes and seconds for "Paid Attention" and "Did Not Pay Attention." The objective is for the parent and child to establish a goal to reach each week. The parent's grade is measured by their behavior, control, voice volume (no hollering, yelling, etc.) voice tone, temper, mood and attitude each week. The parent may need to recite a positive affirmation before doing a story or activity. If you think an affirmation will help the parent and child relationship, then both should say an affirmation. The affirmation should be on the child's comprehension level. You can use phrases from Cultural Virtues.

SOCIALLY CAUSED DISEASES

(Mechanized, Addiction to Computers, Cell Phones or Gadgets, Racism, Social Stressors, Unbalanced Emotionalism, Urbanized)

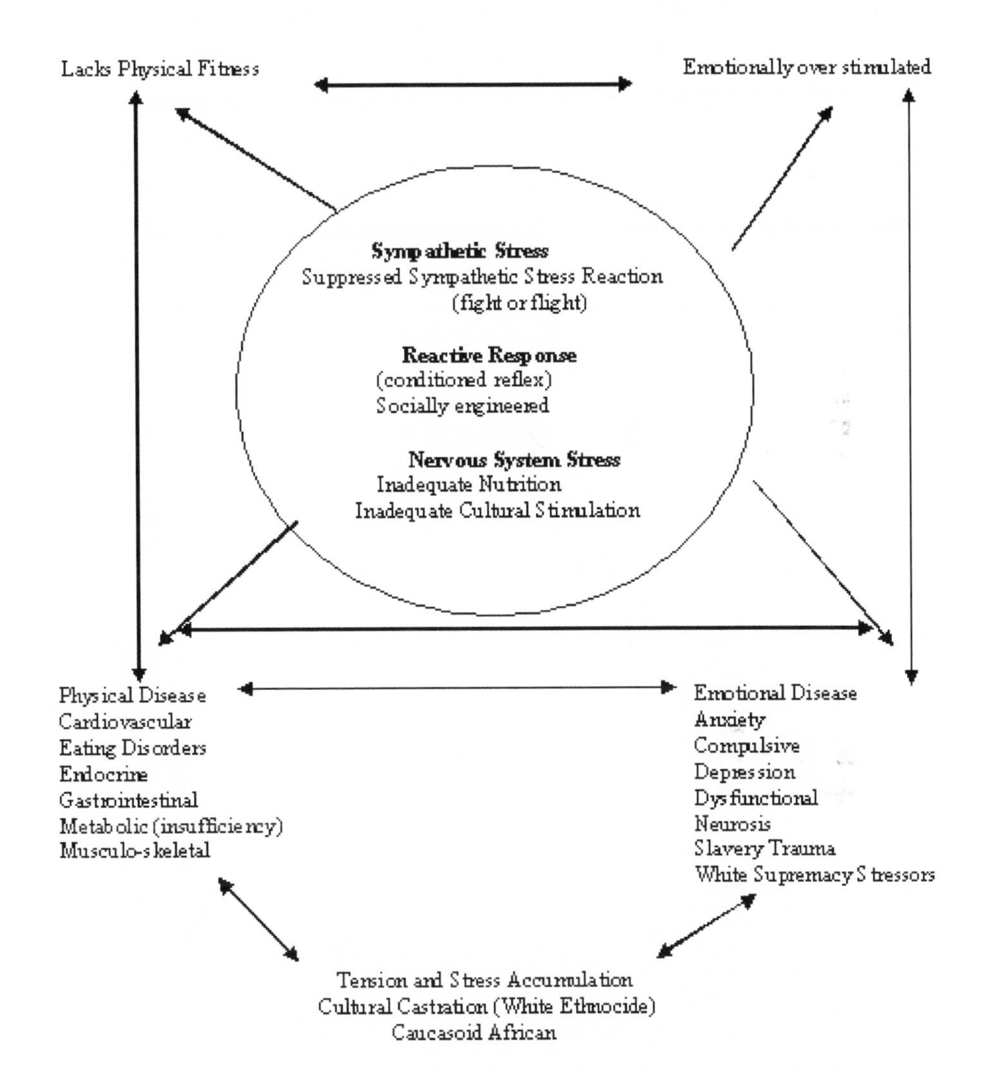

TYPES OF SICK CHILDREN

Hyperactive	Emotionally Immature, Mean	Fearful, Timid	Compulsive
Accident Prone Distractible Immature Restless Talkative Short attention span Underachiever	Acts out Aggressive Breaks toys Fights Has to win No friends Rages Projects Blame Temper tantrums	Cannot face new situations Anxious Clingy Clumsy Depressed, withdrawn Loner Sickly Tearful Tired	Migraine headaches Over achiever in class Stays up late Tense Tics Tries too hard Twitches Ulcer prone
	Causes		
Lack of Oxygen Prematurity	Convulsions High Fever Cause	Intrauterine factors Pregnancy late in life	Drug usage Junk food diet Societal impact
	Contributing Factors		
Sexual Permissive Society Lack of Behavioral Control	Love inadequately given or received Punitive Parents Negative Environment	Love inadequately given or received Negative Emotions	Demands for achievement Rigid Home

Note: Teachers, social workers, psychologists, etc usually make the above classifications subjectively. All Subjective behavior classifications are based upon bias, prejudice and Non-African cultura, standards and classifications.

THE CHEMICALLY ALTERED CHILD

They have:

- Constant thoughts of anticipated fear. "What if?"
- Digestive problems
- Respiratory problems
- Higher pitch crying
- Rashes
- Excessive sneezing, yawning, fevers
- Poor motor skills
- Decreased reaction to what is seen (visual stimuli)
- Excessive crying
- Tends to get less nurturing and care because they do not respond to nurturing appropriately
- Must face objects
- Notochord damage (stem of central nervous system, nerve stem damage that interferes with brain, muscles and bone function)
- Nerve damage (the myelinated nerve covering is incomplete)
- Suicide rate 300 times higher than the average
- Abnormal rhythm in organs
- Decreased weight and head size
- Reduced nipple sucking time (indicates problems with bonding, attachment to mother, self and others)
- Difficult accepting comfort (reduces mother's ability to nurture)
- Coordination problems between nerves and muscles
- Emotional/Thinking/Feeling defect
- Sleep problems
- Tremors
- Confusion and Panic States
- Agitation
- Tantrums (Passive and Aggressive)
- Gaze aversion (looks away when stared at, because staring causes over stimulation of nerves)
- Are easily startled
- Affect disorder (inappropriate responses)
- Must do crazy/weird things, takes unnecessary risks
- Difficulty following sequence (tracking)
- Over excitability
- Mood Swings
- Constant episodes of irritability

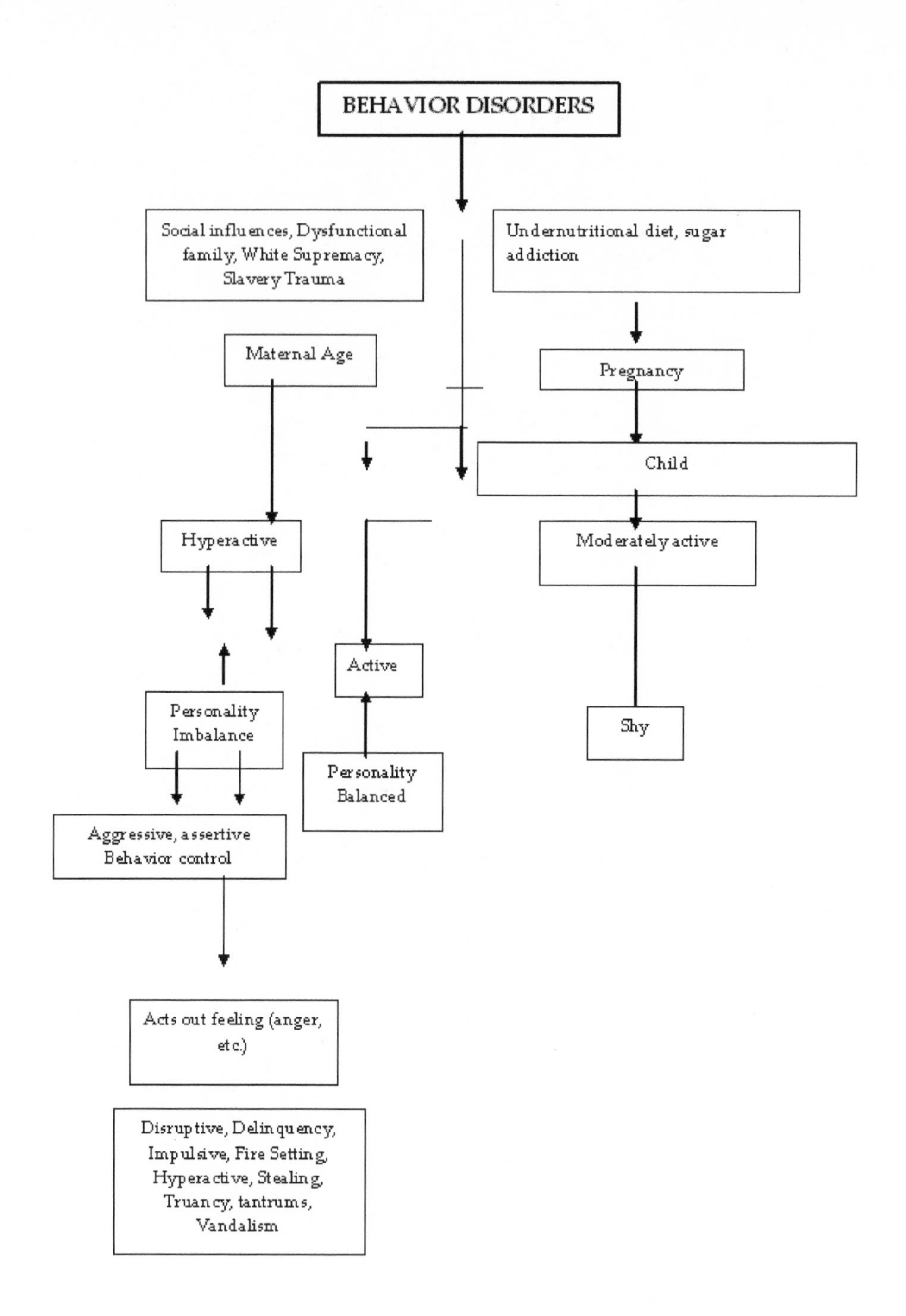
BEHAVIOR DISORDERS
Social influences, Dysfunctional family, White Supremacy, Slavery Trauma
Undernutritional diet, sugar addiction
Maternal Age
Pregnancy
Child
Hyperactive
Moderately active
Active
Personality Imbalance
Shy
Personality Balanced
Aggressive, assertive Behavior control
Acts out feeling (anger, etc.)
Disruptive, Delinquency, Impulsive, Fire Setting, Hyperactive, Stealing, Truancy, tantrums, Vandalism

SUGAR BEHAVIOR PROBLEM
(Sugar Craving Remedy)

Sugar (white sugar, etc.) is an addicting synthetic chemical. It causes learning problems, hyperactivity, attention deficit, mood swings, behavior problems, high blood pressure, cataracts, glaucoma, arthritis, kidney failure, poor circulation, Multiple Sclerosis, Parkinson's, Alzheimer's, Chronic Fatigue, Lupus, Senility, Fibromalgia, baldness and tooth decay. The child develops a Sugar Behavior Problem. The junk food diet, sugary sodas, candy, cake, sugary cereals, etc., addict children to white sugar. They have uncontrollable cravings. Sweets cause the craving for fried foods. Fried foods cause the craving for sweets. Salt causes a craving for sweets. Sweets cause a craving for salt. Children crave salty french fries and salty potato chips because they are biochemically manipulated by the Fast Food and Snack Food industries.

HERBS

Gymenema Sylvestre = sugar craving

Chickweed = craving

Bilberry (Huckleberry), Bittter Melon or Guggulipid = used for diabetes, sugar craving, vision problems

MINERALS

Vanadium (Vanadyl Sulfate) = heals pancreas, reduces craving for sweets

Chromium = increases energy, stabilized blood sugar

YEAST INFECTION HERBS

Usually children addicted to sweets have a yeast infection. Yeast causes a craving for sweets.

Paul D'Arco Herb (yeast remedy)

Garlic (should be capsules or liquid)

SUPPLEMENT

Natrol Cravex or Natures Secret Crave Less or Now Awe Slim = reduces craving for sugar, salt and fried foods (crave less and maintain appetite control)

Lipoic Acid = diabetes, nerve damage, sugar craving

GTF (Glucose Tolerance Factor) = diabetes, sugar craving

FOODS WITH ADDED SUGAR

Apple Butter
Breathe Mints
Brownies
Butterscotch Sauce
Cakes
Candy
Caramel Sauce
Carnation Breakfast Bar
Catsup
Cereals (sugar coated)
Chocolate Sauce
Chocolate Milk
Cobblers (apple, cherry, etc.)
Cocoa
Cocoa Malt
Condensed Milk
Cough Drops, Cough Syrup
Cracker Jacks
Custard
Doughnuts
Dried Fruits
Eggnog
Fiddle Fiddle, Screeming Yellow
Zonkers
Figurines
Frosting
Fruit Cake
Fruits canned in Heavy Syrup
Fruit Cocktail
Granola Crunch Bars
Hawaiian Punch Drink
Jelly, Jam, Marmalade
Ice Cream (bars, cones)
Instant Breakfast
Kool-Aid, Juice Drinks
Lemonade
Licorice
Marshmallows
Milk Shake
Molasses
Peanut Butter with sugar
Pies of any kind
Popsicles
Hi-C Juice
Puddings
Rolaids
Sherbert
Soft Drinks
Space Food Stick
Stewed Sweetened Fruits
Sweetened Carbonated Beverages
Sweetened Mayonnaise
Syrup of any kind
Tang
Toothpaste
Tomato Sauce
Vegetables canned with sugar
Wine (red wine)
Yogurt (fruit flavored)
Yogurt (frozen)
Fruit flavored Gelatin (jello)
Gum
Pop Tarts, Jelly Sandwich (and similar foods)

DYSFUNCTIONALITY IS NO SECRET

Dysfunctionality with relationships, marriages, children, friends, money, spirituality, behavior, thinking, diet, health and lifestyle is taught. Dysfunctional past experiences during childhood influences and rules the present. The past is no secret. The past is revealed by your present behavior and thinking. A child, teenager and young adult raised dysfunctionally has a limited emotional vocabulary and a limited range of thinking and distorted behavior. They are victims of poor parenting and the failure of the Black community to provide the social conditions, which would allow them to reach their highest level of humanism. A goldfish experiment can reveal the impact of dysfunctionality.

In a goldfish experiment, one baby goldfish was raised in a very small fish bowl (dysfunctional) while another was raised in a large fish tank. They were both fed the same amount of food. The goldfish in the large tank grew over 6 inches while the one the very small bowl barely grew an 1 inch (social impact on health). The small goldfish was taken out of its small bowl and put in the large tank. The small goldfish would only swim in an area the size of its small fish bowl. It never would swim around in the large tank. Both fish continued to be fed the same amount of food. The large goldfish continued to grow while the small goldfish remained the same size. This reveals the impact of conditioning (social engineering) on the life of the small goldfish that was raised dysfunctionally. This same affect occurs when an individual is raised dysfunctionally (small fish bowl). The individual's emotions, thoughts and behavior become distorted (dysfunctional). The African Maat culture can heal and rescue the victims of dysfunctionality.

DYSFUNCTIONALITY INDICATORS

Dysfunctionality shows:

- In how you treat people
- In how you treat yourself

When the child's lack of good parenting continues into their teens and young adulthood their dysfunctionality shows when they:

- Abuse or lie to others
- Are petty, start arguments and/or gossip
- Run away from home

- Wear the saggin pants (i.e. shows behinds) or "booty shorts" or thongs. The backward spelling of saggin is "Niggas." It is a word from the social engineering MKULTRA program
- Are doing or selling drugs
- Are making sexual remarks, cussing, fighting and hurting others
- Think material objects, tattoos, jewelry, cars, money and a lot of sex can replace or hide their dysfunctionality or substitute for lack of personal Maat success
- Are looking for love through sex, looking for pleasure by masturbating
- Are gang bang'in
- Staying in or create an abusive relationship
- Have a baby because you want something to love them instead of knowing the baby comes here needing their love
- Pretend to be macho, a dog or bully, so no one will guess that you hate yourself or are hurting inside
- Are smoking marijuana or drugg'in (or a "crack head")
- Are drinking wine coolers, beer, malt liquor
- Use random violence or uncontrolled violent reactions in normal activities
- Are heterosexual and homosexually prostituting
- Leave the child home without a babysitter or abandon or fail to give economic support to their children.

DYSFUNCTIONALITY THROUGH A CHILD'S EYES

A child defines their reality in a child's terms. The following examples reflect how they think and form dysfunctionality. Many times a child has processed their feelings incorrectly or misunderstood them. They become ruled by a past that they did not understand plus they lacked the emotional intelligence to decipher the past. The following thoughts of children can caused dysfunctionality in their lives:

- I am neglected and ignored by my family; I do not get love or positive attention from parents or adults.
- My mother is known as a "player," a "party girl," "crack head," "drunk," or tends to be in and out of many bad relationships.
- My father only comes home to have sex with my mother. He walked out on me and/or my sisters and brothers and I don't know why he left.
- My father is unemployed or in prison or is a known drug addict, player, hustler and/or drunk who has no time for me.
- My mother and/or father died and/or left me and I feel abandoned.
- I feel that if I had just been a little older, I could have rescued my mother and father from being no good or from drugs, alcohol or from having bad relationships, or death and crime.
- I wish I was at "peace" with myself and could accept a past that I cannot change; I want to feel normal.
- Somebody should have taught me my life's purpose, so I can belong.
- One day I found out that the person I was calling Mom or Dad is really not my biological parent and I am adopted. I guess, I really cannot trust anybody.
- I found out that I was given away to a relative, friend, stranger, etc..., I feel like a piece of left over trash, abandoned and deserted like no one wanted to love me.

- I was raised by a relative and told to tell people that my sisters and brothers were my cousins. I am living a lie and my real life must be kept a secret and hidden because it is messed up.

- I found out at a family gathering or at my parent(s) funeral, that my parents had more children by others and they knew about me but I did not know about them. I met them for the first time but do not know what to feel about my feelings.

- School is a waste of time, I would rather watch videos or surf the Web or talk on my cell phone or e-mail my friends. Doing these things makes me feel real and understood.

- I am the "lightest or darkest, fattest or skinniest" of my sisters and brothers. I feel or they make me feel weird, not normal and I don't fit in.

- I feel that there is something wrong with my brain, so I must take Ritalin.

- I have tried sports, religions, computer games, drugs, alcohol, sex and/or masturbation to try to get rid of the pain I feel because I do not want to remember the things that go on in my house or in my head.

- I try to be the "overachiever": I want all "A's". I think it will make me normal and I can be part of a group. My parents cuss and drink and are uneducated, violent and/or druggies. This makes me feel empty and worthless. I wish I had normal parents.

- My mother and/or father are divorced or separated because they did not care enough about me to stay together. I feel I need normal parents to make my life work better. My "thug" friends are better than my parents.

- I have supportive and loving parent(s) or guardian(s) who care for me but I still feel empty because I don't know who I am.

- I have been molested (heterosexually and/or homosexually) by a family friend, or family member or sister/brother. My mama knows, I think she knows and she ignores or denies it and chooses not to do anything about it. She blames me or does not want me to bring it up because it will destroy harmony within the family. I am a freak. I guess I deserved it.

- I was molested (heterosexually and/or homosexually) and nobody knows. I do not know what to do or how to heal or what to heal. I guess God does not like me.

- I feel the only way to get people to show me love is through sex, expensive clothes, knowing a lot of rap songs, cursing or joining a gang.
- I work out (body build) so that I can look good and normal and be accepted.

- I will do anything to get attention.

- My father has a girlfriend or new wife and a new family and has no time for me.

- My parents treat me like a T.V. and they are the remote control. I want to control myself.

- My mother has a boyfriend or new husband and all she cares about is her relationship with him – not me. She has too many boyfriends. She is a slut.

- I allow myself to be used or allow males to beat and cuss me out.

- I see people like my family and/or friends or myself on the Jerry Springer show. It really scares me. I must be sick too.

- I wonder why my parents think they know everything. If they did, why don't they know how I feel.

- My parent(s) think that buying me things is all they need to do. I feel they really cannot help me.

- My parent(s) pretend to be model citizens but our home life is horrible.

- My parent(s) thinks going to church solves everything.

- I don't feel loved, safe from terrorists, safe from AIDS or cared about.

- Why wasn't I born in a good family where you feel much love, concern and support.

- I was raised by relatives who do not like me or love me.
- I feel hurt because I was always told that I was just like my mother or father and that I ain't never "gonna" be nothing!

CONTROL
(MIND AND BEHAVIOR)

OUTCOME BASED EDUCATION
(OBE) and the Child

Purpose of OBE is to:

- Teach values clarification "which changes the child's beliefs, attitudes, etc."
- Force vaccination, Ritalin, Prozac, special education, etc.
- Create Eurocentric International Personality (De-Africanizes)
- Teach the child that feelings about self and others are more important than reading, writing, arithmetic, etc.
- Encourage self-exploration (masturbation)
- Teach that homosexuality is a lifestyle choice (homosexual themes in textbooks, story books, movies)
- Teach that electronic advances replaces civilization advances
- Devalue right and wrong and teach a non-judgmental attitude (right and wrong don't matter)
- Use "Whole Word" learning instead of phonetics (mimic like a talking parrot)
- Emphasize Eurocentric Multiculturalism and Interracial marriages
- Promote "herd" behavior
- Restrain academic performance
- Emphasize the belief that there is no real absolutes or morality
- Promote abortions, cross dressing and self-gratification

OBE was used between 1990 and 1993 in New Zealand, Germany, South Africa with (whites), Australia and Great Britain. This training was not successful. The African culture's music, art, philosophy, Maat, good parenting skills and African centered educational approach protect the child from the OBE.

OBE teaches that Leaches (Tether) are acceptable:

In some parts of the world, tethers are used routinely to keep toddlers safe. In very rare, special circumstances (in a busy bus, train, or plane terminal, for example, or on a subway) putting a toddler on a leash may make sense. This is especially true when there is only one adult in charge and more than one child (or a lot of luggage) to look after. But a child on a leash, restrained by another person, often does not learn self-restraint. In most other situation, when walking down the street, playing in front of the house, or shopping in a department store—it is better to keep your toddler nearby using other techniques.

OBE HISTORY

One of the first documented cases of a MONARCH secret agent was that of the 1940's model, Candy Jones. The book, *The Control of Candy Jones,* (Playboy Press) portrays her 12 years of intrigue and suspense as a spy for the CIA. Candy, whose birth name is Jessica Wilcox, apparently fit the physiological profile required to be one of the initial experiments or human guinea pigs under the government's scientific project, MKULTRA.

The most publicized case of MONARCH monomania has surfaced through the book Trance Formation of America: The True Life Story of a CIA Slave by Cathy O'Brien. The back cover emphatically states, "Cathy O'Brien is the only vocal and recovered survivor of the Central Intelligence Agency's Mk-Ultra Project Monarch mind control operation."

Caucasian therapists involved in deprogramming are Cynthia Byrtus, Pamela Monday, Steve Ogilvie, Bennett Braun, Jerry Mungadze and Colin Ross. Some Christian counselors have been able to eliminate parts of the programming with limited success. Some books on mind control are Walter Bowart, *Operation Mind Control,* Jon Rappoport, *U.S. Government Mind-Control Experiments on Children* and Alex Constantine, *Psychic Dictatorship in the USA*.

Music plays an instrumental role in programming, through combinations of variable tones, rhythms and words. Stephen King's numerous novels and subsequent movies have been used for mind control. One of his books, INSOMNIA, features a picture of King with the trigger phrase "WE

NEVER SLEEP," (indicative of someone with MPD/DID) below an all-seeing eye.

A partial list of other mediums used to reinforce base programming are: Pinocchio, Sleeping Beauty, Snow White, Beauty and the Beast, Aladdin, The Little Mermaid, The Lion King, E.T., Star Wars, Ghost Busters, Trancers II, Batman, Bewitched, Fantasy Island, Reboot, Tiny Toons, Duck Tails, The Dead Sea Scrolls and The Tall Book of Make Believe.

A few movies, which depict or portray some aspect of Monarch Programming, are Hellraiser 3, Raising Cain, Labyrinth, Telefon, Johnny Mneumonic, Point of No Return, The Lawnmower Man and Closet Land.

Programming is updated periodically and reinforced through visual, auditory and written mediums. Computer games are forms of psychological programming. They wire the child's mind so that it is only accessible to the MKULTRA and serves the New World Orders social engineering purposes. Some of the first mind control programming themes are the *Wizard of OZ* and *Alice in Wonderland*; both movies are heavily saturated with occult symbolism. Many of the recent Disney movies and cartoons are used in a two-fold manner: to desensitize the majority of the population, using subliminal and neuro-linguistic programming and to deliberately construct specific trigger and keys for base programming of highly-impressionable MONARCH children.

The Outcome Based Education (OBE) was designed as a Mind/Behavior Control instrument of MKULTRA

MKULTRA = Was a federally funded program that started on April 13, 1953. It was a part of the psychological warfare tactics of the CIA, Military and National Security Council. The acronym MKULTRA is formed by using the letters from Mind = "M" and Kontrolle = "K" and Ultra (alter)—subconscious mind. MKULTRA is a social engineering system used to manipulate and control people. The OBE that is used on children in the public school system, colleges, jobs, games, television and medias is part of the MKULTRA. These behavior control psychological warfare tools are used as part of the New World Orders (one world currency, government and citizen). These programs help the citizens to be uniformed in behavior and filter out terrorists and create terrorists. The programs cause girls to become more physically violent and promiscuous.

MKULTRA uses:

- Behavior Modification via psychology, movies, books, metaphysics, radiation, music, drugs, parapsychology, sex (prostitution, homosexuality) teenagers, adolescents

- Conditioned Stimulus Response sequence = reprogram the mind

Levels of Mind Control (i.e., OBE, MONARCH)

- ALPHA = Alter memory, left (female) and right (male) brain conflicts, fragmented personality

- BETA = Changes in sexuality, morality and behavior DELTA = Self-destructive behavior, violence, devoid of fear, aggressiveness

- OMEGA = Suicidal, self-mutilation (body tattoo, earrings on navel, tongue, eyelids, genitals, nipples, lips, etc.)

- GAMMA = Increase acceptance of misinformation (surfing the Web), misleadership, misdirection Children from birth to 6 years old can be conditioned with radiation, foods, drugs, etc.

AFFIRMATION TO RESIST OBE

Resisting OBE Brainwashing

1. I am an African centered person. I have been partially or completely self-initiated in a Rites of Passage of my culture.

2. I will never give up my African Culturally centered mind or my own free will. I will never betray my people in order to achieve success or power in a Non-African culture.

3. I will continue to maintain African centered focus by all means available to me. I will improve myself and support others of like mind.

4. I will not participate in negative gossip or put down African peoples (includes African Americans, Diaspora) or take part in any action, which will be harmful to my ancestors and culture.

5. I will never forget that I am from a superior African culture, a descendant of the Black people who first civilized and populated the Earth.

6. I am holistic; I will utilize my ancient history, religion, natural diet, culture, herbal medicine, art and science.

7. I am a living example of Maat. I will take holistic care of my spirit, mind and body by eating properly.

8. I worship (African names of God) Onyankopon, Mawu, Olurun, Allah, Imana, Mungu and Ngai.

School Shootings

The schools that have had shootings have had OBE. The adults that have been involved in shooting co-workers at their jobs or at social gatherings (i.e. church) or in their personal life have had OBE. One of the effects of self-esteem (Outcome Based Education) programs is that it distorts and bends the personality. OBE participants feel they no longer have to tell the truth to themselves or others. You do not have to tell the truth because if the truth you have to tell is about your own failure then your self-esteem will be damaged and that is to be avoided. This creates a personality defect. The OBE victim develops a break with reality-psychosis while this OBE psychosis is being created the student constantly plays violent computer games. This subliminally programs the student to use violence as a reward for any type of psychotic thought.

Newspapers are running the psychological "signs" that parents and teachers should be looking for. These OBE symptoms include: "Lethargy... Changes in environment. They may decorate their room all black or go in for gang paraphernalia... Behavior changes. They may develop behavior that ranges from combative to extremely promiscuous."

One of the first states that introduced Outcome Based Education (OBE) – mind altering and behavior modification programming was Arkansas. In 1983, Arkansas was employing the services of a national OBE expert, Ted Sizer of Brown University, who was using a grant from the Winthrop Rockefeller Foundation to fund the experiment. In 1984, Arkansas joined four other states as a pilot for "Relearning" an OBE project. In one Arkansas school, films were shown to students consisting of an ax-yielding young man, a woman having her mouth violently taped while the offender kissed her, a man with his feet in a cement block was shown drowning and rows of dead bodies. This social engineering was deliberate and well researched. The mental and physical response to OBE was known. OBE creates terrorists and the terrorist behavior justifies a Police State, spying on private citizens, random searches, psychological, white Ethnocide, programs, genetic engineering, cloning and Behavioral Disorders drugs.

Psychiatric Institute Or Behavior Modification

The New York State Psychiatric Institute opened a facility on Riverside Drive in upper Manhattan on Friday, May 8, 1998. John Oldham, Director of the New York State Psychiatric Institute said "Technology has exploded, we can do brain imaging and molecular genetics which enables us to learn about the brain chemicals receptors and the inside of the brain in a very huge way that we could never do before."

This technology allows them to manipulate mental illness, terrorism, white supremacy, violence, learning functions, gangs, aggression, sexual behavior, schizophrenia and manic depressive disorders. It will increase the social engineering of people, cloning and make them better servants for Caucasian society.

The genetic manipulation of thoughts and moods can have negative consequences such as an increase in mental illness. It can help identify and label children as genetically inferior and high-risk tendencies for failure, jail, drugs and behavior disorders. One of the drugs involved in the Institute's mind manipulation is Fenfluramine.

The drug Fenfluramine was used on boys in the Institute. This drug was banned from the market by the FDA because it causes serious effects on the heart, which may cause death. Of the 126 boys used in the study, 97% were exclusively poor African American and Latino, and were the younger brothers of convicted delinquents. The program was aimed at drugging the entire family which would eliminate the possibility of them behaving negatively and drugging them would engineer them to be docile.

They paid each family $125.00 to participate in the study. According to the Ad-Hoc Coalition, researchers got the names of the boys for this project from the Manhattan and Bronx Family Courts without the families knowledge and consent.

The experiment on children is designed to validate that aggression in children is biological and that it can be predicted and that children from families with criminal records will become violent criminals when they grow older. This has been proven to be scientifically invalid.

The medical purpose of choosing children who were not problem children was to make sure that these youngsters would not develop problem behavior. The drug was a preventive measure that would change the boys' brains so that they would not mess up their lives later on. This is the reason normal siblings were chosen for the study.

With this psychiatric facility, chemically and genetically altering the brain on a large population allows the Federal Government to engineer Black youths and call it psychiatric help. It is psychiatric terrorism.

CHAPTER 8
EMOTIONS, DISTORTED THINKING, ANGER

"Our destiny, divine or political; social or cultural; economic or ecological, is not tied to what the whites do, nor should it be. And, the sooner we recognize and act on that central fact of our history, the sooner we can begin saving the blood of our children."

Kiarri T-H. Cheatwood

EMOTIONS

"Show Me:" An adult asks the child to "show me how you look mad or glad etc." This gives the child an opportunity to express their feelings and allows for a conversation about feelings and emotions.

INCOMPLETE FAIRYTALE: The parent begins a fairytale such as "A child has a dream and wakes up and says, oh it made me afraid." The child is then asked to complete the fairytale. Fairytales can help reveal-hidden emotions or anxiety within the child.

FEELING COMMUNICATION: The child is asked to tell how much of a given emotion they are feeling and experiencing. Younger children can use Emotion Faces Chart or show the emotion by using their hands (hands close together for a little mad, hands far apart for upset mad). Older children may indicate their level of feeling by selecting a number on a scale from 1 to 10. The number 10 is the most intense. The parent can prepare the child to express feelings by talking about how other children have such feelings. This helps the child to know they are not alone with their feelings and emotions.

EMOTION FACES CHART: These glad, sad, mad, scared and lonely faces can be placed on cards and a game can be made up about the faces. Children can draw faces on cards and explain how they felt that emotion and how they acted when they felt the emotion. They can make up a story about a child who is feeling the emotion expressed on a given face. The parent can make up a story or read a story that has the emotion in it.

EMOTIONAL FACES

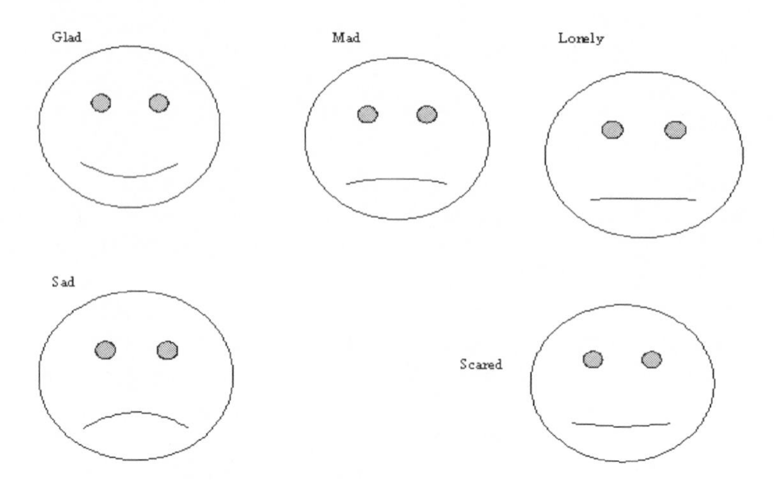

OTHER PEOPLE'S EMOTIONS

The child is usually 5 years old or more before they can consistently put someone else's feelings first. However, you should still teach empathy to them. For example, when the child hits a playmate do not say, "No hitting" say "Ouch!" or " When you hit some one, it hurts them." Instead of saying "Give that toy back, it is not yours," you should say, "When you take someone's (use the child's name) toy away from them, it makes them feel sad." Young children do not have an understanding of ownership and they believe everything belongs to them. You may choose to say "When you take someone's toy, it makes them sad."

The child lacks an emotional vocabulary. They inadequately understand their own emotions as well as the emotions of others. Often they treat emotions like toys or as something to take and play with. Children use emotions without regards to the emotional consequence it can cause others. They can choose an emotion to use, but cannot choose the consequence (reaction) of that emotion used.

EMOTIONAL COMFORT

The emotional "comfort items" are used by the child to nurture, sooth or relax herself or as a source of power (ownership) or for protection or as a companion. The most popular and abusive "comfort item" is the pacifier and thumb. Other "comfort items" are blankets, toteable objects, toys, inanimate objects, pictures, books, music, a particular clothing item, keys, money or an imaginary friend. They can switch comfort items from day-to-day or week-to-week. Some use their parents as a comfort object. When they misplace or cannot find their comfort object, they go through a withdrawal crisis similar to a drug addict or display emotional traumas and tantrums.

It takes time and patience to wean the child from a "comfort item." Do not push the child to give up the extra comfort of a "comfort item." You can try to substitute all "comfort items" but like any addict; they have developed a physical attachment and physical habit, plus an emotional habit as well. Often times, the children associate the "comfort item" with a special feeling that they had in the presence of the object. If the father left or is not nurturing, the child associates keys with the father. Consequently, keys could be their comfort object and a way of making daddy give comfort. "Comfort items" are misplaced and misspent emotions. Children mismatch their emotions as well as their emotional reactions. They use "comfort items" to help them sort out emotions, establish an emotional order and sort mismatched emotions.

EMOTIONAL CYCLES CALENDAR
(Female and Male, Child or Adult Emotional Cycles)

January	1	2	3	4	5	6	7	8	9	10	11	12	13	14	15	16	17	18	19	20	21	22
Feb/Mar																						
Mar/Apr																						
Apr/May																						
May/Jun																						
Jun/Jul																						
Jul/Aug																						
Aug/Sep																						
Sep/Oct																						
Oct/Nov																						
Nov/Dec																						
December																						

Month Days of the Month

KEY:

1. Anger
2. Anxiety
3. Cramps/Pain
4. Cheerful
5. Depressed
6. Excessive Fighting
7. Only eats Sweets
8. Forgetful
9. Headache
10. Hopelessness
11. Impatient
12. Tantrums
13. Insomnia
14. Irritable
15. Stays to self
16. Very hyperactive
17. Wants to sleep
18. Mistrustful
19. Talkative
20. Walks off
21. Stealing
22. Menstruation
23. Back Pain
24. Breaking and Throwing Toys
25. Swelling
26. Energetic
27. Childish
28. Bedwetting episode
29. Much Yelling/Screaming
30. Lack of Energy
31. Nervousness
32. Moody
33. Jealousy
34. Tendency to cry
35. Agitates others
36. Upset
37. Negative Attitude
38.
39.
40.

Add additional categories

Directions for Emotional Cycles

Put the number that coincides with your emotion on the date it occurs. You may have to use a different color pen (red, green, etc.). Record emotions for 2 or 3 months, then you will see a numerical pattern (cycle). This will be the emotional cycle. Knowing the emotional cycle allows you to control your emotions and adapt to your child's or mate's personality. For example, the days that the child (or adult) becomes depressed will be predictable. On these days, the herb, St. John's Wort could be taken to relieve the depression.

OVULATION CYCLE USING TEMPERATURE

(Young Girl or Woman)

1. Get a battery operated oral, ear or temple (forehead) or basal thermometer.

2. Use the Emotional Cycle Chart, a calendar, a piece of lined or graph paper. The first day of your menstrual cycle (period) is day # 1. if your cycle is 28 days, put an 'X' on each day of your cycle. If using graph paper, your chart will be 28 squares across. Write your temperature on the calendar with a red, green or other colored pen/marker.

3. Take your temperature the first day of your menstrual flow. Keep the thermometer near your bed. Take your temperature before you get out of the bed.

4. Record your temperature each day for 2-4 months. If you are ovulating, there will be a drop in temperature immediately followed by a sharp rise of between 0.5° and 1.0° F. While your temperature is raised between 0.5° and 1.0° F, you will be ovulating. This will happen around the 14th day of each cycle. The drop to a low temperature indicates ovulation will start soon. When the temperature rises back up, it will stay there with slight variations until the 2 or 3 day prior to the beginning of the next menstrual cycle. The temperature will drop and a new cycle will begin. If you ovulate and become pregnant, the temperature will remain elevated.

Note: Your emotional and/or ovulation cycle will coincide with the phases of the moon (Blood flow increases on a full moon, etc.) You can use the phases of the moon to predict mood changes and ovulation.

There are small portable hand held microscopes that detect ovulation by using saliva (Ovuscope) and computer programs that can calculate ovulation dates with accuracy (www.ovuscope.com) Call: 866 688 7273

--- Apogee and Perigee ---

The orbit of the Moon around the Earth is an ellipse with the closest approach called perigee, and the farthest point called apogee. The orbit is an ellipse with a focus on the barycenter.

The increase in lunar gravitational force on the Earth at perigee can cause higher high tides and lower low tides than would normally occur. This increased lunar gravitational force combined with the Sun's gravitational force when both the Moon and Sun are aligned with the Earth (New or Full Moon) causes for higher than normal tides.

The Moon's elliptical orbit precesses forward relative to the background stars, taking almost 9 years to complete one circuit.

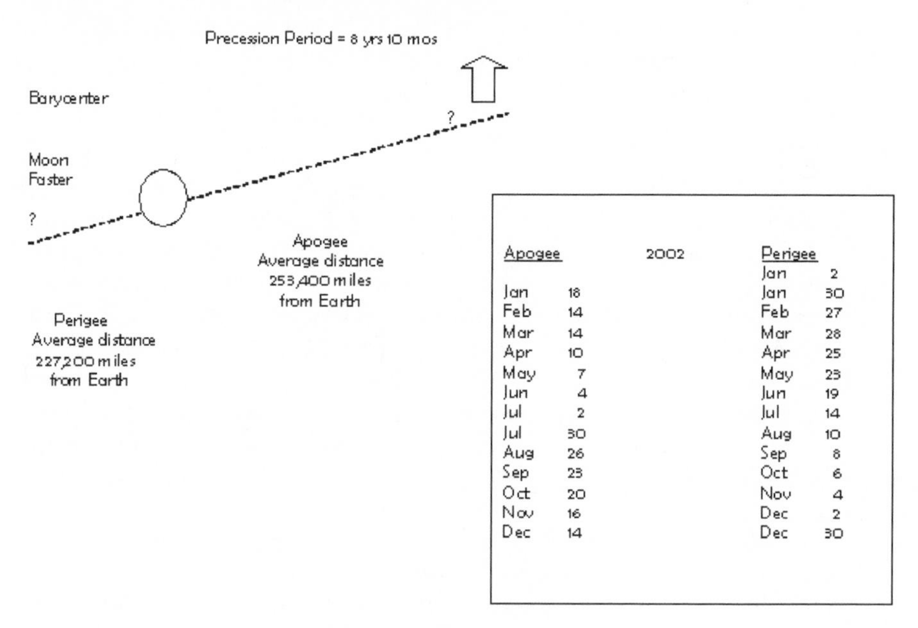

Apogee		2002	Perigee	
			Jan	2
Jan	18		Jan	30
Feb	14		Feb	27
Mar	14		Mar	28
Apr	10		Apr	25
May	7		May	23
Jun	4		Jun	19
Jul	2		Jul	14
Jul	30		Aug	10
Aug	26		Sep	8
Sep	23		Oct	6
Oct	20		Nov	4
Nov	16		Dec	2
Dec	14		Dec	30

Equinoxes and Solstices

Month	Day	Time (UT)	Event
Mar	20	19 : 17 : 13	Spring Equinox
Jun	21	13 : 25 : 29	Summer Solstice
Sep	23	4 : 56 : 28	Autumnal Equinox
Dec	22	1 : 15 : 26	Winter Solstice

BOYS AND EMOTIONS

Emotions are equally the same in boys and girls. They are expressed differently but have the same intensity. The cultural conditioning is what is usually identified as the emotional differences. Boys when they are around three months have a testosterone rise which organizes their emotions differently. However, rearranging the furniture in a room does not make the room (emotions) different (emotional structure). The value of an emotion is subjective. If you feel happy then the emotion of hurt is less. If you feel sad then the emotion of hurt is greater. Your mood and state of consciousness and culture can give increased or decreased intensity to a specific emotion.

Emotions are taught to children. The parent attaches emotions to behaviors. For example, the parent might say, "If you eat your food, you will feel better" or "If you break your toy, you will feel sad."

A boy should be taught emotions. Encourage the boy to express his emotions the same, as you would encourage him to ride his tricycle. When you talk about objects, activities, toys, clothes, Kwanzaa, chores, Maat, baths, sports and food, attach an emotional word to it. Emotional words are not usually spoken to boys. For example, if a girl falls down, she is usually held and soothed and told it is all right to be upset and told she will feel better and be happy again. Meanwhile, boys are checked for wounds, cuts, bruises, brushed off and told to get up and play. Emotional words should be given to the boy. Say, "You fell down and that can make you feel sad or feel like crying." Tell him to say, "I feel sad because I hurt myself but I will feel happy again." Help him to say, "I'm hurt", "I'm sad", "I'm afraid", "I want to cry" etc. He needs to develop an emotionally vocabulary and be able to pick the emotional words or word that matches his feelings.

GIRLS, INTELLECT AND EMOTIONS

Girls are usually encouraged to be emotional and allowed to be emotional in any situation. Girls may need to be challenged intellectually. Do not rush to help girls solve problems, let them make mistakes and try to figure it out for themselves. For example, if a girl drops a toy and it rolls under a sofa. Teach them to use a broom handle to push the toy out from underneath the sofa. Let her climb hills or trees, play in mud, touch worms and attempt to fix broken toys or tighten loose nuts and bolts.

Children learn to use emotions to manipulate their parents and other children. This is especially evident with girls in this Caucasian society. Emotions should not be used to solve an intellectual problem. Emotions weave their own path and emotions communicate directly with emotions. Emotions may trigger a thought. A thought may trigger an emotion. However, emotions have a feeling language and can never be substituted for a thought (Intellectual rationalization). The problems with emotions are that they are mislabeled as a girl's thing. Boys are taught to express their emotions in relationship to sports or cars, while girls are taught to express them in relationships, romance, people and life's situations. This gender classification of emotions handicaps boys and girls and can cause emotional conflicts in relationships.

Girls need to be given intellectual words and rational reasons to attach to behavior. Tell them, "I do not think you thought about this enough and it is causing you to be sad." Tell her to say, "I need to use good thoughts" or "I need to use the right idea and I will not get upset." The young girls may not understand your words but they need to hear the words of intellect in order to be taught intellectual words.

DISTORTED THINKING TYPES

Distorted thoughts contribute to the parent/child relationship and cause painful emotions; low self-esteem, self-hatred, race hatred, worry, depression as well as anxiety can cause you to have conflicts with yourself and other people. Avoid the following distorted thinking:

Personalization

When your thinking is distorted by personalization, you interpret everything around you in ways that mirror your self-worth. Personalization can make you feel good or bad and sometimes it makes you feel great. However, sometimes one bad encounter or negative remark makes you personally feel that your life is worthless.

Catastrophizing

When you catastrophize, you turn everything into a catastrophe and believe that the worse thing will happen. You assume that events and situations have a negative ending.

Example: "I have a cold and have loss weight and that's probably going to turn into AIDS. God, I am going to die!"

Distorted Perception: Weight loss and Colds always lead to AIDS and ultimately death.

Undistorted Perception: Weight loss and Colds do not cause death or AIDS.

Mind Reading

Mind reading occurs when you base assumptions and conclusions on your "ability" to know other people's thoughts.

Example: "He looked at the door while I was talking because he probable wants to leave, he does not like me."

Distorted Perception: "I know what he was thinking about when he looked at the door."

Undistorted Perception: "Only he knows what he was thinking about when he looked at the door (if it was even a conscious gesture)". It more than likely had no reference to your conversation. You were the one worried about whether he likes you. Liking you or not liking you was not involved in the conversation.

Emotional Reasoning

This is a mistaken belief that everything you feel must be true. Using Emotional Reasoning means you feel then see, read and/or listen. Therefore, what you see, read and/or hear is your feelings (emotions), which colors what you see, read and hear. You see, read and hear what your emotions want to feel.

Example: "I feel upset, therefore I must be upset."

Distorted Perception: "My subjective feelings are always real."

Undistorted Perception: "My opinions about myself are cyclical, diet influenced, change all the time, often depend on my reaction to others moods or my mood. No one is just upset or just normal. You probably make poor emotional choices or reasoning sometimes but that's just a part of being human.

Filtering

Filtering means looking at only one part of a situation to the exclusion of everything else. It means that you block out part of reality and see what you believe.

Example: "Our family get together is going to be a disaster. I get along so horribly with my mother and relatives."

Distorted Perception: "My enjoyment of the family reunion depends exclusively on how I get along with my mother."

Undistorted Perception: "Even though I disagree and fuss with my mother or feel hurt by her, I have a functional relationship with my father and siblings and other relatives. They will be at the reunion. Therefore, I will have an enjoyable time.

Fallacy of Fairness

When you use the fairness fallacy, you evaluate people's actions based upon what they do to please you as fair and what they do that does not please your wants or needs are considered unfair. Fairness means it is done your way and unfair means it is not done your way. The fallacy of your fairness is that you are the judge, jury and witness. The person accused of being unfair is not allowed to be at the trial and their defense is automatically considered a lie. These are the fallacy of fairness:
Control Fallacies ♦ Fallacy of Change ♦ Being Right
Shoulds ♦ Global Labeling ♦ Polarized Thinking
Heaven's Reward Fallacy ♦ Blaming

Distorted Thought Elimination

Steps for Distortion Elimination:

1. Identify your emotion
2. Describe the situation that stimulated the emotion
3. Identify the distortion in your thought process
4. Eliminate the distortion

- What emotion (or emotions) are you feeling now?
  "I am feeling angry, upset, sexual, confused, tense and anxious.

- Describe in detail, the event or situation that stimulated your emotion.
  I went to a friend's house to go and exercise as previously arranged. My friend was not at home when I got there."

- Describe your thoughts and identify any distortions in your thinking.
  Because they were not home, I decided that they really did not want to exercise with me and that they really do not like me or respect my feelings enough to let me know that they would not be available.

- Eliminate the distortions.
  There is nothing to support your thought, your friend was not there when you arrived, that was the basis for the distortion. You have been friends for a while. All evidence indicates that they like you. An uncontrollable event or emergency may have occurred. They may have gone on an errand that took longer than expected, they may have been confused about the plan that was made or they may have forgotten about the plan (or you may have misunderstood). The one course of action for you to take would be to call them or wait awhile at their home or leave a note asking them to call you when they get home.

Angry Children/Angry Families

The single most common cause of anger in a child is an angry home. Children learn how angry they should be from their parents, they also learn how and when to get angry, and how much anger is necessary and how to behave when angry.

Angry families do things differently than normal families. They have destructive habits such as:

- They talk to each other and expect an angry response.
- They think a lot of anger is normal and expected.
- No one listens until they get angry.
- They have constant angry moods.
- They try to solve their problems with anger.

ANGRY FAMILIES – ANGER IS NORMAL

Anger indicates a problem. Anger is a symptom of a larger problem. Anger is a sign that something is unjust, imbalanced, not harmonious or wrong. In some families, anger is constantly expressed but never resolved. It makes the child dysfunctional.

Children in angry families get mad sporadically, cyclically or all the time. There may be good reasons to get angry. If there is no reason, they will make up one.

Children and family members in angry families are manipulated to be angry. Someone is almost always angry with someone else. There is/are angry conflict(s) every day or usually everyone is mad at everyone else for real or imagined reasons.

It is like a constant angry boxing match, a dysfunctional soap opera and feelings are always in conflict. There are usually constant angry moments in these families. Moments of harmony or Maat create too much tension. Angry families defuse/discharge tension or harmony by being angry.

ANGER PREVENTION DO'S AND DON'TS

There are ways to prevent anger. Feelings and emotions can stimulate anger episodes. Therefore, it is best to avoid resentful feelings, negative attitudes and issues. The following Do's and Don'ts will help guide you away from being angry with your child.

DO'S	DON'TS
■ Stick to the issue when talking to your child	■ Turn a disappointing behavior into a life sentence for your child
■ Ask yourself what is the child's problem and what you can do to help	■ Let yourself think, act or feel like a victim of a dysfunctional child
■ Throw away old behavior scoreboards concentrate on the child's behavior today	■ Dwell on what the child is doing to you
■ Get help if you need it	■ Go back to old techniques that do not resolve the child's bad behavior
■ Be responsible for your own parenting skills	■ Judge the whole child as bad because of one behavior you dislike
■ Challenge old thoughts about your child that make you stay angry	■ Awfulize (Everything is awful. My life and child is awful.)
■ Think anti-anger thoughts, see joy in the parent/child relationship	■ Devilize (The child was born dys-functional and has an evil streak). That's why they do not follow my rules and instructions. The child's evil streak makes their behavior negative

CONTROL YOUR ANGER

YOU LEAVE. Tell the child that you are really upset. Tell the child you have got to leave before you hurt them or say something that you really do not mean. Promise to return when you can talk calmly. It is important to keep your promise and return to talk. A time-out is not avoiding the situation or running away. It allows you time to think of the appropriate parenting skill needed.

GO SOMEWHERE SAFE WHERE YOU CAN CALM DOWN. Go sit in a quiet area or meditate.

DO THINGS TO HELP YOU CALM DOWN AND RELAX. Drink a cup of herbal tea (kava, catnip, chamomile, passion flower or valerian). Exercise or take a brisk walk, look at a music video or movie, read an interesting book, practice breathing or relaxation techniques. Avoid aggressive things such as watching wrestling, boxing, a violent computer game or film. The objective is to calm down spiritually, physically, emotionally and mentally.

WARNING: Simply walking away from someone when you are angry does not get rid of the anger. You should use positive skills and put them to use. Time-out allows you time to calm down and utilize Maat.

YOU REALIZE THAT YOU ARE CLOSE TO A RAGE OF ANGER. Rages do not just happen. They have a pattern. They are predictable. There are warning signs. You need to learn your Body signals such as sudden sweating, tension, headache, nervous eyelids, squeaky voice, a dry mouth, etc. Thoughts such as "That's it. No more. I can't stand it" or "I won't allow a child to say that to me." Beware of actions like wanting a drink, telling the child to get out of the house, pacing the floor, making fists and raising your voice. If you feel yourself beginning to have these actions and you cannot stop them immediately, you should take a time-out.

LET YOURSELF RELAX. Let go of that out-of-control feeling. Use relaxation techniques. Take your time.

AFTER YOU REGAIN CONTROL, YOU SHOULD RETURN. Ask yourself these questions. Can I be calm and talk no matter what the child says or does? Can I talk calmly even if the child is angry or upset? If not, do not talk with the child. If you do go back to talk without being calm or using positive parenting skills, you will have an anger rage episode.

RETURN. Talk with the child about what happened. Stay calm. Go back to the issue or problem that caused the conflict, stay in a calm and loving mood while you are talking. You will feel better knowing you took a time-out in order to use Maat or a Cultural Virtue. You helped the child feel safe about your anger and their own anger. The child sees you utilizing good parenting skills to bring your relationship closer and united in love.

BE DIRECT. No more ugly moods, loud outbursts and anger fits. No lectures either. Just tell the truth. Say, " I am angry because you said you would do your homework before going out." Make no further comment. No need for angry silence. Save the "if you respect or want to get ahead" generic lecture. They have heard it all before.

BE SPECIFIC. Don't be vague. "I would like more respect and I don't like you splitting your attention." This is too vague and you have just said nothing at all. Compare that remark with, "Please turn off the TV when you are doing your homework, so you will not divide your attention." The child may not like your request. But at least they know what you want. Be specific and honest.

BE POLITE. Polite means using good manners with your children. A child or parent can be polite even when they are angry. Polite children do not talk back to their parents. An unpolite child when told to do something by their parent will say, "Can I finish looking at TV before I do as you told me." Polite children are courteous, tactful and immediately do as they are told without telling their parent about what they want to do. Normal people get angry and they stay polite.

BE A NEGOTIATOR. Do not bribe the child with a reward for good behavior – negotiate. Negotiations are often a better solution than arguing and beatings. For example, you can say, "Take your bath now and then afterwards we can read a story." Do not threaten or promise: "If you do not take your bath right now, I will beat you or I will not read your favorite story." The child's refusal, tantrum or slowness in taking a bath may just be a challenge. Usually, after the challenge and the ignoring of the behavior, the child will reluctantly take the bath.

Children may challenge you by touching an object that they should not and then give you a quick or sneaky glance before they stop touching the object (artwork, statute, crystal, etc.) If the child stops and did not go any further or damage the object, then they demonstrated that they did follow the rules and stopped touching the object which is what you wanted. Forget about it. This allows you and the child to avoid a confrontation. You successfully negotiated the situation without a minor war taking place.

WATCH YOUR ANGER

- You do not have to get angry every time your parents or sisters and brothers get angry.

- You do not have to give in or be nice every time someone gets angry.

- Do not act upon your anger with your parents or on your sisters and brothers. Getting angry with your child will not help when your are actually angry with yourself.

- Tell your parents or sisters and brothers what you want and need without getting angry or attacking them.

- Take responsibility for your own anger and your own life. If you have an anger problem (too much or too little) do something about it now.

Challenge Angry Thoughts

There are four kinds of thoughts that keep children angry:

- Rigid beliefs about the world (family, mother, father, siblings, etc.)

- Rigid beliefs about themselves (low self-esteem)
- Thinking they are helpless (unable to change the way their life is going)
- Blaming others for their anger A Child's Beliefs about the World cause Anger:
- "You can not trust your parent(s) to keep their word."
- "Never believe your parent(s) word or a promise."
- "It's a cruel world. You have to have money to live and be free."

A Child's Beliefs about Themselves cause Anger:

- "I'm an angry child and I will always be this way."
- "Anger runs in my family. That's why I'm angry."
- "I'm naturally a fighter and I need conflicts. Anger is the way to be heard."
- "A Black child like myself is naturally aggressive and angry."
- I'm Black and that means we have to know how to be angry and have an attitude."

CHAPTER 9
PROBLEMS AND SOLUTIONS

"Never forget that intelligence rules the world and ignorance carries the burden."

Marcus Garvey

NOW

(Impatience)

The child has a limited understanding of time (a minute or hour are the same) and the past, present and future are mixed together. "Now" is the only concept of time that they have. "Now" can be a minute or hours to a child. Time is an emotional feeling to them. If it is boring, it is an eternity, if it is fun, time is a second. When they are two years old, they cannot "wait a minute." Waiting a minute is an emotional measurement. By age three, the child waits a reasonable time but usually needs alternative activities to pass time.

The parent has to develop patience with themselves and the child by using the following suggestions:

SET A TIMER

If you ask the child to wait a moment while you do something (talk on the phone, read/check/send E-mail, do a chore, etc.) be sure to give yourself an adequate amount of time before you set the timer. Tell the child when the timer goes off or the hourglass empties, you will be ready. This will give the child a vague sense of time as well as a feeling of control over time and you. When the timer goes off be ready to stop the activity or else the child will not trust you or the meaning of time.

Do not use Colored Peoples Time. Time based upon rhythm or cyclical nature of the beginning and ending of an event. This type of time is based upon nature's rhythm/cycle such as the unfixed beginning and ending of seasons (winter, spring, etc.). Rural Africans such as farmers mostly used Colored Peoples Time. The ancient urban African craft workers, bankers, teachers, administrators, bookkeepers, construction workers and city workers used fixed time and fixed schedules to run the bureaucracy and operate the government.

TEMPTATION

It may be tempting to make the child wait just because they said, "I want it now." This is not reasonable or fair to the child. Remember, you are teaching the concept of time as well patience.

NOW YOU SEE IT

The child wants to do an activity such as play with a toy, ride a bike, slip and slide on a wet floor or wants something they should not have. It probably will be best to remove the item from their view or remove them from the item. If they do not see it, they cannot want it.

BE PATIENT

If you ask the child to stop an activity (reading, playing, bathing, etc.) and they say, "Not now, I'm playing." Tell the child they have to stop playing when the timer goes off. If the child notices that you are impatient, then they will probably enjoy making you irritated and prolong the playing. If you are patient it will influence the child to be patient. If you have the time to wait, it is best that you do instead of grabbing and rushing the child or dragging the child.

ALTERNATIVES TO "NOW"

Remember the child has no concept of time, you do and that gives the child the advantage. You can postpone the urgency of doing something "now" by getting the child to improvise a game, sing rhymes/raps, have them to count or say their ABC's, tell them a story or play a word game.

"NOW" IS REALLY NOW

If the child says, "They are hungry now" and it is not time to eat, give them a light snack. Hunger and thirst are real problems for the energy-using child, especially the hyperactive ones.

"NO"

A child just before becoming two years old or early in the second year may go through the "No" phase. It is a compulsion that they often do not have control over any more than they can control growing or teething. Physiologically, it is easier to enunciate the word "no" than the "yes". It is easier to shake the head from side to side to indicate "no" than to move it up and down for "yes". The child uses "no" emotionally the same way as playing with a toy. They try emotionally to make "no" into a sentence and/or a paragraph. They will say "no" to their sisters and brothers, babysitter, other children as well as their toys. "No" means I am in charge of everything I do, I am myself and I am independent. They will say "no" to your request, rules, eating, sleeping, playing and say "no" to things they want to do. The "no" phase can have a short or long duration. They use "no" to imitate the adults' freedom to control things. Sometimes, they don't mean "no" but say it anyway. This makes them irritated and then they say "no" to "no" and end up in a "no' trap. The "no" phase can test your patience and strain your control. The following suggestions can be helpful:

DON'T GET UPSET

Remember you are the adult, stay calm and relaxed. Tell the child that sometimes they have to do what you say even when they do not want to. Do not punish the child; punish negative behavior or words.

DON'T BE A RIGID DICTATOR

Remember the child is being ordered around all the time. Instead of being a dictator and saying, "Get in the tub and take a bath", try saying, "Now it's time for your bath", "Okay you are undressed and the tub is full of water", "What do we do next?" or "it is bath time what do we do?"

DON'T LAUGH AT "NO'S"

At times the "no's" can be funny. It is a serious character change for the child and should be respected.

BE POSITIVE

Reinforce the positive, praise good behavior and praise when the child says "yes". This makes "yes" rewarding to say.

OPPORTUNITY

If there is no option, do not give one by asking. For example, "Do you want to go home now?" The child will probably respond with their usual "no" answer. It would be better to say, "It is time to go now." If you can give the child several options, it is less likely they will say "no" to all of them. However, if there are no options then give no options. Stick to your decision and when you say "no" mean it.

LET THE CHILD WIN

You may be able to let the child say 'no" and agree with them by saying "okay." If you say "no" to the child and they start screaming or go into a tantrum, you must stick with your "no" response. Sometimes, you may say, "It is time for us to go now" and the child may say, "no! let's stay." If it is not an inconvenience for you, you can say, "Okay I will allow you to play a little longer." "We can go home right away the next time." Letting the child win sometimes can make losing less painful for the child.

LIMIT THE "NO'S"

If you are tired of hearing "no" as an answer, remember to limit your questions. Instead of saying, "Do you want to do a puzzle" say, "It is time to do a puzzle". Do not say, "Do you want to wash your hands?" Say, "Do you want to wash your hands in the bathroom or the kitchen?" Limit your use of using the word 'no", your negative frame of mind easily transfers to the child.

Remember negativism, rebelliousness and challenging your authority is a phase, can last for five to six months. This "no" phase prepares you for the teenager not following the rules rebellious phase. The "Terrible Two's" prepares you for the "Terrible Teens." The teenagers are just as emotionally confused and lost as they were in the "now" and "no" phase except they have added hormone driven mood swings and unstableness.

GIRLS – DO FOR SELF

CONTROL

Girls should be confident, self-sufficient, independent and organized. They should go camping and do outdoor activities, climbing mountains (nothing big), build things (toy airplanes, cars, boats, etc.), help to check the motor oil, air filter and other fluids in the car. Let her play with construction toys. This can help build self-reliance and the attitude that she can take care of herself. She will feel she can control her life.

STRENGTH

Encourage your daughter to exercise and participate in sports. You can demonstrate and encourage physical health by not smoking, drinking alcohol and not eating junk foods. Exercising regularly.

MONEY

Girls need to be taught money management skills. Give her an allowance, help her to budget and make wise decisions about spending and saving. When she is older let her participate in the family monetary spending decisions. This way she will acquire an understanding that spending money is related to monthly bills, savings and emergencies.

FIX IT

Let your daughter do simple household repairs such as tightening nuts and bolts, stopping drips (washer replacement) oiling squeaks and plugging leaks. Read a "how to do" household repair booklet together.

DON'T WANT YOU TO GO

When the parent has to leave the child and the child does not want you to go, this reaction is Separation Anxiety. It usually begins in the last quarter of the first year and continues into the first few months of the second year. Separation Anxiety may not bother some children while others develop it late and closer to two years old and it can continue into the third year or into the fourth. The anxiety can be mild if the child has been prepared for it. The parent can start at an early age by leaving the child with a relative or babysitter for a few hours and gradually progress to a full day and then overnight.

The anxiety can be severe if the child has only been cared for by the parent and has never had a babysitter. Children that have a disease or experience emotional stressors such as divorce, death, family problems, the birth of a new sister or brother, a change in babysitter, moving, a new daycare or have been abused tend to express extreme anxiety. The following suggestions can help them to cope:

❖ Prepare the child for the stress. Start with brief separations such as your disappearance behind a door or into another room. This emotional stressor helps prepare the child and helps the anxiety detox experience. The child goes through attachment withdrawal the same as an adult that has had a broken relationship or divorced.

❖ Reassure the child that you love them and will return. Do not tell the child you will miss them. This will make the child feel obligated to miss you back and they will not be able to enjoy themselves because they think they should be missing you.

❖ When the child pleas with you to stay and starts crying, stay calm, relaxed and do not react to their withdrawal symptoms.

❖ Do not tell yourself, "The child needs to learn even if it is the hard way." The child learns faster when you give them love and attention. When you are sensitive to their feelings of separation anxiety it lessens the stress.

❖ An anxiety attack by the child must be handled with care, patience and understanding. When the child clings to your legs, tries to follow you, hollers, screams and cries to manipulate you into taking them with you; they are using the typical withdrawal tactics of an addict. Their addiction is you and it is a natural addiction. Do not say, "Stop acting badly", "Oh, you are acting silly", or "You make me feel bad, behave yourself and stay here." It would be better to say, "I know you want me to stay but I will be back soon. I love you."

CARRY ME ATTITUDE

The child has an emotional reaction to walking all the time. They were nurtured and comforted by you constantly carrying them in your arms, baby carriers and pushing them in strollers. Walking has caused a lost of that one-on-one comforting. When they say, "Pick me up" or "Carry me" they are going through a slight withdrawal symptom. You are pressuring them to walk all the time and this creates a conflict. The child refuses to walk by protesting and acting like their legs will not carry them or that their legs are made out of rubber is protesting. A child still going through the two years old "no (negativity)" feels that you want them to walk and that's a good enough reason not to walk. The child feels that the feeling of interdependence and the joy of walking is no longer fun. Walking has become a task, a chore, a requirement and every step they take means they have to keep taking steps. Walking to them was treated like a toy but now walking is no longer fun to play with, so the child says, "Pick me up." Assist your child with the walking process try the following suggestions:

- Let the child push their stroller, walker and/or shopping cart to help put fun into walking.
- Play word games; sing raps and/or rhymes to put fun into walking and to distract them from the activity of walking.
- Try taking breaks during a long walk (long for the child, short for you) skip, hop, and jump on one leg or jump like a frog. Put fun into walking.
- Talk about where you are going. Make your destination into the prize for walking. The prize can include a reward such as reading their favorite story, etc.

WANDERING OFF ATTITUDE

A child that wanders off thinks that their journey (wandering) is a way to explore and discover. They are motivated by the excitement of learning new things and danger/caution are not important. The moment they are in a different place or outside the house, their attention and focus is straight ahead to an adventure. It does not matter if the parent wants to go up or down the steps, turn right or left or stop at a traffic intersection; wandering is an adventure that takes them in the opposite direction. The following suggestions may be helpful:

- Take the child places in order to train them how to behave on outings. Take them on training walks for crossing the street, getting on and off escalators or elevators, riding the subway, buses or shopping, etc. This provides you with an opportunity to instruct.

- Take the child on outings that are just for them to wander about. Make it clear to the child that this outing is for them to experience going places.

- Take the child on a parent-in-charge outing. If the child starts to ignore the rules and attempts to wander or even looks like they are going to cross the street, put him or her in the stroller (you may need to bring it along) or firmly hold their hand or put the child in a chair or on a bench for a "time-out" and have them recite the rules for outings. Constantly, repeat the rules and ask them to recite the rules as well as the punishment for breaking the rules. Do not let the child break a rule without a punishment as a consequence. By allowing them to break a rule without a punishment they will often try to break it again and then proceed to break another rule. Be consistent and calm.

- Keep the child's attention on outings by singing or reciting Cultural Virtues or Kwanzaa or Maat principles, raps or songs, playing word games or saying rhymes.

TOOTHBRUSHING ATTITUDE

Children need to learn how to brush their teeth even if they have only one or two teeth. The problem with tooth brushing is that it is not fun and cannot be treated like a toy. The child wants to control their mouth and may not like you controlling it by invading it with a toothbrush.

- Let the child choose a few toothbrushes that they like. Let them select which one of their toothbrushes they want to use each morning and evening. Then proceed with helping them to brush their teeth.

- Let the child practice brushing on a doll that has teeth.

- You may need a doctor, dentist, teacher or an authoritative person to tell the child to brush their teeth. If you have difficulty with them remind them that the dentist (or authority figure) said, "You must brush your teeth."

- Have the child open their mouth and check their teeth for bits of food and then you check behind them. You may have them check your teeth for particles of food after you have brushed your teeth.

- Tooth for tooth is the best approach. Let the child brush your teeth after you brush theirs. It may be best for the child to brush his or her own teeth. Disregard their efficiency technique and excess toothpaste usage. Tell the child that they did a good job; they need encouragement and praise. The child usually does not develop good skills until they are six years old.

- Buy toothpaste that does not contain fluoride (from the health food store). Commercial toothpastes are dangerous and carry a warning on label – "should not be swallowed."

- If you brush the child's teeth, let them sit in front of a mirror so that they can watch and feel apart of the process. Approach their mouth from behind; slightly tilt their head back for better mirror visibility. If you like, sit on the floor with the child in your lap and leaning on you. Let the child help hold the toothbrush. Talk about brushing while you are doing it, you can say, "That tooth looks clean, let's do the next two."

I DON'T WANT TO GO TO MEETINGS, LECTURES, CHURCH, ETC. ATTITUDE

Children have not developed control over their impulse to talk or do something physical. Whatever their emotions lead them to do; they usually do it. When asking a child to do two tasks at the same time such as being quiet and sitting still, you are pushing them to their limitation of control. Most children cannot sit still while watching their favorite TV show, a movie or doing a favorite task with paper/pen (crayon, pencil, etc.). This does not mean not to take them to places that require quiet alertness. They have to be prepared emotionally, physically and mentally to sit still and be quiet and that takes practice. The following suggestions may be helpful:

SEATING
Choose a seat on the aisle, an empty row or in the back of the facility.

PRACTICE
Play going to the meeting and listening to a lecture. Use dolls and stuffed animals as the audience. Practice talking to each other in a soft quiet voice and whispering. Use a timer to see how long the child can sit quietly and work gradually to improve on the time. If necessary, take breaks by walking out of the lecture (church, etc.)

CARRY DISTRACTIONS
You may need to bring quiet toys and picture books or computer learning games along on the outing.

DRESS
Do not put uncomfortable clothes on the child or tight shoes. If they feel best in play clothes, then let them wear them. If they like dressing up, let them do so.

OPTIONS

You may need to consider using a babysitter or only taking the child to short lectures or festivals that provide children's entertainment or child care (some religious organizations do this for their services).

PERSONALITY TYPE ATTITUDES

In order to communicate with someone or understand a person (child or adult) or their problem, you must identify their personality. Listed below are general personality type attitudes:

Positive Attitude	Negative Attitude
Assurance	Doubt
Follows Instructions	Does not follow/forgets
Confidence	Fear
Cooperative	Does not cooperate
Calm/Self-Control	Stressed/No control
Trust	Distrust

COLORS, BEHAVIORS AND PERSONALITY

Excess usage	Causes	Healing Color
Blue	Emotional Deficient Personality	Yellow
Green	Obsession with Money or Sex	Violet
Red	Lack of Anger or Control	Turquoise
Turquoise	Lustfulness	Red
Violet	Uses religion to mask issues	Green
Yellow	Lack of Mental Control	Blue

Excessive use of color choices in clothes, toys, toothbrushes, decorations, jewelry and/or household items can reflect the child or adult personality. The excessive color usage may need to be balanced by other colors. These balancing colors can help heal a subconscious problem and/or behavioral problem.

DROPPING THINGS

The child develops the dexterity with their hands and exercise the dexterity. They develop control over their fingers to the level where they can drop things. Dropping things is another toy for them to play with.

They like the power of being able to drop things and throw peas, food, spoons, stuffed animals and watching things break or scatter over the floor. It is fun and the fun is increased if a grown-up toy (parent) is around to pick up the things that are dropped. Encourage the child to stop dropping things by using the following suggestions:

NO MEAL
If the child drops or throws food., tell the child, "You may eat the food but do not drop it." If the child continues, take the food away from them.

DROP IN THE BUCKET
Let the child drop things into a parent-approved bucket. They can be given blocks, balls, small toys and unbreakable items to drop in the bucket. Let them drop food in a bowl if you are making a salad or drop raisins/dried fruits in a nut mixture or cookie/cake batter. Tell them "You can drop things when it is okay. Dropping food and things on the floor is not okay."

TRUST
Do not trust a dropper around things or with things such as glass dishes, ceramics, breakable drinking glasses and cups, etc. There is no need to tempt the child.

DO NOT OVERREACT
The child will get more amusement if the parent gets upsets, hollers, screams or fusses. Pretend that the dropper is not upsetting you, remain calm, talk in a relax manner and do not point your finger at the child and say, "Don't do it" or "Naughty, Naughty."

THE FLOOR
If the dropping seems to become an addiction, put the child on the floor. Prepare an outdoor lunching in doors. Dropping and watching you pick-up is less fun on the floor.

PUTTING THINGS IN HOLES
(Ears, Nose, etc.)

The child enjoys the adventure of doing things because they can be done. They put things in holes to see where it will go or if it will come out. When the child puts an object in a body opening (orifice) tell them "It is not okay." For example, say, "Crayons are for coloring not for pushing into your nose." A child may put an object into a hole without you observing it. This can cause a bloody discharge, complaints of pain and/or a foul odor. Objects in the nose can cause bleeding, objects in the mouth – choking, in the ear – eardrum damage and in the vagina – bleeding. Any object in a hole can cause an infection.

- If the child continues the behavior, do not make them feel bad or guilty for what they are doing. Constantly tell them in a calm voice "Putting objects where they do not belong is not okay," for example, "Crayons go in the crayon box not in your mouth."

- Do not give the child objects small enough to put in holes (body orifices) such as marbles.

THROWING THINGS

The child learns the new developmental skill of throwing. Now, they want to throw everything that is light enough for them to pick-up. The parent has to identify the appropriate things to throw and the appropriate time to throw them without jeopardizing the household or the safety of others.

- Let them throw a ball in a safe area. They do not have the eye-hand coordination to catch. Therefore, you can play throw and retrieve. They can pick up the ball that has been thrown close to them. You can use a Frisbee.

- Use various sized balls, from beach balls to small rubber balls. Do not use balls that can fit into their mouth or spongy balls that they can bite a piece out of or hardballs. Paper airplanes can be thrown in the house along with beanbags or a ring toss set can be used.

- The child may get upset or angry and throw things. They do not have good impulse control. Tell them it is okay to feel angry but not okay to throw objects. They may need a squeeze ball or a punching bag or punch a pillow to vent their anger on.

- Tell them what is to be thrown and what is not to be thrown (cups, books, toys, dolls, spoons). "This is a ball – a ball is for throwing. You do not throw books – books are for reading."

- When they are getting ready to throw or fling an inappropriate object, take it away from them and give them an appropriate object. Tell them, "If you throw that book, it can hit and hurt someone and make them sad." If they persist, put the object in a box with the word

"JAIL" on it. Tell the child the object is in jail until they decide to say, "I won't throw it anymore."

BUMPING INTO THINGS

Children are usually focused upon their emotions, imagination, the mechanics of walking and where they are going instead of what's in their way or the obstacles in their path. If they do see an obstacle, they usually have too much speed or lack the coordination to avoid it. The one year old is slightly farsighted with limited depth perception and lack of spatial (distance) judgment. Around two years old their vision improves to about 20-60, just before they turn three years old, they can navigate around obstacles better and have about 20-40 visions. Between eight and ten years old, their vision is 20-20 and their coordination has improved.

- Protect the child by having clear paths in the house.

- Remember any distraction (TV, dials, clocks, toys) can cause the child to crash into a table or toy and fall down.

- The child can get lost in their emotions and imagination and fall down without bumping into anything. They have bumped into their emotions/imagination.

SWALLOWING THINGS

Children can swallow small objects and/or coins. These objects most often are passed in the child's bowel movement. If the coin has not appeared in a bowel movement in the potty or diaper and a fever is present, the object may have to be removed.

Large objects can get stuck in the digestive tract. Sometimes a medical procedure with an endoscope may have to be used. This instrument is inserted in the mouth and down the digestive tract, it will reveal the object or an x-ray can visualize the object. If the object is a small button, a battery, sharp needle, fishbone or pen, it may have to be removed. Do not give the child fish that have small bones to eat.

- A child that has difficulty swallowing and is coughing or seems to have chest pain may have swallowed a foreign object.

- Do not let children play with objects small enough to swallow.

GETTING INTO EVERYTHING

Children learn touching (tactile) and their lack of impulse control combined with curiosity causes them to grab, push, squeeze, poke, rub and touch everything. The parent should encourage the child to touch and yet discourage the child from touching unsafe, breakable and/or dangerous objects.

SUBSTITUTES

Give the child toys that have push buttons, knobs and dials to replace the urge to touch the DVD, TV or VCR. Let the child have their own remote-remove the batteries. Give the child adult play clothes to dress in or drape in or to drag on the floor or drag around the house. When you are folding and stacking freshly cleaned clothes, give the child a stack to fold and unfold or to mess up. Give the child various sizes and colors of bottles to fill and empty during their bath time as a substitute for the urge to get in fluid filled containers.

DON'T TOUCH

If don't touch is said in a harsh tone and very often, it will inspire the child to touch. Children like the attention. Whenever possible use a calm tone of voice say "Do not touch", "Please do not touch, "Let's touch something else."

MAKE RULES CLEAR

Every time the child tries to touch the DVD, VCR, glass items, stove, microwave, computer or other untouchables, redirect them immediately and say, "Please do not touch." This has to be repeated until the child stops reaching for the untouchables.

HAVE TOUCHABLES

The more the child is allowed to explore and touch, the less the urge is to touch. Have safe objects and places the child can touch and explore.

RISK LIMIT

The best way to limit the risk of a touch disaster is to childproof your home. Avoid places with breakables, put valued possessions away and teach the child how to touch breakables on an item that you do not mind being broken. Keep such items around so the child can practice touching. Avoid a touch disaster by buckling the child in the shopping cart and stroller.

GETTING INTO EVERYTHING

The child that gets into everything will grow up and get into everything. It is best to monitor and teach them how to touch. Show them how to turn off and on the TV. Let them be in charge of selecting the stations while you are present. Let them squeeze the toothpaste tube properly while you are present. They can be taught to turn on and off lights, hand you clothes to fold, remove flatware from the dishwasher (you should remove the knives, sharp utensils and forks) and use the computer keypad/mouse (store your work first).

- Always demonstrate and supervise the activity.
- Make instructions clear and do not become angry or shout at the child when they accidentally or purposely do not follow instructions.

THUMB SUCKING AND WEANING (Breast Milk, Pacifier, Cup)

THUMB SUCKING

Children use thumb sucking as a comfort and support activity. They may thumb suck if they are stressed, bored, tired, want nurturing, feel upset, cranky, irritated or emotionally struggling with a feeling or with their independence and dependence. Most children usually stop thumb sucking (or fingers or fist) before they are one year old.

- It does not harm the teeth if it is not done day and night and past three years old.
- The redness, irritation and sores usually heal and are not problematic.
- If it interferes with eating, playing, talking, learning and using their hand; then each time the thumb is put in the mouth remove it. Tell the child, "Let's find something else to do with the thumb" or "Please do not put your thumb in your mouth." Have the child do an activity or game that involves using the hand (finger painting, riding a toy, playing catch, kneading dough, etc.).
- If you overreact or fuss, the child will continue just for the attention and the fun of seeing you react. You become another toy.
- Your thumb sucking child may cause you to be stigmatized and get pressure from other parents or frowns or hear whispered remarks and conversations about your lack of parenting skills and the emotional unstableness of the child.

WEANING FROM BREAST MILK

The activity of breastfeeding is physical, emotional and spiritual. The physical attachment to the mother helps the baby to develop language and thought. The skin, pulse and aura of the mother as she reacts to the words of others and her own words, her reaction to sounds, the weather, the home's atmosphere and her reaction to her own body's movements and sounds are translated and transmitted to the baby. The nutritional value of the milk is adjusted spontaneously in order to meet the baby's nutrient needs. No bottle milk can do this. The sound of the mother breathing and her heartbeat are rhythms and fluctuate according to the spiritual and emotional state of the mother and this is also translated and transmitted to the baby.

Breastfeeding is the baby's holistic Rites of Passage into the physical independent world. The baby cannot adequately regulate it's own body's temperature, the baby clinging to the mother's body provides a heating and air conditioning system. Consequently, gradual weaning is best for both members of the nursing team, (mother and child) weaning can start when the child can take solid foods in place of breast milk. Gradual weaning decreases breast engorgement. If the breast gets engorged, hand express some milk to relieve the pressure. The baby needs extra love and attention during weaning. The child may substitute a comfort habit such as thumb sucking, a stuffed animal or blanket during this process. It is best to avoid the amputated nipple (pacifier) unless it is necessary. The following suggestions may help during the weaning process:

- Do not start weaning if the child is having an emotional challenge such a new babysitter, has a new baby sister or brother, adjusting to a divorce or a bad relationship, starting a day care or is having a disease crisis. Wait until the issues are resolved or the child is calm.

- Be sure your child can drink from a cup.

- Nurse before instead of after the bedtime ritual. Try to use distractions such as singing, music, talking or other people in the room to prevent the child from falling asleep at the breast.

- Offer the child vegetable milk from a cup, a snack or a solid food meal when they wake up in the morning, after a nap or when they are hungry. Offer breast milk at bedtime. If the child is still hungry after eating and or still wants the breast, give them breast milk.

- The child eating solid foods and drinking vegetable milks will reduce the milk quantity in your breast.

- For a few nights, let someone else (spouse, friend, relative) put the child to bed at night. Put the child to sleep in a room that they do not associate with breastfeeding or give them a distraction such as a new toy, song, book or rhyme at bedtime.

- Reduce the number of breastfeeding. Start by eliminating the midday feeding. You may try taking the child to the playground or on an outing or changing your daily rituals to distract the child from a scheduled breastfeeding. Eliminate the bedtime feeding; it is usually easier to do than the morning feeding.

WEANING FROM THE BOTTLE

Weaning the child from the bottle while they are one year old is ideal. When the child goes into the "no" phase they are more rebellious, non-cooperative and negative towards your authority, so it is best to start the process before then. Use a cup with a spout or use a glass of vegetable milk instead of giving the child the bottle. Bottle milk drinking tends to decrease the appetite for solid foods and compromises their nutritional needs. There are health problems caused by bottle drinking. A few are listed below:

- Bottle drinking cavities are caused as the result of the natural sugars in vegetable milk or in natural juice pooling in the mouth just before the child falls asleep. The sugars are broken down which causes acid to form and thus teeth are destroyed. The teeth have to be pulled and the child is given false teeth (bridge).

- Children tend to drink from their bottle while flat on their back and this causes ear infections.

- The child drinks excess fluids (three to four quarts a day). This stresses the kidneys and can cause excess electrolytes, which can weaken veins, arteries and dehydrate the muscles and bones.

DON'T WANT THE CUP

The ideal time to get the baby to drink from a cup is around the second half of the first year. Cup drinking is still an adventure and almost considered another toy at this stage. However, if you wait later, you may get resistance. The following may help them start using the cup:

- Prepare the child for cup drinking. Let them use a cup to feed their dolls or play with cups in the tub by filling and emptying it, or serving juice/vegetable milk to you or one of their friends.

- Let your child shop with you and pick out a few cups they like. The cups should have a weighted bottom, which helps prevent tilting, and breakage. Cups come in many varieties of shapes, designs and colors with built in straws, spouts and one or two handles.

- Offer your child the cup before you do the breastfeeding or bottle feeding. At each meal, let them drink a little from the cup and offer them the cup between meals. Always keep the cup within their reach.

- Serve a liquid the child is unaccustomed to or dislikes this can make them reach for the cup with their favorite liquid in it.

- Continue to reduce the bottle feeding even if the child rejects the cup. The child's craving for fluids will eventually make them reach for the cup.

- Do not make a fuss about messy cup drinking. This can cause the child to dislike cup drinking. Make sure the child wears a bib or a shirt that you do not mind them getting messy.

PACIFIER USE

Pacifiers are comfort objects. The child does not expect milk to come out of them. Pacifier use is associated with a child developing the habit of always wanting to chew gum or eat a snack (candy or sodas). It can lead to an Eating Disorder. The pacifier increases the risk of biting the tongue, accidentally injuring the front teeth. They can cause ear infections, misaligned teeth, speech problems and damage to the structure of the mouth. Children should be weaned from pacifiers by the close of their second year. Usually, a child will stop on their own by the ages of four or five. However, they may tend to substitute the pacifier for a lollypop or chewing gum or for sucking on candy. The following are suggestions to assist in the weaning process:

- Be persistent with weaning the child from the pacifier. If they ask for it say, "We no longer need the pacifier."

- If the child uses a substitute such as sucking on an empty cup with a spout, chewing on a small toy or their clothes, gently take the comfort object out of their mouth and say, "Please do not do this."

TANTRUMS

Tantrums have a pattern and a cyclic behavior. The tantrum pattern is made clear if you keep a record of the episodes for a one or two week period. Write down the time of day the tantrum occurs, the stimulus that triggers the episode (eating sweets or a particular food, before meals or before or after an activity, playing a computer game or watching a violent show or movie, signs of stress, frustration, sudden changes in activities, tiredness, or hungriness or being denied an activity or food, before or after homework or a bowel movement, etc.). Examine the tantrum record and note whether there is a tantrum trigger then eliminate or change the tantrum stimulator. The following can be helpful in preventing tantrums:

- Do rituals and ceremonies (routines) to prepare a child for an activity, use a rhyme, rap or song, recite a Maat/Kwanazaa principle or Cultural Virtues before a regular scheduled nap/meal/exercise/bath or bedtime. Do activities that fit the child's learning style and personality.

- Be aware that tantrums can begin at the end of the First year and can get worse around the Second year and continue until the child is four years or older.

- Encourage the child to talk about what's on their mind and how they feel. You can say, "You look like you are upset because you did not finish playing. Are you?"

- Have activities or free time or let the child choose an activity. This will help the child who has been restricted physically or emotionally because of daycare or preschool rules. If the child is not allowed to have free time, they may explode with a tantrum.

- Children constantly spend energy and need to constantly replace it. Make sure there are nutritional natural snacks available and be sure to carry snacks with you on outings.

- Avoid or reduce the need to say "no". The negativity of the parent emotionally triggers a tantrum. When possible try to say "yes". Do not make saying "no" consistent to your child's request to do something. Instead of giving an absolute "no" negotiate by saying, "You can not skip brushing your teeth after dinner but you can play for a short while and then go and brush your teeth".

- Do try to control or supervise every action of the child. Do not stack one rule on top of another rule. Being too restrictive and controlling can lead to a tantrum. Absolute control is only needed when absolutely necessary.

- Do not say "maybe": which to child means "a little no" or "a little yes." Either say "yes" or "no". "Maybe" usually means "yes" to a child and gives the child the signal to do what they want.

- Do not set standards so high that the child can never completely meet them. This makes the child feel frustrated and frustration leads to a tantrum. This does not mean to stop giving the child activities or chores that are not challenging or that they may not successfully accomplish.

- Allow the child to make decisions by saying, "Do you want to drink milk or juice." This lets the child feel in control and is less restrictive. Too many restrictions can cause a tantrum.

- Make the baby sitter and other caregivers and relatives aware of the child's tantrums. When they may occur, preventive techniques and discipline for the episodes.

- When you have noticed that the child has reached their limitation of exhaustion, boredom, frustration, over stimulation or under stimulation, try to get their attention off the negative feeling by using an alternative activity such as talking on the phone, using a learning computer game or give them a book, toy or a rap, song or rhyme to say.

- When the child has a tantrum do not allow them to manipulate you to change your decision that caused the tantrum. Try to be calm even when you are angry, this helps the child avoid a tantrum when they are angry.

- If your child has avoided a tantrum, give them praise and positive reinforcement, say, "I like it when you do not have tantrums" or "You are really behaving good."

TANTRUM CAUSES

- Children have a limited vocabulary. They are action and emotions motivated and express themselves impulsively. Impulsive outburst of their actions and emotions are called a tantrum.

- Many times the child is put in behavioral and emotional restrains by parents and added to this are the intellectual restraints of a limited vocabulary. These restraints are compounded by a button on a shirt, the selfishness of another child, the inability to complete a puzzle, a walk that gets stopped by an accidental fall, etc. Eventually the child is forced to explode with a tantrum.

- Life seems like everybody older than they, are telling them "no," "do not touch" or a spoon fails to find their mouth or a drink from a cup misses their mouth and spills on the floor. A tantrum is a good way for the child to say, "I am tire of it," " I won't take it anymore" "I am taking control."

- Children can be used as a political pawn by their parents and grandparents. Divorced or single or a separated parent can be too busy with household chores, solo childcare chores and work to parent the child. A parent that visits the child may have another relationship plus a demanding work schedule, are unable to parent the child or the parents may try to be the child's favorite by giving gifts and relaxing the rules. The child becomes frustrated with the social complexity, which results in a tantrum.

- Children lack emotional impulse control. The emotions that they are experiencing plus their impulsive emotions from their fantasies are both out of control. So, the child does something to stop all the emotional movements by having a tantrum.

- When the parents give the child too many choices or constantly tell them to make decisions, the child gets overloaded with the burden of making independent decisions and choices and has a tantrum.

- When the child has too much freedom or is around other children that lack control or appropriate behavior, the child has a tantrum to bring parental control to the social crisis.

- Children that have speech problems, stutter, hearing impaired, have health problems (asthma, allergies, sickle cell, etc.) are hyperactive, born after a long struggle with infertility or after several miscarriages or prematurely tend to get spoiled and have a tendency for tantrums.

- Parents that have a severe disease, money problems, depression, are overweight, workaholics, fatigue, worried with relationship problems and many other issues tend to make their problems the child's problem – the child uses tantrums to turn off the their involvement in adult problems.

TANTRUMS IN PUBLIC

Then a child has a tantrum in public, parents feel ashamed and embarrassed. Your feelings come second. Consider how the child feels. They feel emotionally congested, emotionally loss and mixed up as they are hollering, kicking and lying in the floor. The parent has to stay calm and treat the tantrum with the same methods they use at home. Consistent behavior, rules and discipline make the child feel secure with themselves and their emotions. This will help the child to detox from the tantrum.

Prevention is the best way to avoid giving the child an excuse to have a tantrum. The following suggestions can be used as preventive tips:

- Do not disrupt the child's sleep and nap schedule
- Avoid long periods of confinement and forced sitting, sporadic eating, etc.
- Have distractive (alternative) activities for boredom or over excitement. Plan activities.
- Give snacks if a meal is delayed. Carry snacks with you on outings.
- Make time for reading, singing, saying rhymes, hugging, listening to relaxing music, playing with games/puzzles and playground activities.
- If the parent has a tantrum (uncontrolled emotional outburst or behavior) it can inspire a child's tantrum, the adult must control themselves.

TOYS

When selecting toys choose toys that are multipurpose. Choose a variety of toys from different categories. Some toys crossover into other categories. Select toys that provide the following functions:

- Toys that stimulate interest, learning and teach cause and effect or how things work, toys that teach shapes, numbers, colors, patterns: construction trucks, leggos, building blocks, shape sorters and nesting toys, sand and sandbox toys. Buy toys for the bathtub or pool that squirt, float, pour and fill – interactive toys.

- Toy musical instruments such as horns, flutes, and rhythm instruments (maracas, drums, tambourines, keyboard, xylophones, kalimbas, cowbells, etc.).

- Children's cassette players and musical tapes or stories on tapes. You can record stories for the child.

- Toys that require imagination and improvisation: cars, trucks, missiles, spaceships, pretend electronic gadgets, kitchen equipment, building systems, dolls and accessories such as handbags, hats, briefcases, household items, cell phones and board books.

- Toys that improve small motor skills (plastic jigsaw puzzles) especially those with knobs to aid putting in and taking out skills, pop-up toys with dials, knobs and buttons to manipulate, interactive hand manipulated computer toys, nesting and stacking toys, shape sorter boxes and plastic containers for filling and emptying.

- Toys for creativity, play clay of various colors, artistic computer games, interactive creative computer games, crayons and paper, finger painting, painting on poster (paper) with sponges and brushes, collage making.

- Toys for large motor skills: pull toys, riding toys, swings, balls of all sizes, slides, push toys and climbing toys.

- Toys that improve knowledge: computer learning games, vehicles (space ships, cars, boats, fire engines, trains, trucks, airplanes) garden and farming tools (shovels, back hoes, bull dozers, lawn mowers, brooms), household items: fake food, refrigerators, microwaves, alarm systems, stoves, dishes, pots, pans, sinks, dolls, and accessories – hats, shoes, carriages, strollers, car seats, cradles, baby sitters, clothes, money, etc.

PLAY AREA

The home of the child should have a designated play area. Tell them this is where we play with our toys. The young child will get emotionally involved in play and take toys all over the house. This can be a danger and stressor as you and the child will be constantly tripping over or stepping over or bumping into puzzle pieces, blocks, cars, dolls, books, bikes and other small items. The following are suggestions to assist with maintaining harmony in the home:

- Designate a play area. It should be an area that you can easily see or if you cannot see this space place a camera or listening device in the area. Tell the child that this is their play area. If the child takes toys out of this area get the child to take them back and/or help them take the toys back. You must consistently place/return the toys in this area so that eventually the child will know this as their play area.

- The play area should have at least two toddler size chairs, a small sofa, a blanket for short naps, a small table, non-slip carpet or an indoor/outdoor rug for when the floor is cold, a big pillow or cushion, good lighting (full spectrum lights) easy-to-reach and easy-to-use storage for toys and books, educational pictures, mobiles and the area should be colorfully painted.

- You can use different colored baskets for each type of toy. This helps develop the child's organizing skills and makes clean up easier. You can use plastic milk crates, clothes hampers or storage containers of various colors.

- Maintain a regular clean up schedule and routine – have twice a day or once a day clean ups. Start with a rhyme, rap, song or drum rhythm and say, "It's time to clean up. Can you put the blocks away." You may do most of the cleaning up but do have the child participate because it helps teach responsibility.

- If the child constantly leaves a toy or toys outside the play area, warn them that the toy will be put in a box marked JAIL. The toy timeout box (JAIL) is used to reinforce the cleanup rule. Remind the child why the toy is in JAIL (or Storage or Penalty off limits).

PLAYMATE VISITS

When the child has a playmate come for a visit it is very exciting for each child. It means there are two or more children together that can escalate each other's spontaneous impulsive behaviors and fantasies. The playtime can change from togetherness to a tug-of-war to fights to compatibility to shouting to whispers or a total disaster. The following rules can be helpful in maintaining peace:

Compatibility

The children may be happy playing separately, side by side, together or in separate areas of the room. Do not force them to be compatible or expect them to become good friends. Playing together and being compatible are separate issues.

Visit Schedules

Do not try to use one toddler to baby-sit another toddler. It may bring you a few minutes of relief to have another toddler over but it is also extra duty for you. Scheduled playmate visits once or twice a week gives the children something to be excited about. However, visits every other day or everyday can be a chore. Visits can be demanding for the child because they have to control their urge to be selfish and make themselves nice and have good behavior for the duration of the visit. If the child is in preschool or daycare daily then they may be tired of socializing. Too many visits can push their limits of control. If the child does not seem excited or cheerful on the way to a playmate visit or while waiting for a playmate to visit, then it may be an indication to reduce the visits. Sometimes, a child may act grumpy before a visit then after the play starts, they may cheer up. Being sensitive to each child and using parenting skills can make a visit worthwhile.

Timing Visits

It is best to choose the opportune time for a visit. Do not schedule visits at naptime, or when the child is fatigued, cranky, hyper, or just before meals or during the nurturing (hugging) time because it may trigger bad behavior.

Nurture the Visitor

The playmate may go through ups and downs during the visit. Use your parenting skills and reassure the child that they are safe and loved. They may need lap time and a friendly touch (nurturing) or a smile of approval. You may have to say, "I'm here, call me if you need me, don't worry."

Monitor

The children want to be left alone to play but only feel safe playing if you constantly monitor or occasionally supervise an activity. Monitoring prevents the children from getting into mischief.

Conflicts and Fights

Children breakup and makeup and are very forgiving to each other as well as to adult parents that lack parenting skills. If fighting is too regular, use a timer for activities that they do together. This will stop them from reaching their socializing limit. When the buzzer goes off, they should separate and play independently.

Snacks

When the children have a snack be sure that each child has the same number of cookies or crackers, the same amount of juice or vegetable milk, the same size sandwich, the same amount of ingredients in the sandwich and the same amount of ice cubes. This will avoid favoritism and fights.

Be a Host

Greet the visitor at the door and be cheerful towards them. The visiting child is stressed when they have to leave their parent and the child being visited is stressed because they have to share their parent. You can relieve the stress of the children sharing by setting aside some toys for the visitor. Plan a few activities and have snack foods available. You need an alternate supervised activity in case tempers flare and combat breaks out.

Be Realistic

Do not expect fun and harmony to exist for the duration of playtime. There will be minor conflicts.

Brief Visits

When children are less than two years old their ability to focus on playing for a long duration is limited. Limit visits or one-on-one activities to an hour or an hour and a half. Young children tend to play with their own imagination more than with each other.

Clinging instead of Playing

Children have personalities, emotional cycles and different growth and development patterns. Some children are socializers (gregarious) while others are more comfortable clinging to their parent and watching others socialize. The clinging child needs to be prepared and encouraged to leave the warmth attention and nurturing of their parent. They should not be forced or pushed without tact and skill. Listed below are a few suggestions to assist with the process.

Gently sit the child down near the other children. Give the child an activity they can do while sitting such as a shape sorter, books, blocks or coloring. Then gradually move over to where the other parents are. If the child follows you, do not stop them. After a few minutes with you gently take the child back to the play area. You may have to repeat this process many times during each visit with playmates or the playground until the child's builds enough confidence to stay with the other children for a few minutes. When the child feels secure, they will join in with the other children.

SHARING

The child has to understand **ownership** before they understand **sharing**. They have experienced ownership and enjoyed it and feel the sensation of autonomy and self-identity that ownership gives. Possessiveness is a normal developmental phase and necessary before the child can develop the ability to share. Children usually understand ownership by the second year and do not understand sharing until they are almost four years old. Between the concept of ownership and sharing are the confusing concepts of **borrowing** and **lending**. They think that lending is the same as giving and borrowing is the same as receiving (it is now their possession).

The child does not grasp **temporary** use as different from **permanent** use. If the child offers one of their possessions to a playmate or family member, it is their way of showing the possession to them. It is not sharing or a gift but a gesture of empathy. Toddlers will share things that belong them and play with things that belong to others and take possession of it and say "mine." Because the child owns nothing, they are free to own everything. Saying "mine" identifies that the child has emotionally attached ownership to something. They naturally object to sharing and have to be taught to share. The following concepts are a few suggestions for teaching sharing:

Lending and Borrowing

An example may be the best way to teach these concepts. Let the child borrow your keys (use old keys) then ask for them back. Borrow one of your child's toys for a few minutes then return it. Tell the child when they are at the playground they borrow the seesaw or at school they borrow the chair and desk, they do not take these items home or own it.

Explain to them that when you lend something you give it back; when you borrow, you have to give it back. Borrowing means you can use it and give it back. Lending means, others can use it and give it back to you. You will have to repeat these lessons many times in order for the child to grasp the concept.

Do not Trust

The child feels that borrowing; lending and sharing are ways to take their possessions. If the child does not trust or feels insecure, they will have a difficult time with sharing. To them "sharing" is a game of peek-a-boo, now it is mine, now it is not mine. They may not want to share a toy that they do not play with and will hold on to their possession to feel secure. Build their confidence by borrowing or lending an item together and returning it together. Borrow another child's toy. It may be easier if the child that is going to lend has two or three of the same toys. Then return the toy together. This can teach trust.

Praise

Encourage the child to share and when they reluctantly decide to share give them praise. Tell them that sharing toys helps them and the other child have more fun. If the child does not want to share one toy ask them to share another toy. When they are around children their age or size or play with toys that belong to others it makes it easier for them to learn sharing.

Do not Share their toys for them

Ask the child's permission before you offer their toys to another child. It may be necessary for visiting children to bring their own toys. This may help them to exchange toys while they are playing. Before a child comes for a visit, talk about the toys they will leave out for sharing. You may want to put away their favorite toy in order to prevent fighting. If the children do argue over a toy, ask them to stop arguing and have them each play with the toy at the same time or work out a way for them to use it without arguing. You may use a Timer to separate scheduled playtime with the toy.

Share with them

Use every opportunity to say to the children that you are sharing and you need to share. If you are reading a book or eating, you can say, "This is my apple but I like sharing it with you" and give each child a bite.

Cannot Do It

When a child feels that sharing for a few minutes is horrible, it is a true feeling. The child's concept of time is based on their feelings; they feel ten minutes is ten days. Lending, borrowing and sharing means losing ownership of a possession permanently. They refuse to lose control of the possession because it means they lose it, so they "cannot do it."

Share the Feeling

The child is fearful of losing a possession and hesitates to share. If you show that you emotionally understand, it will help the child attempt sharing. Do not tell the child they are being naughty, bad or selfish. Tell them, "I know it is very hard to share your toy. It is a favorite toy that you like very much", "Your friend really feels bad when they cannot use it for a little while." Forcing the child to share does not teach sharing, it teaches the child to do as they are told or get punished.

Taking Turns is Sharing

It may be easier to ask the child to take turns than to share. When at the playground children take turns on the swings and sliding board. Encourage taking turns. Tell the child, "Let the other child use the slide" Let the other child borrow the slide, and you will get the slide back." If they do not fairly take turns, you may have to remove the child from the slide when it is the other child's turn. The child will gradually begin to accept group sharing.

Sharing Game

Make sharing into a game. Say to the child, "You let me play with your toy and I will let you play with my sunglasses."

WON'T TAKE TURNS (SHARING)

Children may go through one developmental phase easy and find difficulty in coping with another. Giving use of their toys to others may mean giving the other child power over them. The toys are the same as a part of them. The child wants to stay in control and being first in using a toy, water fountain, slide, a crayon color, the shape sorter or swings keep them in control. It is easier for the child to overcome developmental difficulty if they are in a daycare or have a group of playmates. The following suggestions can be useful:

TIMING

It is easier to encourage the child to take turns if they are not fatigue, sleepy, cranky, hyper or hungry. Try to pick a time when they are feeling good or very happy about something.

TIMER

Use a timer to help the child to stop using a toy and allow another child to use it. The Timer can reduce fights, arguments and act as a referee. Tell the child, "I will set the Timer. When the Timer rings, your turn will be over and it will be the other child's turn to share." The children will often let their emotions tell them to keep using the toy even after the Timer rings. Be persistent with the rules and eventually the children will accept the timer. It is best to put the toy in the child's hand or let them get on the slide before you set the Timer.

PRACTICE

You and the child can practice sharing by taking turns. When you are reading a book to them, you turn a page and they have them to turn a page. Share a sandwich, let them take a bite then you take a bite. Say, "I enjoyed sharing with you" "We both have fun when we share" Alternate being first. Sometimes, let them bite first then the next time you share you bite first.

BE PATIENT

It will take time for your child to accept that they must share. Usually they will not regularly share with their playmates until they are almost three years old.

"MINE"

The babies are raised with individual ownership of the parent. The parent devotes a lot of time and gives their undivided attention to the baby by feeding them, giving them breast milk, changing diapers, hugging and carrying them. It is a part of the developmental phase to feel the parent is "mine" and the toys are "mine" and everything I touch and see is "mine." The child's emotional impulse wants them to protect and guard what is "mine." The willingness to share is difficult. When two children get together their "it's mine" emotions collide. They want to share but do not know how and when they try the "it's mine," alarm clock goes off in their head.

GUNS

Children are raised in a violent, physical and emotional abusive gun society. The child will need to learn how to use a gun, wait until they are a teenager to teach them. They need to be taken to a gun club and rifle range in order to learn. First and foremost, they must not be given a gun of their own nor should a gun without a lock be kept in the house unless it is stored out of their reach and is locked in a container (box). They must be taught when and when not to use a gun and the emotional and social consequences of legal and illegal gun use. It is not wise to let children use toy guns and practice murdering their playmates. Avoid the computer games that allow your child to practice murder. The following suggestions may be helpful:

PRETEND GUNS

The child may be forbidden to have and use weapons. However, their imagination will create guns out of spoons, sticks, and pencils or make gun sounds with a pretend gun. Make your rules clear about guns and when the child has a pretend gun say, "You are not to use guns, you can play with another pretend toy", "It

is not nice to pretend to hurt others." Parents will find it difficult to ban the use of the imagination or to monitor the imagination. Whenever the child is acting out with a pretend gun, calmly repeat the rules.

COMPROMISE

Some parents allow the use of water pistols, plastic swords, bow and arrow toys and six shooters and ban the use of modern machine guns, laser guns, hand grenades and super water blasters. They do not allow the child to murder people but they can kill animals or aliens. The compromise decision is usually an attempt to keep harmony and not make their child seem weird around others.

TOM BOYS (BOYISH GIRLS) AND GENTLE BOYS (GIRLIE)

Children just before they are three years old begin to establish strong gender tendency, boys choose male type toys and usually want to play with boys; girls choose female type toys and enjoy doing activities with girls. Preschool boys may imitate their fathers if their father washes dishes, changes diapers, helps clean the house, irons clothes, cooks and prefers non-athletic activities (reading, computer work, etc) then the boy may do these activities while playing with girls or other boys. Boys that like playing house, reading, or coloring rather than playing football, wrestling or basketball should not be considered homosexual. Boys may cross gender lines if they have sisters, playmates that are girls or to satisfy their curiosity. Do not be suspicious of gender confusion, criticize or tease the boy for his behavior. If the behavior continues and the boy takes on a girl role with boys, physically acts like a girl and in a mixed group constantly plays only with girls, then there may be a need to seek help. A child's choice of toys is not an accurate indicator of homosexuality; so do not make a hasty conclusion.

Children tend to learn by trial and error, experimentation and wisdom. Parents do not tend to get too upset when trial and error and experimentation learning is used when it comes to a child finding out how long they can hold their breath or how many grapes they can put in their mouth at one time. A child learning a gender by trial and error and experimentation is normal and necessary. For example, if your daughter wants to see how it feels to wrestle a boy or play with boy's toys it is a developmental phase. She has noticed that boys get more freedom to do things she cannot, so she assumes that acting like a boy will get her the same freedom. She may say, "She wants to be a boy" which means I want more privileges.

Girls and boys should be treated differently because they are different. Around the third month after birth there is a testosterone rise in boys and an estrogen rise in girls. These hormone shape their emotions and thought processes differently. Newborn boys tend to be physically active while newborn girls tend to be quieter. Girls tend to react to voices and faces. Boys tend to react more to movement of objects. Cultural conditioning causes boys to handle rough and girls to be gentle. Boys are usually left to figure out problems and are "fix it" or "break it" oriented while girls are usually given help for problem solving. Girls are talked to with nurturing and the use of more emotional words "What a pretty little girl with a nice personality" boys are told "What a handsome and strong boy you are."

When girls prefer to put on clothes that boys would wear, it is probably because too many rules come with wearing a dress. They cannot sit with their legs open or let their panties show, they have to bend down instead of bending over and showing their panties. They are told, dresses are not supposed to get dirty or torn like boy's clothes. Sweatpants, T-shirts and pants are more comfortable. Allow the girl to experiment instead of constantly saying, "Girls are not supposed to do that." Provide a positive example of how a female is supposed to behave and carry herself. If the cross gender behaviors continue into the third year, there may be a need to seek help.

A parent should be aware that children have an imagination. What is believed to be gender confusion may just be a girl playing with a car to take her pretend family somewhere or playing with a police car because she is a female policewoman. The boy playing with a doll may be using it as the Momma and the baby boy doll going to church or using the doll as a female soldier. You may try to restrict the toys to a gender but you will not be able to restrict the child's imagination.

AGGRESSIVENESS

A child does not understand that their aggressiveness that causes them to push, hit or pull others hurts. If they do understand their emotional immaturity and lack of impulse control will still create aggressive behavior. The following suggestions may be helpful:

SKILLS

Social skills are learned they are not automatic. The child will use trial and error, experimentation and role models to acquire social skills. Encourage good manners and behavior. Often times, hitting is trial and error experimentation. The child says to themselves, "I wonder what will happen if I hit my playmate on top of the head." The next experiment maybe to hit them in the ear. The result will always be pain and crying. However, the experiment is out of curiosity and requires your punishment.

RESULTS

The child may hit a playmate, and then after the playmate starts crying realize the results of their actions. They lack ability to foresee the results just as playing is spontaneous so is hitting. Tell the child to say, "I am sorry, I did not mean to hurt you" encourage them to say, "I feel like hitting" instead of hitting the other child. This will warn the child and alert you to use your parenting skills. Remember, that the child lacks a vocabulary to match each behavior that they want to do or have done. Therefore, they will just do the action because they do not know how to say, "I have reached my limits with my playmate" so the hitting is the same as saying it.

Be a Model

Children learn more from what you do than what you say. Model aggression control. When you are upset with your spouse, friend, another adult or child make sure your child sees you control yourself. If you lose your temper with someone make sure your child sees you apologize.

Step In

Know when to step in or step out of the way of a pulling, shoving or pushing episode. Allow the children the opportunity to resolve the issue. They need to develop their social skills. Your intervention in an aggression is based upon whether it is harmless pushing or fist fighting. If the children are fighting over a toy choose another toy or a similar toy that they can play with. If it is over a one of a kind toy, then use a Timer to impose sharing. If they do not want to share tell them you will have to take the toy from them. You may put the toy in JAIL (Penalty or Off Limits or No Trespassing Box).

Breaking up a Fight

Your immediate concern is the safety of both fighters. Help the one that is losing first and comfort them both. If the fight involved pinching, biting, scratching and/or hitting, look for wounds and treat them. If your child started the fight give the victim another activity to do while you take your child aside and calmly tell them "You hurt your friend when you attacked them." Tell them that they have to have a consequence for their bad behavior; it can be a time out, sitting beside you for a while or sitting by themselves and repeating a Maat principle or affirmation. Have the child apologize to the victim. Warn both children to behave. Sometimes the victim teased or provoked the fight as an experiment or as a way to have a toy to themselves. Therefore, you should warn both children.

It's Okay

Let the child know it is okay to feel upset, angry, cry or feel like fighting when they do not get their way, when they do not want to share, when a toy is grabbed from them or when they break a toy but it is not okay to hit. If they want to holler or scream tell them it is okay but they have to go to another room and ask permission before they do.

Know the Limits

Observe the warning signs of irritation, fatigue or frustration that your child may exhibit. They usually lead to explosions of aggression, irrational impulses and conflict. Teach the child words that identify how they feel (i.e. upset, want to hit) and ask them to tell you or others. This can help you diffuse the emotion before it makes the child reach their limits. Remember, that the child has a low tolerance for frustration. Frustration causes them to reach their limit fast. It is the leading cause of aggression.

Boredom

When the child no longer finds a game or toys interesting, they will get bored. If you do not respond with a challenging activity or game the boredom will lead to aggression, a tantrum, fight or stress. Take scheduled breaks for reading, nurturing (hugging, cuddling, etc.), rhymes, singing and/or drumming. This can stop boredom and prevent aggression.

Control

The child likes to be in control as much as possible. They like to control toys, games and a living toy called a playmate. When the playmate toy does not behave the way the host child wants, the host child will hit or assert themselves aggressively. They will crash their trucks and crash their "real playmate's toys." The child wants to be the center of attention and feel they are the central controller unit until they are a little older than two years of age.

Don't take Sides

It is difficult to decide who is innocent and who is guilty. The parent did not see the first punch, the instigator's method of teasing or who is taking revenge. Investigating the conflict will not help as children will claim to be innocent. You should be a mediator and try to make both parties happy with the verdict or punish both parties. Do not take sides or judge or blame, seek to establish Maat.

Monitor

The children need your supervision. Children with good behavior can create mischief and start fights at any given moment. They are impulsive and let their emotions manipulate them.

Don't Lecture

Keep your sentences short and do not use long paragraphs of dialogue, long speeches about how to behave. This is not going to stop a child from being a child. Make sure the rules and consequences for breaking the rules are clear. Long speeches tend to make the child ignore your words and can irritate the child which will more than likely cause aggressiveness or anger. If your speeches do not get good results, do not spank, scold or bully your child to behave. You will be training the child to be a bully.

Breaks

Aggressive behavior flare-ups can be diffused and taking breaks for snacks, painting, singing or drumming can restore peace. Schedule parent supervised activities as a prevention.

TV/Movie/Game Violence

Point out the types of bad behaviors. Make it clear that harming people or hitting people is not the best way to solve problems.

Praise

Whenever the child does not use aggressive behavior, pushing, hitting, shoving, scratching or biting to solve a crisis, give them a word of praise. Give plenty of attention for good behavior (smiles, hugs and gentle touch) and very little attention for negative behavior. Encouragement is desired and needed by the child.

Punishment

A parent that is too strict and uses physical violence on the child and a parent that does not punish or discipline will get the same results. A parent has to allow the child to make some choices and the parent must set limits, rules and discipline criteria and follow them. This will prevent aggressiveness.

INTERRUPTING CONVERSATIONS
(PHONE/VISITORS)

Children may demand that they be the main focus of your attention. They have become addicted to you and when you are in a one-on-one conversation with any one other than them, it puts them immediately into a lack of attention withdrawal crisis. Like an addict their emotions and body craves the "attention addiction." In their attempt to get high off "attention" they may cling to your leg, turn your head towards them, act silly, crawl over your lap, interrupt, whine, whimper, make loud noises, put their hand on your mouth or pull on your clothes. The child dislikes the intrusion of the visitor. It will take patience to help the child develop control and stop you from hurting them. The following few suggestions can help your child accept visitors:

TIMING

You could arrange for your visitor to come during naptime or when the child is distracted by an activity. Keep your visits short; your child has limited tolerance. A long conversation with the visitor can tire you out as well as tire out the child and overtax the child's tolerance.

DON'T INTERRUPT

When you are involved in an activity with the child do not stop or interrupt it with a chore or conversation that you can have at another time. If you do interrupt the parent/child activity time with one of your chores or personal conversations with an adult, it is not showing respect for the child's time with you. When you cannot avoid interrupting a parent/child quality time or activity with a chore, involve the child. If you must make juice have the child help you wash the fruits or vegetables as well as hand them to you so you can put them in the juicing machine. If you have to write out some checks have the them doodle in a notebook, if you have to check e-mail have the child play with blocks. When an uninvited guest or a phone call interrupts your parent/child activity, tell the visitor or phone caller to wait until you finish with your child. Let the child hear you say this. Resume the activity with the child for a few more minutes them talk to the person. In the case of an uninvited guest, invite them to join the activity.

SPECIAL PLAY AREA

When a visitor does arrive do not completely ignore your child's desire to want to be included in the socializing. Give them a task such as helping to clean up or have the child place their favorite pictures in the room. If it is a repairperson allow them to watch the repair from a safe distance. If the visitor sits and talks and if you do not mind being interrupted have a special play area set up near where you are talking. Put books, blocks, puzzles and toys in the area for your child. Do not make the child interact. If they seem to want to interact ask the child to show one or two of their favorite books or pictures. The child can have pretend visitors in their play area such as dolls sitting and having an herb tea party. After the visitor has left the child can help you clean up and you can help the child clean the area where their pretend visit took place (use a play broom, duster and wear an apron). If the child feels like they are part of the visit, they more than likely will not interrupt.

SNACK

When your visitor comes you may want to have a snack prepared even if your guest is not hungry. Avoid messy foods. The food should be appropriate for the child. Invite your child to have a snack with your visitor. This will decrease the child's interruptive behavior and whining. With a mouth full of food, they cannot talk or whine much.

PLAN INTERRUPTION

Children cannot be expected to amuse themselves for the duration of a visit. If it is a long visit, take breaks at intervals in order to interact with the child (help with an activity, read a story, sing or rap a song etc.). Tell the child that you have stopped talking with your visitor only to read one story or do one puzzle. When you have finished, you will go back to your visitor. Before you return help the child get another activity, puzzle or book. Stay in contact with the child in between breaks by saying a few words of encouragement such as "You are doing a good job of reading" or "I bet you can read the book better if you do it again." Keep visual contact and physical contact with the child, frequently give the child a smile, a hug, rub their back or gently touch their arm.

STAY IN CHARGE

You need adult conversation and time with other adults. Do not give up your rights. If you let the child take over your visits or rudely interrupt too many times without a consequence, you will lose your rights and the child will not let you forget it. When having a visit be friendly and calm with your child but be firm with the rules. If they break the rules too many times – discipline is necessary.

PRAISE

When the child fails to follow all the rules for visitors, reinforce their positive behavior instead of scolding about the negative behavior. Tell the child, "I like the times you were quiet and did not interrupt. Now you and I are going to do something special." Finger painting together or a trip to the playground or playing a computer learning game together can be the reward.

INTERRUPTING PHONE CONVERSATIONS

The phone will ring. If you miss a telephone call there is "call waiting." The child will want attention. If you miss giving them attention there is not "child waiting." The child makes sure that when they ring you for attention, they get it. They use inappropriate behavior and whining to stay on the line even if you hang up. You should treat the phone call with the same rules as those for a visitor.

DON'T FORECAST

If the phone rings do not say, "I do not want any problems out of you" or "Do not bother me while I'm on the phone." Instead say, "Who could be calling me." If you say, "Do not bother me or "Do not be a problem" you will more than likely be bothered with problems.

PARTICIPATION

When the caller is a close friend or a family member you can let the child participate in the conversation. You could offer the phone to the child with "Do you want to talk?" or use a speaker phone. If the child pushes the phone away, do not force them to talk. Wireless phones allow you to keep an eye on the child and do interactive activities. It does split your conversation but it is better than no adult conversation.

KEEP CALM

Remember that your child craves attention tactile (touching), visual (seeing you constantly) auditory (talking to them) and/or rhythm (being massaged, rubbed, cuddled, rocked, etc.). Do not get frustrated, angry or upset about it. It will increase the child's need for more attention because you will have to soothe them. Either way they will get attention be it negative or positive. The child needs your patience and empathy so keep calm.

PRIVACY

Remember the child can be listening or pretending not to listen to a private conversation. It is best to have conversations with adult topics or adult words when the child is not present. Conversations that are R-rated and X-rated in the presence of a child is child abuse.

ANOTHER PHONE

Buy a toy phone or give the child a real phone that is not being used (remove the cords, battery). Let the phone be reserved for use only when you are on the phone. When you answer your phone, answer the child's phone and hand the child the phone and say, "It is a telephone call for you." This will keep the child occupied with a one-sided garbled conversation. It does not matter if the child can speak or not.

Stay in Contact

Stay in eye contact with the child as much as possible. This will let you still be with them in an emotional way. Smile, cuddle, massage their arm, shoulder, back or leg. Be interactive, stack blocks with them, bounce the child in your lap, hold their hand or hug them while talking. You may want to consider getting a phone that has a headset attachment or one where the attachment can be placed on your waist, this will free your hands.

Praise

You have a right to use the phone. Give your appreciation and praise to the child for not interrupting or the partially successful attempts to not interrupt. Tell them "You behaved well. Thanks for letting me talk on the phone." If your phone calls tend to interrupt the parent/child time, let the answering machine screen the calls or use caller ID.

TELEVISION (VISUAL MEDIAS)

Children watch their movies, educational videos, music videos, television shows and educational shows on television. Television can decrease social interaction because children ignore each other while watching TV. A child that excessively watches visual medias (i.e. TV) does not want to put time into using their imagination for free-play and the child tends to do little sharing of their thoughts and feelings. Peer pressure often forces the child to watch TV because if they are unaware of the characters (i.e. Big Bird) they will feel left out of discussions about the character. Children are often force to watch TV because parents with inadequate parenting skills use TV as a tool for peace and as a substitute for a babysitter.

The TV is used to occupy the child's attention while dinner is being prepared or while the parent is doing laundry, talking on the phone, E-mailing, surfing the Web or in a chat room or reading mail, etc. If the child is watching a TV program then the commercials makes them want junk food, the latest gadgets or sex toys as well as want the trendy clothes. The TV can be considered as a "salesperson" with bad manners or a "teacher" that is visiting. The parent needs to monitor anything the child watches on visual medias (computer games, TV, DVD, etc.).

SUBSTITUTE

Instead of letting the TV screen entertain you and your child substitute activities in its place such as exercises, making raw juices, working on art projects, a garden, growing plants or herbs in a flower pot, or going to the park or museum. When you do watch TV talk about the characters use of Maat or, talk about good and bad behaviors, morals and ethics of the characters, ask questions – why did the character do that or say that?

AGGRESSION

Watching violence on TV causes children to be violent. If TV did not influence children and adults then companies would not spend billions of dollars on commercials for their products. Watching violence makes it easily acceptable and dulls the reactions to violence done to others. Violence seems unrealistic because a cartoon character or an actor that is violently harmed tends to be immediately recuperated. Talk about the violence with the child, asks if there is another way to behave or how would it make them feel to be hurt by others?

FEAR

The children's emotional vocabulary is not broad. Emotions feel real. Fantasy on TV is emotionally real. If the child watches horrible frightening scenes, it will cause them to easily be scared and believe it may happen to them or their family members. Children tend to be concrete thinkers and do not differentiate between a real fear and unreal fear. Fear is fear to the child. Just before the child starts preschool they begin to separate the real (fact) from the unreal (fiction). Keep in mind that news programs and your talk about the news is full of violent and scary things to a child. Explain to the child that they are safe and nothing bad will happen to them. Remind them that television shows, movies and cartoons are pretend and make-believe. Color a picture together and tell the child that this is how cartoons and pretend movies are made except machines do the coloring.

BE SELECTIVE

Use a VCR to tape appropriate shows and avoid taping the violent, aggressive, fear causing shows as well as the hidden pornographic images and obvious sex themes shows. Show the recorded programs during your child's scheduled TV viewing time.

LESS

Children that view TV get accustom to the special-effects style and hi-tech format of TV learning. This causes the child to become bored with their schoolteachers and school learning. Boredom leads to the inability to concentrate as well as causes the child to become fast paced like the TV shows. Children that are less TV viewers do poorly in school and score lower on reading tests. They do not develop their social skills and intellectual abilities adequately. The parent should read to and with the child. Encourage your child to talk about stories you have read and make-up stories. Ask questions about the characters in the child's improvised story. Challenge the child to come up with different character types and different places for the story to take place.

TV REWARD/PUNISHMENT

Do not make watching a video or TV show a reward for good behavior. The child will think that good children only watch TV because TV is good. Do not take away TV viewing as a punishment. The child will think that bad children do not watch TV.

INTERACTIVE

Encourage the child to participate in the activities on the TV show or in the video such as sing-along, arts and crafts, exercise or dance-along. Ask the child to tell you about the show/video, talk about the good and bad behaviors. Discuss the story's main point, what they learned, draw the characters in the story or improvise the way the story could have gone. This makes TV viewing a teaching instrument.

TV Cannot Nurture

When parents turn on the TV because the child is upset, fatigued, bored, hyper, cranky or aggressive, it does not solve the problem, it creates a problem. The child is not taught how to cope with or explain their feelings. This may cause the child to look for solutions elsewhere such as mediating problems with food (Eating Disorder), Temper Tantrums, and Bedwetting, being combative or stubborn. This draws negative attention to the child and indirectly soothes their misplaced feelings. Turn off the TV and talk and nurture your child.

Imitation

Children follow what you do and not necessarily what you say. Parents need to model responsible behavior and TV behavior. If the parent watches educational, exercise or history shows, the child will tend to watch them. If the parent reads more than watch TV, the child will imitate them. Do not keep the TV on for background noise or keep it on when you are not viewing it. If quietness in your house irritates you play the radio or some music periodically.

Limitations

A child can very easily do without TV until they are sixteen months old. After sixteen months, an hour a day of educational viewing is adequate. After the child is two years old, two hours of TV is more than enough. More TV viewing will limit the time the child needs for their proper growth and development. It is best to set limitations on TV viewing while the child is young as it is difficult to do so with older children. The parent has to turn off the TV when the time limit is up. There are times that a special video or TV show will be on and the rule has to be changed but tell your child that it is an exception because of the video or the show.

DISCIPLINE

Discipline is the art and science of using rewards and punishments to help the child to utilize self-control, respect the rights and feelings of others, determine right from wrong and know how and why they should protect themselves and their happiness. Discipline means, "to teach." Very seldom are rewards associated with disciplining but rewards are the foundation of discipline. If the child does things that stop them from receiving a reward for good behavior then they should be punished. Unfortunately, discipline is only associated with strict rules, physical abuse, slaps, beatings, hitting, disrespect and humiliation.

- Children are learning how to be disciplined and how to accept discipline while they are being disciplined. The parent knows what they mean when they tell a child to clean up their play area; they should not assume that the child knows exactly what was meant. The basic orders, rules and rewards and punishments have to be clear and spelled out.

- Rules should not be too rigid and strictly followed. The child has to feel that they still have some control over their lives. It will not be easy for the child to follow every rule precisely, when it is possible allow for a little variation. For example, you may tell the child to put the book in the toy box. The child may put the book on the table and make a little area for the book in the toy box and then put the book in the toy box. It may not always be possible for the child to follow the rules in their way but when it is let them.

- Parents are in an ongoing process of learning and within a learning process mistakes will be made. When you realize you have made a mistake with an instruction, do not be embarrassed. Say you made a mistake. Let the child know that you make mistakes.

- A child that is tense, tired, hungry, sleepy or thirsty tends to lose their ability to focus on rules and may have difficulty following instructions and cannot cope with discipline.

- Children have to be allowed to make mistakes and learn from their mistakes. If your strict rules and harsh discipline make the child afraid to make mistakes it will slow down their developmental process. Allow room for errors so your child can learn. For example, if the rule is no cookies before lunch then keep all the cookies put away until then. The child will have to follow the rule but they will not have self-discipline. Every now and then leave a few cookies in a bowl in order to give the child the opportunity to practice self-discipline.

- Praise the child in order to reinforce their positive use of self-discipline.

- The punishment should fit the crime. If the child writes on the wall with crayons, immediately tell them that the rule is to write on paper then take away the crayons. Tell them "no crayons until tomorrow" put the crayons in the JAIL box and when you give back the crayons also give the child some paper. Do not wait until later on or around dinnertime to tell the child they cannot watch their favorite TV show because they wrote on the wall. This punishment is too delayed to be effective plus it does not match the crime. A crime punishment schedule should be; **mild crime** – take away the item used in the unacceptable behavior, **moderate crime** – take away the item plus something they like, **severe crime** – take away the item plus something they like and restrict their activities. For example, if the child hits a playmate over a toy in the sandbox take them out of the sandbox (restriction) and do not allow the child to play with the toy (item taken away).

- When a child does something unacceptable let them suffer the consequences of their actions. Do not protect your child from the consequences of their behavior with reparations. For example, if the child plays with their favorite video tape movie and breaks it. Tell them "The rules are to watch video tapes not to play with them." When they want to watch that same video, show it to them and say, "You have broken it so we cannot see it." Some parents would immediately do reparations and buy another tape. Replace it if the breaking of the video was an accident. If it was done on purpose then put it in JAIL and wait awhile before replacing it. The child will suffer until a new video is purchased. Suffering allows the child to feel the consequences of their actions.

- When the parent is preoccupied with a chore or with thoughts and is unable to give the child attention; the child may get into mischief to get your attention. Avoid overreacting. Stay calm, do not holler or scold, the child's objective was to get your attention whether it is by being calm or hollering, it does not matter. Attention was the child's objective and getting the attention was achieved. Take breaks from your preoccupation and give smiles, gentle touches, nurturing or say a few words to your child. They want to be a part of your life. Your life makes the child feel secure and loved.

- Incorporate humor as a disciplinary tool. It helps to relax the child, releases tension and helps the child to avoid a confrontation that would hurt their pride. If the child refuses to sit and read, suggest that Big Bird will read for them. Place Big Bird in a chair or you can pretend to be the child and act like them or sing a silly song "This is the way I hold my book, hold my book, this the way I read my book, read my book". Hold the book upside down and say, "I don't understand these pictures or words. Can you help me?" When the child volunteers to help you, the objective is achieved. It does not matter if they sit or stand to help you read. Here is another example, if the child refused to wash their face, pretend the washcloth is a talking puppet that flies around looking for dirty faces. Let the talking washcloth clean a doll's face then clean your child's face. Be creative, improvise and use silliness.

- When discipline is being enforced or rules of discipline are given it is natural to say, "No, you cannot do this or that" or "No fighting, no lying, no running in the house, etc." Children like to challenge the parent's "No's." Do not let your "No!" become wishy-washy (easily changed to yes) or become funny. The child will not take you seriously if you say, "no" one-minute then "yes" the next. If you say "no" you cannot have a cookie or watch a video mean it and stick to it.

- A child finds it stressful to live all day hearing "no." Too many "no's" can make the child feel their life is impossible to live or happiness is just a lot of "no's." Try to limit your "no's" to things that may be harmful to the child, yourself or another person. If the home is childproof and has a play area it will limit the "no's" needed.

- Discipline requires that you have rewards and punishments "no's" and "yes's" and a preferred activity and an alternative activity. For example, you can say, "You cannot play with Momma's watch but you can play with your toy watch or do puzzles." Try to stress positive behavior. If the child has emptied the fruit out of the fruit basket onto the floor, say, "The fruit belongs in the fruit basket, not on the floor. Let's see if you can put the fruit back into the basket" instead of "Why did you do that, look at the mess you made".

- Discipline is most effective when it is given face-to-face. Do not holler from another room "Stop jumping up and down on the bed." Go to the room, look the child in the eyes and calmly say, "Please stop jumping up and down on the bed. Jumping on the bed is bad behavior. Now, you have to be punished. Go sit in your chair and say, I will follow the rules three times. I will let you know when the punishment is over."

- A child is not bad. A child does bad things. They learn through trial and error, wisdom, experimentation, imitation and observing cause and effect. Children are emotionally and impulsively driven. Rather than doing what they are told, their emotions cause them to see how other possible actions feel, they are curious and want to see the results of their actions. They may seem to be deliberately not following the rules when they are actually distracted by what they are seeing, feeling or imagining. Children have difficulty keeping their feelings, the real and unreal (imagination) separated. Dividing their attention is a developmental skill that is immature. When they are busy with one activity, they tend to be unable to focus on another activity or a chore you told them to do.

- Disobedience is an incidental side effect of lack of attention. The child gets information overloads and sometimes shuts out the parent. They hear some of what the parent said but not all of it. The child may not follow rules because they lack understanding plus they want to see the results of the broken rules. Added to this, they lack impulse control. Sometimes, words, rules, punishment, impulses and emotions are just another toy to play with. They may be sitting in a chair calmly but their impulses are with Batman and their emotions are with Big Bird. It is a world of excitement interrupted with some parental rule. Their imagination is the attraction and the rule is the distraction.

- The child has to learn to cope with limits and restrictions. Learning to live with limits can help reduce the child's and the parents' stressors especially when the child starts saying, "no" and "mine" to situations and things. Start early with "limits." The limits of behaviors are set based upon your priorities and what you feel strongly about. Etiquette must be used at all times in your home. Use "Please", "Excuse me", "Thank You", "Good morning, afternoon, evening and night", "May I", etc. You may not allow shoes to be worn in the house or never leave an empty toilet paper roll on the holder. When you come in from outside, wash hands before going into the refrigerator, etc.

- Parents have to keep promises. Unless an emergency or a crisis causes a promise to be broken. If a promise is made to take the child to the playground but then you decide you would rather answer your e-mail, talk on the phone or iron clothes, and ask yourself if the e-mail, phone conversation and clothes ironing can be postponed or done later. The parent has to be responsible and keep their promises if they expect the child to act responsible.

- Do not emotionally bribe a child to behave. This can cause the child to feel guilty. For example, saying, "If you loved me, you would not be bad." The child should not be asked to behave in order to prove that they love their parent.

- The child's disobedience or failure to follow rules or running to hide from discipline should not cause you to have an uncontrollable anger. Uncontrolled anger frightens young children, triggers anger in older children, damages and humiliates children emotionally and mentally and teaches the child how to behave inappropriately. During an anxiety and anger explosion the parent may say things that hurt, scream or become physically abusive to the child. A parent on occasion may find it impossible to hold back their rage; parents are not perfect and are expected to have human imperfections. If the anger outbursts are few, brief and far between and not attacks on the child's personality (focuses on behavior) then it will not damage your ability to have good parenting skills. After an anger outburst, apologize to your child and tell them you love them. The child may have done something deliberately wrong to cause your anger such as throwing a ball at a lamp or damage something that was given to you by your grandmother or taking your cell phone and flushing it down the toilet. Do not feel bad about your inappropriate attempt to discipline feel bad about losing your temper.

- When you feel like your parental behavior has deteriorated to that of a child's level take a time-out. If you realize that you have an adult tantrum as a reaction to your child's tantrum or you are being just as demanding as the child, take a time-out. Time-out allows you to re-evaluate what's going on in your personal life and assess whether you need to work on a specific parenting skill or review cultural virtues.

- You have to feel sure of yourself and confident. If you act wishy-washy (unstable) and are always saying, "I don't know how to help my child", "I am lost as to what to do with this child", "And everything I try to do to help fails". When you talk like this, your child feels insecure and frighten because you are not in control. Your behavior must be consistent.

- Do not treat your child like a remote control by passing them from preschool to after school care to a babysitter and then to a friend or relative. Do not treat your child like an object or as a material possession that you have to buy clothes for and feed. Listen to what your child is saying even when they are very young and they can only use monosyllables, hum, point and grunt to communicate. It will be difficult to interpret their language of sounds and garbled words. When they are between three and four years old their speech will become clearer. The main thing is that they see and feel you are listening. Be understanding and feel the emotions in their words and have sympathy for their needs even if you will not or cannot meet their needs. Do not humiliate the child in front of friends, playmates or strangers. Always use manners with them and around them such as saying, "Please", "Excuse me" and "Thank you." Give them simple explanations to their questions or your rules even if they don't understand your reasons still explain them as simply as possible.

- Do not live your life as if you have no children or as if you want to be a teenager. Do not take your child to adult parties, R-rated movies or lectures because you want to go, consider the child's rights. When you made the decision to be a parent, the child's life became a priority in that decision. However, do not live your life for your child, do not give up all of your rights in favor of the child, do not plan your life completely around the child. Maintain your friendships and spend time with your friends. Have activities that you do without your child.

- Do not rely on the child to be obedient. The child is emotional, impulsive and lacks self-control. The responsibility of keeping the child safe, out of trouble and obedient belongs to the parent. When the child is not old enough to understand and accept the responsibility of recognizing what is safe, unsafe, and permissible and off limits then their parent has to do it for them.

- Always use love and nurturing with the child. Do not use love as an object to give or to take away in order to discipline. Withholding love is not the way to discipline. It causes the child to feel lost, abandon, unimportant and creates a variety of emotional problems. Always let the child know you love them and say, "I love you" with feeling and not in a matter-or-fact manner. For example, do not say, "I do not like you" instead say, "I do not like your behavior", "I will help you do better because I love you."

- Discipline is a fine art; it cannot be too gentle or too rough, too rigid or too loosely enforced. A child that is disciplined only when the parent is present is not good. The child needs to be encouraged to use self-discipline. A child that relies on their parents to keep them in control usually behaves out-of-control when the parent or authority figure is not present. Most people associated this with artist (painters, musicians, actors, dancers, etc.). When artists are doing their art, the artwork disciplines them and keeps them in control. When they are away from their art, they are out-of-control (wild). A parent that is loose with the rules, changes rules, unpredictable, lets the child have their way or sometimes doesn't enforce rules or ignores giving consequences when rules are broken usually has children that are rude, quick to anger, selfish and act good as long as they are having their way.

- Children have an untrained memory. Memory has to be taught and children lack the skills to train and develop a memory. They cannot learn a lesson and at the same time memorize the lesson. Their memory capacity is limited. Be patient and prepare to repeat rules and lessons over and over. Do not expect a child to learn a lesson then lose the impulsiveness, urge to experiment and desire to observe how things act and react. You can tell them "Don't play in the toilet" everyday. The child still has their curiosity and fascination with the toilet water and flushing things in the toilet. You can't expect a child to stop being a child.

- Customize and personalize the discipline to match the child. Some children will stop an inappropriate behavior after you have warned them or told them that it is bad, another child may not listen to the warning unless they feel they will get a beating, another one has to be removed from the room, another hears a single angry word and starts crying, another will ignore the warning while another child if you give them a harsh look will obey. The mood, state of health, tiredness, hunger or being upset can cause a child that usually ignores your warning to start crying if you give them a harsh look. Discipline is an art and science that requires the parent to know that how they are feeling influences their discipline style for that moment or day.

SPANKING

Spanking is a succession of sharp hits. It is not to be confused with a tap on the hand or buttocks, which is used to get a child's attention. Anything more than a smack on the buttocks (usually the child has a padded diaper) can harm a child. Shaking a young child can physically damage the child's nervous system or eyes. Spanking is not an effective means of discipline. Children that are spanked will stop their bad behavior because they don't want to get spanked. They learn what they will get spanked for and what they will not get spanked for. They very rarely learn to differentiate between what is "right" and what is "wrong." The child is obedient because they are afraid of getting hurt by a spanking. Spankings are usually done with the hand, a belt, shoe, switch (tree branch), a child's plastic sword, a ruler, rubber hose, telephone cord or any other weapon available.

Children that are spanked are more likely to use physical violence and/or force with other children and grow up and beat their own children. Spanking teaches the child that conflicts are best settled with violence. Spanking does not demonstrate to the child that there are alternatives for violence and it teaches that anger and frustration leads to violence. An adult that spanks is an over powering, very large, a strong bully that attacks a very small and weak little child. The parents that lack parenting skills use a spanking to replace their inability to be an effective parent. Spanking is usually done while the parent is upset or angry with the child. In a state of anger, the parent is liable to hurt and abuse the child. Spanking the child after the anger has subsided may cause less physical damage and trauma but then this is calculated cruelty. If the angry parents wait until they are no longer angry then the spanking is so far removed from the child's bad behavior incident that the child may have forgotten or the child lives in fear waiting for the spanking. Spanking is humiliating, cruel and demeaning for the parent and the child. It can create a love-hate mentality in the child that they carry into adult (marriage) relationships.

If a parent feels that they are too upset or angry with a child and want to spank the child, they should take a time-out to recite a positive affirmation or Cultural Virtue or principle of Maat or Kwanzaa, or walk away from the child and stay away until they regain their composure. If you need to seek help, talk to a friend or a private counselor. If you call a Child Abuse or Community Service Agency or an Emergency Help number, you will be put into the system and tracked by computers and may have to deal with being labeled a Child Abuser or risk having the child taken away from you or even being given jail time. It is best to not use a city, state or federal agency or an agency that receives government funding.

A smack on the hand or buttocks may be necessary if a child continuously keeps trying to touch a hot stove or runs into the street. Such a smack on the hand or slap on the buttocks should be followed by an explanation such as, "If you run into the street, a car may hit you and hurt you or kill you." If the child understands that the reason for the smack or slap was used to get their immediate attention and understands the danger of the situation then the smack or slap is appropriate.

TOILET LEARNING (TRAINING), DIAPERS, POTTY AND ACCIDENTS

PUBLIC TOILET USAGE

When using toilets in public places always cover the toilet with toilet paper or a paper seat cover. The parent can also carry toilettes or wipes that can be used to wipe off the toilet seat as some children tend to accidentally push off the paper that covers the toilet seat. Tell your child never to sit on a toilet in a strange place without lining it first with paper. Encourage the child to use a piece of toilet tissue on the flusher handle before flushing. Warn your child to look at the toilet roll before using the toilet. If the roll is empty they should choose another toilet or tell you. If the roll of toilet paper has sheets touching the floor, throw away those sheets of tissue.

When the child is learning the potty, it is best that they wear "on" and "off" clothing. In the winter, the house should be kept a little warmer than usual so that the child can dress with lighter clothes – avoid winter clothes. The fewer the clothes the easier to undress, sweaters and belts may present problems. A child dressed lightly is more able to successfully make a run to the toilet and do their last minute rush to undress.

TOILET LEARNING (TRAINING)

Toilet learning is a separate developmental task. A child that reads well or talks or walks early does not usually start toilet learning early. Children can be ready for toilet learning around their first year, most around the second year and others may not be ready until their third year. Listed below are indicators that will let you know when to start training:

- A child that stays dry for a few hours during the day and/or regularly wakes up dry after their naps is ready to begin toilet training.

- If the child's bowel movement has a regular predictable schedule such as right after meals or first thing in the morning.

- A child that likes to be clean, dry and neat. When a child desires to be changed immediately or does not like soiled soggy diapers or sticky fingers.

- A child that communicates what they want and understands and can follow directions.

- A child that wants to wear underwear instead of diapers.

- When the child is curious about what people do in the bathroom and tries to follow them into the bathroom so they can watch and/or try to imitate what the person did in the bathroom.

- When a child seems to keep playing and ignores urine flowing down their legs or makes the grunting sounds signaling a bowel movement in progress. They are not ready for training and if you start there may be some difficulty in learning.

- When the child lets you know by pointing, grunting, having a certain look, holding their genitals, trying to squat or saying words that mean bowel movement or urinate. Then they are ready.

- Children learn by trial and error, imitation, wisdom and experimentation. A bowel movement is something new for them to learn about by touching it, finger painting with it or smearing it on themselves or other things. Make it clear to the child that a bowel movement is not to be handled. "Bowel movement is not to be played with – it belongs in the potty (or toilet) and must stay there until it is put in the toilet and flushed." The child should be expected to learn about the bowel movement by touching, smelling and at worse tasting. Do not make the child feel bad about handling it and you should stay calm about it. Give the child an alternative activity such as finger painting with paint. You can ask the child to empty the potty contents into the toilet. Monitor the child while on the potty to prevent further artistic episodes.

STARTING TOILET TRAINING

- Before beginning toilet learning be aware that emotional and social issues may make the task difficult or require a postponement such as relationship problems, a new baby, divorce, an illness, a new day-care, moving, etc.

- You must decide on potty vocabulary. It is best to use bowel movement and urinate instead of babyish language. Then tell everyone in the household, the baby-sitter, day-care, family, friends and visitors to use these terms as well.

- Explain to your child the symptoms and signals. Tell the child "When you feel like pushing, it means a bowel movement is coming. Soon, you will be able to use a potty." The child must be prepared for the potty and learn to feel their body's signals before actual potty use. Start by telling them, "When you want something to drink, say, I am thirsty, when your eyes start closing say, I am sleepy, and when you want something to eat say, I am hungry."

- Try to catch your child holding their genitals or tell them to say "Urinate." When you hear them or see them in the act of having a bowel movement in their diaper tell them to say "Bowel Movement." This helps them to beware of their body signals and to identify the signal.

- You may have to demonstrate sitting on the toilet and urinating. It is best that a boy have a male to demonstrate urinating. If you have an anatomical correct doll (a doll with genitals) you can use it to demonstrate as well as putting clay on the buttocks to demonstrate wiping. The child can practice with the doll. There are dolls that drink and urinate. Tell the child to help the doll use the potty and to help the doll switch from diapers to training pants.

- Make going to the toilet/potty learning sound like a glorious achievement and a step to becoming a "big girl" or "big boy." Tell the child, "Very soon you will be going to the toilet just like your big sister (or big brother) and grown ups", "You can have more fun wearing underwear than diapers", "You will be just like a big girl (or big boy) when you are able to use the toilet." Tell them, "When you are ready you can use the potty instead of diapers."

- Help the child adjust to using the potty. Let them sit on the potty while reading a potty book or any age appropriate book, or sit on the potty to watch TV. Use a potty that they can take from room to room. Put the potty in their control, let them put pictures on it or write their name on it. Once the child feels comfortable with the potty, they will be comfortable using it for urination and bowel movements.

- Be sure to get the potty that will not tip over when the child gets up to look at their bowel movement and/or urine. It should be sturdy with a stable base and be a color that your child likes. Avoid the potty's waste with a plastic urine deflector shield. They are designed to stop boys from aiming their urine on the floor while in a sitting position. The child can get accidentally scraped or cut by this while getting on or off the potty.

- Some children want to use the regular toilet and not the potty.

- When using a potty seat that fits on top of the regular toilet make sure it fits. If it is loose and shaky it can scare the child. Get a stepping stool for toilet use only. Some potty seats come with built in footrest as well as stepping stools.

- Change the diaper in the bathroom (if possible) or near the potty so the child can make an association. Put the bowel movement in the toilet and flush it. If the child is frighten of the flushing, flush the toilet when they are not in the bathroom. If you have the time, you can let the child see you putting the bowel movement from the diaper into the potty. This will be extra work for you because you will have to clean the potty afterwards as well as flush the contents down the regular toilet.

- If you force the potty before the child is ready, you will require extra patience and have to prepare the child for something they have no concept of. You may fail. Toilet learning is another developmental task. It is usually before they are two years old that the child has established a predictable bowel movement and urinating pattern. Predictability will not make the process easier to learn. The child has to know their body signals, be able to judge time, be able to stop the emotion of joy while playing and switch to the serious attitude needed and be able to physically coordinate sitting on the potty, getting on the potty and wiping themselves, be able to maneuver through obstacles such as furniture, toys and people in their path and have good running ability aside from being able to walk without falling down. You should expect a few accidents.

- If you force the child and put pressure on the child to be toilet trained, it will not work. Toilet learning is a developmental task and most successful when the child is ready. At any sign that the child is ready – start. A new baby can postpone the learning and cause a child that already is toilet trained to start having many accidents or not go to the potty.

DO'S AND DON'TS

- ✓ Don't expect the child to be successful too soon. It will probably frustrate the child and you. Children usually take two months to learn the process.

- ✓ Don't' punish, say they are bad when they have an accident, spank, shame, scold or get angry. Your attitude and emotions will be tested. The child says they have to go to the potty every minute while you are busy. You will stop and take them to the potty, they will not have a bowel movement or urinate, then you will take the child off the potty and they will have results. The child will sit on the potty a long time without results, then stand up and have results. The child will refuse to go to the potty or go to the potty before leaving home then have results as soon as you put them in the car seat. They will have a bowel movement or say, "I have to go to the bathroom." You will ask them not to wait until the last moment to go to the bathroom, they will start on a last minute charge to the potty leaving a trail of urine and bowel movement droppings as they are running. The child's justification for their behavior is "I had an accident." Remember that the child is learning a complicated task and will have relapses, trials and errors and experimentation. You may need to use a few phrases from "Cultural Virtues."

- ✓ Do limit the fluid intake late in the evening. It is unwise to give a child a glass of water an hour before bedtime.

- ✓ Don't' limit fluids during the day. The more fluids the child drinks the more chances they have for practicing their potty usage. Denying fluids can cause dehydration and it is unfair and does not solve the problem of them urinating on themselves.

- ✓ Do calmly remind the child to use the potty. Saying, "You better use the potty" or "I do not want any accidents" or "If you do not use the potty, you know what will happen." Fussing, nagging and scolding will not help. You can say, "I am going to the toilet, you can go to the potty" or "Your potty is here waiting for you to use it."

- ✓ Don't make the child stay on the toilet when they are ready to get up or make them stay on the potty when they refuse to go. Calmly and politely encourage them to use it when they are holding their genitals and watching TV or playing with toys or watching a video, you can say, "Why don't you use the potty, then come back to the toys or (video)." If you force the child, they may hurry the bowel movement by straining or decide to be constipated in order to keep playing. Don't use a laxative to make the child feel the urge to have a bowel movement or use a laxative to make them have conveniently timed bowel movements.

- ✓ Don't make using the potty a "good" and "bad" issue. If they have an accident do not say, they are being "bad" and if they use the toilet say, they are "good." When you make a remark always talk about the behavior and never label the child. For example, do not say, "You are being good" say, "You did a good job and acted like a big girl (or boy) and a grown up."

- ✓ Children learn at their own speed. There is no need to keep a report or comment on their progress. There is no slow progress or fast progress, there is only, they have finished or have not finished learning. Slow learners are not less intelligent and fast learners are not to be considered brighter. Give praise and encouragement.

- ✓ Don't make learning confrontational. If the child refuses to learn there is no need to confront the child daily about using the potty, frown or become upset or angry when changing diapers, or say, that their friends are using the potty and wear underwear. If the child has relapses and starts ignoring the potty do continue toilet training. Do not give up. The child that refuses the potty will eventually get tired of the diapers and make using the potty a routine.

- ✓ Don't force the child to allow you to wipe them or check their wiping. The child usually will not successfully wipe themselves for several years. Put a little wet oatmeal or clay on a doll and show the child how to wipe until nothing is left on the toilet paper. Periodically ask the child to let you see if their last piece of toilet paper used to wipe is clean. If you do force the child to let you wipe them, they may stop using the potty. Some children feel if they cannot do it, then nobody can do it for them.

- ✓ If the child is frightened of the flushing sound from the toilet do not force them to stand by the toilet while you flush it. This may change the fear into an emotional problem or phobia. You may want to hold the child while you flush it if they allow it. Or you can try holding the child in your arms while you stand in the bathroom doorway and someone else flushes. You can also flush the toilet while they are in the next room or in the hallway. If you wave bye-bye to the bowel movement then flush the toilet it may help. You and the child can practice flushing toilet paper or you can sing a song to the bowel movement and then say goodbye bowel movement and then flush.

- ✓ Children that are hesitant about toilet training may need to accompany their parent to the bathroom. This will help prepare them for the potty. On the trips to the bathroom, casually talk about them starting to use the potty and if they would like to try the grown up toilet or use a potty. A toilet is a large and tall item to a child and can be scary; so most children like a small low to the ground potty.

- ✓ Children need to have a series of success using the potty before switching to training pants. Accidents in training pants tend to be uncomfortable and embarrassing and can cause the child to not want to use the potty or the wear the training pants. When the child is ready or motivated to wear training pants switch to them. Children see other children with them on and want to wear them so even if they are not fully ready for them do not refuse to use them. When the child is self-motivated, using training pants will be successful.

- ✓ Girls want to stand and urinate because boys do and boys want to sit to urinate because girls do. They do not understand or see why they should be restricted to one position. Tell them a girl's urine aims down so it is best for girls to sit and a boy's urine aims out so they should stand. The explanation may not satisfy the curiosity or their desire to use another position. The best instructor and demonstrator for boys is a male and for girls is a female.

ACCIDENTS

(Incontinence of bowels and bladder)

Accidents mean the failure to have a bowel movement or urinate in the toilet despite having successfully completed toilet training. Toilet training does not mean toilet-learnt expert. Accidents do not require an apology because it was not meant to happen. Accidents may need a confession if there is a dog in the house. They will be unscheduled, frequent, sporadic, occasional, accidentally on purpose and sincere accidents because the child is learning a skill. You would not punish a child that is learning to walk for falling down nor would you ask for an apology or a confession.

Your reaction to accidents should be calm and as polite as possible. The child is attempting to learn so reassure them that they can master the skill. Say, "You were trying – you had an accident. Next time you will get to the potty." But, if the accidents are happening every bowel movement and urination then the timing for toilet learning is probably not correct. Return to diapers unless the child wants to stay with the potty. Remember, the child has many things they are learning at one time plus they lack impulse control, get lost in other activities, can be easily distracted by their imagination and feelings. Listed below are some things to consider and a few suggestions to decrease accidents:

- Emotional and social issues such as relationship problems, a new baby, divorce, a new baby-sitter, moving or an illness can cause accidents even in a child that has had no accidents for awhile.

- Do not overreact to an accident, threaten, lecture, scold or humiliate. You will further upset the child and may cause retaliation accidents.

- Children that are fatigued have less control and more likely to have an accident.

- Do not lose control when the child is fully dressed to go out and has an accident. Do not tell the child they are acting like a baby in order to encourage them to act like a grown up. This remark will not mean much if they know an elderly person that wears diapers or if you are wearing a "Depends" diaper.

- Encourage the child to help clean-up, if the child is willing have them wipe up their leaks on the floor and/or put the bowel movement in the toilet or wrap up the diaper and throw it in the trash.

- When children get excited they often lose control.

- A child stressed or tensed will have accidents. Identify and evaluate the stress indicators and reduce the stress. See Relaxation and/or Cultural Virtues.

- Use a natural bubble bath, soaps and/or bath oils (you can get these items from a health food store). The commercial toiletries have harsh chemicals and allergens, which can irritate the anus and genitals thus causing bedwetting and accidents.

- If the child is learning a new skill, they will concentrate on it and ignore the toilet learning and this can cause accidents.

- Praise and encourage the child. A few accidents can depress the child and hurt their pride. When the child successfully gets to the toilet in time, let them know how proud you are of them and tell them they are really learning.

- A child may refuse to be successful at toilet learning because they are refusing to grow up. They enjoy the attention and nurturing of being a baby. Some have accidents to rebel against authority and may be angry with their parents. They have found that a bowel movement is a good non-verbal way to tell their parent to "Shut-up", "Leave me alone"' or "I got issues." A parent preoccupied with bowel movements and urine turns them off so they retaliate with an accident. Bowel movements, urine and food are political tools that are used by children and the elderly. Look for political issues for the child's accidents.

- A urinary tract infection can cause a child to hold in the urine as long as they can in order to avoid the irritation and/or burning the urine causes. The child with an infection holds urine until the last minute then unsuccessfully makes a run for the toilet.

- A child that seems to urinate if they laugh, giggle or have a weak urine flow, blood in the urine or is always a little wet may have a disease.

BOYS
(Standing To Urinate)

Boys should sit on the toilet until they have successfully learned to stand and urinate. Do not rush the boy to stand and urinate because it may make them confused. They do not know whether to urinate first or second and then have a bowel movement. The boy has to be able to tell whether the urine is the most urgent or the bowel movement. If they choose the wrong one, then they can start having a bowel movement while they are standing up and urinating. Urinating while standing up requires mastering which urge is the most urgent

Standing to urinate requires coordination, lifting the toilet seat, speed and the ability to aim the urine. If the boy is too slow lifting the toilet seat or aiming they may start urinating before the penis is in the proper position. It is best for the instructor to be a male who can pass on the man-to-man tips and demonstrate the technique. Do not select a male that is having some gender problems. The boy can practice aiming by trying to sink a toilet paper square in the toilet commode.

Boys that are having aiming problems may have to sit on the toilet backwards to practice aiming. This will be the position he will be in when he stands. When his aim is good, he will need a stepstool (some potty's have steps attached) to be at the right height to urinate in the grown-up toilet. The stepstool should be sturdy otherwise; when he is rushing to urinate he may fall off it or fall into the toilet. If he does not want you to hold his penis in order to help his aim, expect misfiring and urine to be on the floor, toilet seat cover and walls. When rushing to urine the boy may forget to lift the toilet seat up or worse the toilet seat cover. It is best to give praises and positive words of support for even small amounts of success.

ACCELERATED POTTY LEARNING

- Some preschools will not accept a child that is not toilet trained while others will. If it is required that the child is toilet trained then you will have to use accelerated training and pressure the child. You may have to offer rewards for each successful potty use. Do not tell the child that they must learn how to potty in a few weeks or they will not be able to go to school.

- A movable potty chair is best. It does not matter where the child uses the potty the only thing that matters is that they use it. The child may want to take the potty from room-to-room, let them. During accelerated learning too many rules and restrictions about potty use will slow down the process. If they move the potty and forget the toilet, you can get it for them or they can wipe later.

- If they do not want you doing "a have you wiped cleanly inspection" do not force the issue. You can clean the area during their bath or shower. If while using toilet paper they accidentally use their hand to wipe themselves, smile and tell them may be next time they will do better. Let them carry a few sheets of toilet paper for emergency use. Put them on the potty after each meal even if it is only for a few minutes.

WON'T POTTY AND OLDER

A child two and half years or older that refuses to be successfully toilet trained after several months of training should not be given up on. They may have shown all the signs of being ready to be trained but just will not put any effort into it. Listed below are a few suggestions to assist in the process:

- Let the child have the responsibility for toilet learning. Talk to them calmly and do not scold. In a learning process you can study and put sincere effort in learning and still do not comprehend what you have been studying because you have a learning block, then one day you are fully aware of and understand the process(the light comes on). Children have learning blocks and do not always understand. It is best tell to them "It is your bowel movement and urine and you can use the potty. I can help you, if you need me just ask me."

- Let the child feel in control of their body. You can do this by letting them make choices such as potty or toilet, diapers or training pants, you can start now or later.
- Ask someone else to give words of encouragement such as another child or adult, teacher or nurse, it is sometimes more effective than the parent.

- You should not constantly talk about or remind the child. The child understands and knows how to use the potty so do not pressure the child to use the potty. You do not have to talk about potty training with others as a way to remind the child.

- As an incentive or challenge you can indicate on a calendar with a sticker or mark the days that the child had three or more successful potty uses. If the child has three successive days of use offer a reward. If the child seems too embarrassed with failures marked on the calendar, stop. If the child gets too upset when they fail to get a reward, stop. Potty training is learning and learning should not cause them emotional traumas or scars.

POTTY LEARNING

Learning to use the potty is a new developmental task for the child. It will take trials, errors, wisdom, experimentation, concentration, muscle control, timing, false starts and coordination. Most children learn to control their bowel movements before they can control urination. Many children learn bowel and urine control at the same time. Boys usually learn control later than girls. They have to know how to pull out, aim and control their penis. Children that do not like changes in their daily rituals and ceremonies (routines) usually have difficulty making the transition from diaper to the toilet.

Children have to master the art of wiping themselves after bowel movements. Encourage gentle wiping of the anus; rough wiping can bruise and irritate the skin resulting in infections. Hand washing after using the potty has to be made into an automatic response. If the parent does do the wiping for the child or if the child only urinates, both the parent and the child must wash their hands after using the toilet. Girls have to wipe themselves after bowel movements and urinating. Girls wipe from the vagina to the back. This prevents bacteria from the anus getting into the vaginal area. The most common vaginal diseases are vulva vaginitis and vaginitis. They are both inflammations. The vulva is the external area called the labia (lips); clitoris is the vaginal opening and vestibules (entrance). The usual symptoms are vaginal bleeding, a foul, smelly discharge, itching, irritation and redness. Liquid herbal extracts with vegetable glycerin (no alcohol, no vinegar) such as Cat's Claw and/or Feverfew are good for inflammations of any type. The child will take the vegetable glycerin extracts because they are naturally sweet.

- If the girl is in diapers you may have to spread open the labia (lips of the vagina) especially after messy bowel movements.

- Rinse the vagina with clear water; use a cotton washcloth or a cup. If the girl is using underpants use all cotton so the vagina can get air.

- Only use natural shampoos and soaps from the health food store.

- Change diapers immediately as urine and bowel movement can irritate and cause health problems.
- When children use the potty for urinating and diapers for bowel movements, do not insist that they use the potty. Some children will hold in the bowel movement as a way to protest your insistence. This could lead to constipation. When the child ask for a diaper, you can suggest the potty, if they refuse the potty, give them the diaper.

- Some children's skin tends to be less sensitive to acidic urine while others get inflammation and combative behavior. A child that tends to hold in urine will concentrate it and make it very acidic and irritating to the skin. It is best to keep the child dry. Have the child check their diaper or pants for dryness. A child's skin will develop an immunity to wet diapers and will not suffer any skin problems. However, it is best to keep them dry.

TRAINING PANTS

The transition from diapers to training pants helps the child feel grown-up and more aware of the toilet learning process. It is usually better to use disposable and then non-disposable cotton training pants. Cotton training pants feel uncomfortable with urine or a bowel movement in them. This helps the child to focus on getting to the potty in time. Training pants are for the child to put on and pull down. This helps the rushing child to make the potty in time.

- Heavy duty, extra absorbent cotton training pants hold more urine. Do not use them too early in the learning process because if too many accidents occur in them, the child will begin to feel depress and will want to stop using them and revert back to diapers. Make sure they are not too tight.

- Disposal training pants absorb so much water that the child does not feel the wetness and tend to ignore the wetness. The disposal pants tend to be treated like a diaper so it is best to stop using them as soon as possible. You may find them more convenient on outings to the store, movies, traveling, visiting someone's house, etc.

DIAPER REJECTION

A child may not like the diaper and feel uncomfortable like they are a walking or crawling unflushed toilet. They will put up a struggle with you when you are putting on their diaper. The struggle may continue until the child starts using the potty. The following suggestions may help in easing the process:

- A skin rash can cause the diaper to be irritating. Check for a rash. Wearing a diaper will irritate a child with sensitive skin.

- Use a diaper with Velcro closing (plastic tabs) because the faster you change the diaper the shorter the confrontation. Have everything already set-up before the change (i.e. wipes, lotion, cornstarch, ointments, etc.).

- Do not inspire the child to be combative by struggling against their struggle to resist. The child can lose the desire to struggle with you when you are calm and passive.

- If it is possible have your spouse, another adult or an age appropriate older child change the diaper. Children assume that the way to act with the parent is to resist. They think and feel that this is the way the parent likes it. The child has to figure out how to be combative to a new diaper change. By the time they have figured out a new combative behavior, the new person has already changed the diaper.

- It may be necessary to hold the child down or restrain their legs. Be calm and as gentle as possible, friendly and firm. Do not feel you are being a bad parent or feel guilty. The diaper has to be changed. A smack on the child's buttock will shock them and quiet them for a few minutes but it will not solve the problem. They will start letting you change them with a struggle because they fear being hurt. They will learn that hitting is the way to get what you want.

- When a child is doing an activity and they are wet or smelly, the child will ignore the soiled diaper and keep playing. If you can wait until they finish the activity but if you cannot give them a toy or find another distraction when you change them.

- When a child is walking around with a soiled diaper it may be best to change the diaper while they are standing. Approach the buttocks from behind as an element of surprise. Use distractions such as toys, music box, kalimba, tambourine, mobiles, chimes or talk about shadows on the wall or sing/rap a song. A distraction can shift the child's attention away from the diaper changing.

If you use one area or place to change the diaper, the child when taken to the area will immediately go into their combative routine. Try a different place or area such as a chair, floor, your bed, the crib or playpen or the bathroom. You may have to protect the surface with a towel or plastic pad.

CHAPTER 10
FOOD

"We must be about the business of liberating the minds of Black children. In order for that to occur, the minds of all Blacks who interact with them must also be liberated."

Bobby E. Wright

FOODS

The following sections are provided for those parents who like these type age appropriate foods and want their child to eat them in a healthy way. These parents usually feed their children the same foods they eat. The foods in this section are health food and junk foods combined wrong. Therefore, this section teaches you the right way to do something wrong. Ideally, the baby should be breastfed from 3 to 5 years, eat the right food combinations, eat raw non-genetically engineered organic foods, drink spring water and bath in spring water. A totally organic foods diet is very expensive and the majority of Black folks cannot afford an organic diet. Most have to purchase some organic foods along with synthetic chemicalized freak foods. You have to have wealth to have health (healthy foods) in a Caucasian controlled country. It is suggested that you constantly use blood purifying herbs to flush out some of the toxins in your body that are accumulated from eating non-organic foods. Herbs such as Chaparral, Red Clover, Burdock Root, Echinacea Root, PauD'Arco, Goldenseal, etc. can be used in Extract/Tincture (alcohol-free) form or as a tea or in tablet/capsule form. One or a combination of the herbs should be taken daily ir order to constantly flush out toxins. Most parents cannot or will not provide the ideal organic diet for themselves or their children. They ask sincerely "What should we eat?" This section has age appropriate foods that should be eaten as your child works their way to an organic raw food diet. You should be trying to follow the Food Combining Rules Chart. It will help your child to obtain optimum health.

BABY FOOD

Breast milk or modified vegetable milk is the basic food for the baby for at least six months. Ideally, breast milk in traditional cultures was given between three to five years. Solids foods can be given usually after six months. Cereals (usually brown rice) is given after the eighth month.

The first food can be a very ripe mashed banana or plantain (should have black skin and be uncooked).

A modified vegetable milk formula can be prepared as followed:

- Bottle of Vegetable Milk (Almond, Rice, Soy, etc.)
- Liquid Multiple Vitamin and Mineral = 1/3 adult dosage add to each baby bottle
- Vegetable Protein Soy Free Powder = 1/3 to ½ tsp per bottle

- Digestive Enzyme = 1/3 to ½ dosage per bottle (Empty capsule or crush tablet or get the liquid form) Bean – O if the child has gas, add a few drops to the bottle

COOKING

Stainless steel or glass pots should be used for cooking. Do not use aluminum; it is toxic and dangerous to the nerves and brain and hampers digestion. A pressure cooker, crock pot and microwave can also be used. A steamer basket that collapses can fit into most pots, make sure it is stainless steel. Use a pot with a tight fitting lid. You can steam most vegetables with it. Cooking vegetables and fruits in a microwave is a form of steaming them from the inside of the plant to the outside. Fewer nutrients are lost because little or no water is added when cooking in a microwave. Microwaves are dangerous to your health and should be avoided.

- Do not season any food that you give to a baby.

- You can puree the food by mashing it with a fork or chewing it yourself and then giving it to the baby or use the following:

- A **blender** can be used to puree any food. Vegetables puree best in larger quantities. Use the highest speeds for a finer puree for the younger baby. For older babies, use the slower speeds for a coarser consistency. Blenders can be used to make shakes and nut butters. It can be used to mix green vegetables with powdered juices or mix with frozen juice concentrates (add water).

- A **food processor** can be used to puree foods. It is difficult to puree small amounts in a food processor, so be prepared to do large quantities and freeze most of it.

- A **standard food mill** can be used. Place food in the basket; as you turn the handle, the blade presses food through holes in the bottom of the basket. The food mill strains cooked foods to a smooth consistency.

- A **baby food grinder** (a smaller type food mill) purees small amounts of food. The food fits in a well; you place the turning disc on top. As you turn the handle and press down, the pureed food comes to the top and can be served right from the grinder.

It will grind fruits and vegetables. The grinder sifts out the skins of peas and the hulls of corn. It can be used for grinding dried fruits (i.e. raisins) mashing plantains, bananas and cooked potatoes and softening soy or safflower margarine.

FROZEN FOODS

Freezing foods allows you to have an adequate supply of prepared baby foods. It eliminates the need to rush to prepare food for a hungry baby or a child that says, "I'm starving."

Freeze small portions in ice cube trays or in freezer bags. Thaw frozen foods in the refrigerator; use an egg poacher cup over boiling water, warm the food in a warming dish or microwave oven. A baby can eat slightly cold as well as cold food. Food that seems warm to you can seem hot to a baby because their taste buds are not developed.

ICE CUBE TRAY FOODS: Put pureed food in plastic, pop-out ice cube trays. Freeze immediately. Pop out the frozen food and put in plastic freezer bags. Label and date the food (expires in two months). Use a few cubes for meals or as many as necessary.

COOKIE SHEET FOODS: Put a spoonful of finely ground or pureed foods on a cookie sheet. The size of the spoonful (one or more tablespoons) depends on the baby's appetite. Freeze immediately. Put the cookie shaped frozen foods into freezer bags. Label and date the food.

Open jars of commercial baby foods can be kept in the refrigerator for two to three days. The commercial foods must not contain any preservatives, dyes, salt or white sugar. Do not feed the baby from the jar, their saliva from the spoon gets into the jar and can speed up the spoiling of stored open jar foods. When feeding from the jar, there is a tendency to finish the jar. This can cause the baby to overeat. Pediatric obesity is very high and a health hazard. A fat baby is an unhealthy baby.

BABY'S CEREALS

Cereals can be made from any whole grain by running the grains through your blender before cooking. Commercial whole grains are nutritious and convenient. Brown Rice and/or Millet is usually the first cereal given because they are easier for the baby to digest. You may have to add carrot or vegetarian acidophilus or a digestive enzyme to the cereal in order to relieve the stress on the digestive system. Breast milk can be expressed and added to cereals or any food because the smell and taste is familiar to the baby and it helps with digestion of the food. A cereal can be sweetened to mimic breast milk's taste. Add a little pureed fruit or fruit concentrated juice to the cereal. Avoid honey as it causes fermentation in the digestive tract. A little vegetarian yogurt can be added to help digestion and give the grainy cereals a creamy texture.

Fresh cooked fruits and canned natural fruits (cooked during canning) can be pureed. They can be given to a six to seven month old baby.

BABY'S VEGETABLES

The first choice is fresh vegetables then frozen and lastly canned for the baby. Cook yams, beets, peas, sweet and white potatoes, plantain, green beans, mustard greens, kale, collards, etc. should be steamed and then pureed.

PREPARATION

VEGETABLE STEAMER BASKET: Peel and slice or cut-up food. Fill the pot with water; it should not touch the basket bottom. Cook until tender. Puree or blend, add water for the right consistency.

WATER METHOD: Peel and slice for fast cooking or use frozen. Cook in 1 to 1–1/2 inches of water for 20 minutes. Puree or blend with water.

STEAM METHOD: Peel and slice for fast cooking or use frozen. Steam over boiling water under tender. Puree or blend, add cooking water for right consistency.

MICROWAVE METHOD: Cook a single item or a batch for pureeing and freezing. In a microwave-safe dish, with a touch of water, cook clean vegetables until tender. Yams and potatoes need to be pierced several times to allow interior steam build-up to escape. Single yams and potatoes generally cook in 3-5 minutes.

MICROWAVING: BROCCOLI (Good for constipation). Wash and cut broccoli into one inch pieces, place in non-metal bowl. Cover with a water soaked paper towel, microwave on high for 3 to 5 minutes – the time will vary depending on the strength of your microwave. The broccoli should be well cooked in order to be mashed. Puree until smooth and for new eaters, strain.

SIMMERING: PEACHES
Wash and peel peaches, cut into slices. Simmer until soft in enough water to cover the fruit. Put in blender and process until smooth.

BAKING: POTATO
Preheat oven to 350º, wrap potato in foil and bake for one hour. Peel off skin, chop into cubes, to puree add breast or soy milk for desired consistency.

STEAMING: CARROTS
Place baby carrots in a steamer basket with a small amount (about one inch) of boiling water, cover and steam for about 10 minutes or until tender. Puree until smooth add cooking water as needed.

FRUIT PREPARATION

BANANAS
Use one medium-size, fully ripe (speckled-skin) banana or black skin plantain. Cut it in half and peel one half to use. Cover the remaining half (in the peel) and it can be stored in the refrigerator for two days. Mash the plantain or banana with a fork or use a grinder. You can peel ripe plantain or bananas, wrap tightly in meal-size portions and freeze. When ready to use, thaw and use immediately.

A child that will eat chunkier foods can be given a banana out of the peel with a spoon, one bite at a time.

OTHER FRUITS
Mango, apples, papaya, pears, plums kiwi and peaches can be prepared by using the following methods:

VEGETABLE STEAMER BASKET: Wash fruit, peel and cut into small pieces or dice. Fill pot with water, it should not touch the basket bottom. Steam until tender. Blend or puree. Fix enough to store for the next day and freeze the remainder.

WATER METHOD: Wash fruit, peel and cut into small pieces. Add ¼ cup boiling water to 1 cup of fruit. Simmer until tender (10-20 minutes). Blend or puree until smooth. Refrigerate a serving for that day and freeze the remainder.

STEAM METHOD: Wash fruit well, remove skin and steam for 15-20 minutes. Cool. Remove pits. Blend or puree until smooth. Refrigerate a serving for that day and freeze the remainder.

MICROWAVE METHOD: Wash one piece of fruit. Remove core or pit. Place in a small glass with 2-3 tsp of water on the bottom. Cover dish lightly. Microwave 1 to 2 minutes until fruit is tender. Cool and remove skin. Mash or puree until smooth.

RECIPES

Baked Yam or Sweet Potato and Apples

¾ cup cooked yam or sweet potato
1-cup applesauce or apples
¼ cup rice, almond or soymilk

Preheat oven to 350º. Peel, core and slice apples. Mix yams or sweet potatoes and apples in an oiled baking dish. Put liquid over. Cover and bake for 30 minutes. Puree or mash with a fork.

Banana Treat

½ very ripe avocado, mashed or pureed
½ very ripe plantain or banana, mashed or pureed
¼ cup soy cheese or soy yogurt

Mix the ingredients together.

Fruit Gelatin

Dissolve 1 envelope unflavored gelatin in ¼ cup warm water. Add 1 cup of a single or combination of pureed fruit and chill.

Vegetable Soup

¼ cup cooked pureed vegetables
1-tablespoon whole-wheat flour
1-tablespoon soy or safflower margarine
¼ cup liquid (vegetable broth)

Combine together in a saucepan, warm and serve.

Meatless Stew

1/3 cup whole grain flour
2 cups of green peas
2-tablespoons olive oil
4 medium potatoes or ½ cup of brown rice
3 cups water
5 medium carrots
½ pound of texturized vegetable protein

Coat texturized vegetable protein with flour and brown in oil. Add water and cover pan tightly. Simmer 15 to 30 minutes. Scrub, peel and cube potatoes and carrots. Simmer 15 minutes. Add peas and simmer for 5 minutes.

Adults can eat this dish. The baby's portion has to be pureed.

MICROWAVE DO'S AND DON'TS

DON'T microwave frozen breast milk stored in a bottle. Let the milk thaw by running lukewarm water over the bottle or set the bottle in a pan of warm water. Reheating breast milk in a microwave reduces its anti-infective properties, genetically alters the milk and creates harmful toxins.

DON'T microwave formula in a glass bottle the glass may crack, microwave in colored plastic bottles unless they are labeled microwave safe.

DO use clear plastic bottles – without bottle liners – when heating formula or milk. For a general guideline, heat a cold eight ounces on high for forty-five seconds. Leave the bottle uncovered in the microwave to allow heat to escape.

DON'T shake a micro waved bottle. Microwaves heat liquids unevenly. The fluid at the top can be slightly warm while fluid in the middle may be burning hot. It can burn the baby's mouth.

Note

Egg whites, citrus fruits, cow's milk and wheat products may cause allergic reactions especially in food-sensitive families. It may be best to withhold these foods until the child is over one years old.

Be flexible. Respect strong food dislikes.
And remember,
Love is not equal to the amount of food your child eats.

There are many healthy foods for your baby. If you cannot find them in your local stores, call the companies and ask for the nearest distributor or mail order companies. Two popular companies are "*Earth's Best*" brand 1-800-442-4221 and "*Growing Healthy*" 1-800-ABC-GROW

FAST FOOD RESTAURANTS

Many fast food restaurants and oriental fast food restaurants have veggie burgers, vegetable submarines, vegetable sandwiches, vegetable entrees and whole grain bread. Restaurants have salad bars with grated carrots, peas, broccoli, cauliflower, onions, celery, tomatoes as well as baked potatoes. Avoid the high fat salad dressing and squeeze the juice of lemon slices on the salad. Get orange, apple or tomato juice. Some restaurants provide nutritional information upon request.

Toddlers' calorie needs temporarily decrease. During the first year, their calorie needs are high because the growth is fast. Birth weight triples and height nearly doubles then their growth and energy needs decline between eighteen and thirty-six months of age. Toddlers simply do not need a lot of food and may seem to be picky or finicky eaters. They will eat when they are hungry. Toddlers start to develop food likes and dislikes and do not know what they like except by using trial and error and experimentation. They will basically eat what their parents eat and may need a few novelty type desserts and snacks such as the following:

RECIPES

Raw Vegetables

Toddlers usually prefer raw vegetables overcooked. They will even eat frozen green peas from the freezer bag. They like sweet Chinese pea pods, snow peas and baby carrots. Some toddlers like mashed avocado (guacamole) mixed with onions, red and green peppers and veggie salt. They dip celery spears, cauliflower, cucumber spears, sliced zucchini, mushrooms, slivers of green peppers and broccoli in the mashed avocado or eat them plain.

Alphabet Soup

1-teaspoon alphabet noodles
2/3-cup vegetable broth
2 teaspoons instant tapioca
a little sea salt
a little soy or safflower margarine

Cook over high heat for 3 minutes stir constantly. Remove from heat then stir in sea salt and the soy margarine.

Carrot and Raisin Salad

Grate carrots, mix with raisins or other chopped dried fruit. Mix in a little egg less mayonnaise or mix in a raw lemon or lime juice and a small amount of honey.

Drinks

If you do buy sodas, avoid sodas with caffeine. They over stimulate children and are addicting.

Apple Juice Soda: Concentrated apple (add water) or fruit juice. Mix with carbonated soda water.

Grape, Lime or Lemon Juice: Add an equal amount of water to a bottle of grape juice. For each 2 cups of water added, use ½ cup honey and squeeze 1 to 2 fresh limes or lemons.

Fruity Milk: Add fruit sweeten jelly to plain or vanilla enriched soy rice or almond milk.

Water: Keeping cold water in the refrigerator is an excellent way to encourage consumption.

Frozen Juices

Fruit Ice Cubes: Freeze fruit juices in ice cube trays and add to drinks.

Ices

Base Syrup:

2 cups water
2 cups honey or 1 cup concentrated juice

If using concentrates, cook on a low boil for 10 minutes or until approximately at the jelly stage. Cool. Use as a base for the ices below:

Orange Ice

2 cups fresh orange juice
¼ cup lemon juice or juice from 1 lemon

Grape Ice

1-1/2 cups grape juice
2/3 cups orange juice
3 tablespoons lemon juice

Lemon Ice

¾ cup lemon juice
1 tablespoon lemon peel, grated
2 cups water

Pour into ice cube trays or a small bowl and freeze. Watch for "mushy" stage (1 hour) then mix in the tray and refreeze. Good alone or served by the scoop in a fruit drink.

Vegetable Ice Cream Sandwiches

Softened rice or soy ice cream and spread it on a whole grain cookie or graham crackers. Cut into squares whole grain waffles and use instead of cookies. Gently press another cookie on top and make into a sandwich. Wrap individually or put them together in foil or plastic wrap and freeze.

Ice cream cones can be made. Soften rice or soy ice cream and put in cones and freeze. Cones can be brought from the store.

Carobsicles

1 4-ounce regular carob pudding mix or 2 ounces of carob powder
3-1/2 cups rice, soy, almond or spelt milk
1 tablespoon of arrowroot powder

Sweeten to taste. Freeze in molds or paper cups and insert Popsicle-stick handles.

Popsicles

In a mold or paper cup, mix papaya, apple, pineapple, mango, orange, tropical or grape juice with 1 teaspoon melted vanilla soy or rice ice cream. Mix well and freeze. Add handle when partially frozen. Mash or blend pitted honeydew, watermelon or cantaloupe cubes, pour into a mold and freeze to make a Popsicle.

Banana Popsicles

Peel 3 bananas, cut in half. Push wooden stick up center of each half and freeze. Serve this way or dip in carob syrup or honey and roll in nuts, toasted wheat germ or desiccated coconut.

Cooked Vegetable Ideas

- Use up any leftover vegetable by mashing it, mix it with arrowroot and cook it like a pancake or bake it in a muffin tin.
- Sprinkle shredded soy or rice cheese over cooked vegetables or let the child do it.
- Puree steamed vegetables and add vegetable broth for a creamy soup.
- Spaghetti squash can be cooked whole in the microwave until soft. Cut it in half, remove the seeds and the pulp. It comes up like spaghetti strands. Serve with vegetable seasoning mix with olive oil or spaghetti sauce. It is a good finger food.
- Sliced vegetables can be mixed with rice or soy cheese to make an omelet.
- Make yams, plantain or sweet potato chips. On a microwave-oven rack place 12 thin circle slices. Sprinkle with cinnamon, date sugar and microwave 4 to 5 minutes until dry. Rotate during cooking. Let cool then eat.

- Pureed vegetables can be put in any sauce or in mashed potatoes, mixed in a rice/soy cheese omelet, etc.
- Be artistic and create faces, animals, buildings, cars, boats, airplane and other items out of their food. It can stimulate the toddler to eat.

Graham Cracker Dessert

Crumble 1 graham cracker into a bowl. Add 1 teaspoon of honey and a little warmed vanilla rice, soy or almond milk. Mash, mix and serve.

Carob Cream Cheese

1 ounce of rice or soy cheese
½ teaspoon honey
1-teaspoon vanilla vegetable milk
1/8 teaspoon carob

Blend cheese with milk until smooth. Then blend honey and carob.

Banana and Apple

1 small banana
1-teaspoon vanilla vegetable milk
1 small apple
¼ teaspoon honey

Wash, peel, grate or cut apple into small pieces. Add the remaining ingredients. Put into blender. Blend until smooth.

Yogurt Sundae

Put soy yogurt in a dish. Add fresh fruit and pour honey over the fruit. Sprinkle with granola, nuts or wheat germ. Top with dried fruits.

Baked Plantain

Peel plantain and place in a well-greased (canola or olive oil) baking dish. Brush with canola oil and bake at 350º for 12 to 15 minutes. Remove from oven. Eat as is or with the tip of a spoon, make a shallow groove the length of the banana and fill with carob syrup, applesauce, honey or date sugar.

Apple Custard

1 apple
1 tsp arrowroot powder

1 tablespoons date sugar or honey or fruit sweeten apple jelly

Preheat oven to 350º. Wash, peel and core apple. Slice very thin and sprinkle with date sugar. Mix arrowroot with water until silky smooth and fold into the apples. Put these into a well-oiled (canola or olive oil) baking dish. Bake for 30 minutes.

Nut Butters Sandwiches

(Almond, soy, peanut, cashew, sunflower, sesame, etc.)

- Nut butter and ground dates or raisins mixed with fruit juice
- Nut butter and grated raw carrots
- Nut butter topped with apple butter (or puree pears into sauce)
- Nut butter and plantain or banana slices
- Nut butter and soy or rice cheese blended with 2 tablespoons mango, papaya, pineapple or orange juice or honey.

Vegetable Cheese Sandwich Ideas

- Soy or rice cheese with jelly
- Soy or rice cheese with ground raisins or chopped dates
- Soy or rice cheese with peeled and finely chopped (or grated) cucumber
- Soy or rice cheese with grated pineapple

Keep your sliced bread in the freezer. That keeps it from tearing when nut butter is spread. Sliced bread thaws in only a few minutes.

Pancakes can be used as bread for sandwiches. After applying spread, put them in the microwave for 30 to 45 seconds before serving.

Honeyed Carrots

3 tablespoons soy or safflower margarine
¼ teaspoon ginger
4 cups carrots, sliced
4 tablespoons honey or fruit sweeten jelly
3 tablespoons mango, papaya or orange juice

Mix the ingredients in a saucepan and cover. Cook over low heat for 30 minutes or until tender. Stir occasionally.

Gelatin Beets

1 cup cooked and pureed beets
1 cup boiling water (or jar baby food beets)
3 ounces of Jell-O (health food brand)

Chill strained beets then mix with cold water and make 1-cup liquid and set aside. Dissolve Jell-O in boiling water and add beet mixture. Chill until set.

FINGER FOODS

Children eat when hungry and eat enough to satisfy their hunger. They do not eat a lot of food because they think they will get hungry later. Children do not eat for hunger prevention. It is best to serve small portions first. If the child is still hungry, they will ask for seconds. Ideally, the child's food should be served on small plates or in small bowls. Slowly introduce a new food. If the child does not like it, try the new food again in a few days. Many times a child's taste for a food or rejection of a food is based upon how they feel that moment or another child's rejection or like of a food. Children can change their likes and dislikes for food day-to-day and meal-to-meal. Some finger foods and ideas are listed below:

- Serve thick nut butters or peanut butter thinned with vegetable milks.
- Do not let the child eat while running or lying down.
- Serving dishes do not have to be used. Put the food on a paper towel or a tray.
- Serve half a plantain or banana.
- Serve cereal in a mug with a handle.
- Put finger foods in a freezer bag or a paper bag and serve.
- Serve toasted bread sticks or raw carrot sticks with caution.

SIX TO EIGHT MONTHS OLD

Applesauce
Arrowroot cookies
Plantain or Bananas, mashed or in small slices
Soy or Rice Cheese
Non-Sweet and Sweet White Yams
Yams or Potatoes, mashed
Pudding
Rice Cakes
Soft-cooked vegetables, mashed
Whole Grain Crackers
Whole Grain Cereals

NINE MONTHS TO ONE YEAR OLD

Whole Grain bagels, soft
Carrots and other vegetables, cooked soft
Rice or Soy Cheese
Natural Custards
Scrambled Tofu

Whole Grain French toast "fingers" (sliced in strips)
Whole Grain macaroni and pastas
Soy Meats
Orange sections, peeled with loose membrane removed
Peaches ripe and peeled
Peeled and sliced mango and papayas
Brown Rice
Whole Grain spaghetti with soy meat sauce
Whole Grain toast
Vanilla Rice or Soy Ice Cream

Babies with two to four teeth can be given lumpier foods to chew. Soft foods can be adequately chewed with their gums. The more teeth the baby has, the chewier fruits and vegetables they can be given.

ONE YEAR AND OLDER

VEGETABLES

Asparagus tips, cooked
Avocado, ripen
Broccoli florets, cooked
Carrot sticks (soft-cooked or grated)
Cauliflower, cooked
Celery (remove strands)
Cherry tomatoes, halved
Baked French fries
Green beans, cooked
Lettuce, shredded
Mushrooms, cooked
Peas, cooked
Yams (sweet and non-sweet) or potatoes, mashed
Whole Grain spaghetti squash
Sweet yams or sweet potato, cooked and mashed
Tomatoes, peeled

FRUIT

Apple, peeled
Plantain or banana, whole or cut into sections
Blueberries
Cantaloupe, cut into bite-size pieces
Dried fruits (avoid raisins) unless they are the moist type
Grapes, halved for young toddlers

Kiwi pieces, peeled
Mandarin oranges, mango peeled and sliced
Navel oranges, peeled and sectioned
Peaches, papaya, peeled and sliced
Pears, peeled
Strawberries, halved
Sweet cherries, pitted
Watermelon, honeydew, pitted and cut into bite-size pieces

NON-DAIRY

Vanilla or plain soy yogurt
Soy cottage cheese (add fresh or canned fruit for interest)
Small squares of rice or soy cheese
Grated or shredded rice or soy cheese

FINGER FOODS NOT RECOMMENDED FOR BABIES YOUNGER THAN TWELVE TO EIGHTEEN MONTHS OLD

Difficult to Digest	May Cause Gagging
Baked beans	Grapes, whole
Chocolate	Hard candies
Corn	Ice cubes
Cucumbers	Nuts and raisins
Leafy vegetables	Olives
Onion, uncooked	Popcorn

TEETHING ITEMS/FOOD

The teething developmental phase can be relieved with hard baked whole grain cookies, biscuits and crackers. The child may also relieve teething with cold or frozen whole grain bagels, the hard core of a pineapple, frozen peeled, pitted grapes, frozen pitted cherries, frozen cubed watermelons, cantaloupes, honeydew, mango, papayas and other foods on a stick or a plastic spoon. Ice cubes in a cotton washcloth and held in place with a string or rubber band can be chewed on. Rubber toys or rubber pet toys, toothbrushes, chilled pacifiers and/or teething rings can be used. There are various types of herbal chew sticks such licorice sticks that the child can chew as well as a damp cotton washcloth.

Teething Bread

Harden any type whole grain bread by baking it at a low temperature (150º to 200º) for 15 to 20 minutes. Pita bread can be cut in strips and toasted and used for teething.

Banana Bread Sticks

¼ cup date sugar or honey or fruit sweetened jelly
1-¾ cup whole grain flour (whole wheat or a combination)
½ cup olive or vegetable oil
2 teaspoons baking powder (aluminum free)
1-cup plantain or banana, mashed
½ teaspoon baking soda

Combine ingredients and stir only until smooth. Pour into an oiled loaf pan. Bake at 350º for about 1 hour or until firmly set. Cool, remove from pan and then cut into sticks. Spread sticks out on a cookie sheet and bake at 150º for 1 hour or until the sticks are hard and crunchy.

Graham Crackers

1-cup flour (graham or whole wheat)
¼ cup soy or safflower margarine
1 cup unbleached whole wheat flour
½ cup honey or fruit sweetened jelly
1-teaspoon baking powder (aluminum free)
¼ cup vanilla rice, almond, soy or any type whole grain milk

Combine flours and baking powder. Put in margarine until consistency of cornmeal. Stir in honey. Add milk to make stiff dough.

Roll out on floured surface to ¼ inch thickness. Cut into squares. Prick with a fork. Brush with milk.

Bake at 400ºF on an ungreased baking sheet for 18 minutes or until golden brown. Make the crackers thicker for teething.

Oatmeal Crackers

3 cups oatmeal, uncooked
3 tablespoons date sugar or fruit sweeten jelly
1-cup wheat germ
¾ cup olive oil
2 cups flour (any type whole grain, whole wheat or a combination)
1-cup water

Combine ingredients and roll onto two cookie sheets. Cut into squares. Bake at 300º for 30 minutes or until crisp. Make thicker crackers for teething.

SNACKS

FRESH FRUITS: Plantain, banana, pear, apricot, melon, grapefruit, avocado, papaya, persimmon, guava, fig, mango, kiwi, watermelon, strawberries, dates

FRESH VEGETABLES: Carrot sticks, celery, celery sticks with pure nut butter or soy cream cheese, zucchini sticks, raw cabbage or cauliflower, broccoli flowerets, Jerusalem artichoke slices

JUICE: Pear, mango, pineapple, papaya, grapefruit, kiwi

CHIPS: Whole corn chips, baked potato chips, pure carob chips, banana chips, seaweed chips

DRIED FRUIT: Pineapple, apples, pears, banana, mango, etc.

CANDY: Sesame honey candy

SEEDS/NUTS: Sunflower seeds, peanuts (soak nuts and seeds in water and store in refrigerator)

BREAD/CRACKERS: Matzo crackers, cracker bread, pita bread, whole-wheat pretzel sticks, rice cakes

POPCORN: Plain (can use soy or safflower margarine, sea salt, liquid amino acids spray or nutritional brewer's yeast to season)

NATURAL VEGETABLE CHEESES: Rice or soy

Fruit Roll

Make with apples, apricots, peaches, pears, mango, nectarines, papaya or other fruits. Mash or puree the fruit.

Blender Method: Peel and core fruit, blend until smooth and then cook 5 minutes in a saucepan over moderate heat.

Freeze-Defrost Method: In advance, peel and core fruit, wrap and freeze. Remove from freezer 1 hour before using so fruit can begin to defrost. Cook in a saucepan for 5-10 minutes. Mash the fruit while it is cooking drain it of watery contents.

While cooking, add 1-teaspoon honey for each piece of fruit used.

Layout clear plastic wrap on cookie sheet or broiling tray. Use one piece of plastic for each piece of fruit you have cooked. Spoon mixture onto the wrap then spread it as thin as possible. Spread another piece of plastic wrap over the mixture and to evenly thin it, press down with a wide spatula. Remove top sheet of plastic before drying.

Turn oven to its lowest possible heat. Place tray in the oven and leave overnight (6-8 hours) or until it is dry. Roll up the plastic wrap with the dried fruit in it.

Then peel and eat!

Apples on a Stick

Core a whole apple. Mix nut butter with dried fruit, raisins, granola or toasted wheat germ. Stuff the mixture into the hole of the cored apple. Slice in half or put on a Popsicle stick or plastic spoon handle.

Grinder Snacks

Grind any type of dried fruit (figs, dates, raisins, etc.). Add a small amount of raw lime or lemon juice to a cup of whole-wheat graham cracker crumbs. Make small balls out of your ground mixture and roll in crumbs for coating.

Oatmeal Bars

2 cups oatmeal, uncooked
¾ cup date sugar or ½ cup fruit sweeten jelly
½ cup soy margarine
add a pinch of baking soda

Boil date sugar, margarine and baking soda. Add oatmeal. Blend. Spread mixture in a canola oiled 8-inch square pan and bake at 350º for 10-15 minutes.

Apple Cookies

½ cup soy margarine
½ teaspoon cinnamon
1 cup date sugar or ½ cup fruit sweetened jelly
¾ cup wheat germ
1 cup apples, peeled, cored and finely chopped
2 tbsp arrowroot powder
1-1/2 cup whole grain flour
½ cup oatmeal, uncooked
2 teaspoons baking soda

Puree soy margarine, date sugar and arrowroot. Mix dry ingredients and combine with creamed mixture. Add apples. Drop spoonfuls onto a canola oiled cookie sheet. Bake at 350º for 10-15 minutes.

Stuffed Celery

Stuff celery sticks with soy or rice cheese or any type of nut butter. Diced dried fruit can be added on top of the spread. Remove the strands from the celery.

Cookies

1-1/2 cup whole oatmeal, uncooked
1 teaspoon cinnamon
½ cup vegetable protein powder
1/3 teaspoon cloves
½ cup wheat germ
½ cup canola oil or soy margarine, melted
¾ cup date sugar or fruit sweeten jelly
½ cup honey
2 tbsp of arrowroot powder

Mix dry ingredients. Add melted soy margarine and arrowroot powder. Spoon onto canola oiled baking sheet. Bake at 350º for 12-15 minutes.

Nut Balls

½ cup nut butter
1-cup peanuts or soy nuts
½ cup honey or date sugar
½ cup sunflower seeds
½ cup carob powder
1-cup dry coconut flakes

Combine all ingredients except coconut flakes. Roll into balls and then roll the balls into the coconut flakes. Refrigerate.

Nut Butter Roll-Ups
1 container peanut butter or nut butter
4 slices whole grain bread
Honey or fruit juice sweeten jelly

Remove the crusts from the bread slices. Place each slice on a hard surface. Roll mixture flat with a rolling pin. Spread a thin layer of nut butter on the flattened bread. Spread the jelly onto the nut butter. Roll each piece of bread into a jellyroll. Slice roll into pieces.

Brownies
¼ cup vegetable oil
1-cup wheat germ
1 tbsp molasses
2/3-cup vegetable protein soy free powder
1-cup date sugar
½ teaspoon baking powder (aluminum free)
2 teaspoons vanilla
¼ cup carob powder
½ cup almonds, pecans or walnuts pieces

Mix together the first seven ingredients. Spread in a canola oiled 8-inch square pan and bake at 350º for approximately 30 minutes. Take out of pan while still warm and cut into bars.

Wheat and Cheese
4 cups spoon size shredded wheat
½ cup soy margarine
1 cup shredded soy or rice cheese

In a large saucepan, melt soy margarine then add cheese. When the cheese begins to melt, add shredded wheat. Toss to coat well. Refrigerate.

Bars
1 loaf of whole grain bread (whole wheat or other)
1-cup peanut butter
Add a small amount of peanut oil

1-package peanuts, chopped
1 tbsp carob powder

Trim the crust from the bread. Cut bread slices in half. Put bread and crusts on a cookie sheet and bake at 150º for ½ hour or until dry. Put the dried crusts in a blender until finely crumbed. Combine crumbs with chopped nuts. Thin the peanut butter with oil and add 1 tablespoon of carob powder. Spread or dip the bread slices in the peanut butter, then roll the bread in then nut-and–crumb mixture. Dry them on a cookie sheet. Refrigerate.

Peanut Butter Balls

½ cup peanut butter
3-1/2 tablespoons vegetable protein soy free powder
Add a little honey or date sugar

Mix ingredients together roll into balls and store in refrigerator.

Cereal Sticks

½ cup soy or safflower margarine
¼ teaspoon baking soda
1-cup date sugar
½ cup plus of a whole grain cereal
2 tbsp arrowroot
1-teaspoon vanilla
1-1/2 cups whole grain flour (whole wheat or a combination)

Blend together all ingredients plus ¼ cup of the cereal. If the dough is too soft add more flour. Roll a small piece of dough into a stick. Coat the stick by rolling it in the extra cereal. Place on a lightly oiled cookie sheet and bate at 400º for 8 minutes or until slightly browned.

BREAD, MUFFINS AND ETC.

Bread Making Procedures

To tell if the bread dough or batter has doubled in bulk, press lightly with one or two fingers near the edge of the dough. If your finger indentation remains, it has doubled. If the dough has not, it will spring back up.

When bread is browning too fast (light brown after only 10-15 minutes). Then lightly cover the top of the bread with a piece of aluminum foil.

To knead dough – fold the dough and press it down with the heel of your hand over and over again until the dough is smooth and elastic (not sticky). Sprinkle flour on the dough and your working surface until the dough loses some of its stickiness

Whole Wheat Bread

1-cup warm water (105º - 115º)
1/3 cup honey
½ tbsp sea salt
2 packages yeast
5 cups whole-wheat flour
1 tbsp honey
3 cups whole grain pastry flour
2 cups vegetable milk
¼ cup wheat germ
¼ cup soy margarine or vegetable oil

Dissolve yeast in warm water. Stir in 1-tablespoon honey. Set aside for 10 minutes. In a saucepan, combine vegetable milk, soy margarine or oil, honey and sea salt. Heat to lukewarm. Pour warm milk mixture and dissolved yeast into a large mixing bowl. Add the whole-wheat flour, one cup at a time, beating after each addition. Add wheat germ.

Add enough pastry flour to make soft dough. Put dough on a lightly floured board and knead until smooth and elastic (approximately 8-10 minutes).

Place dough in a greased bowl turning it to grease the top. Cover and let rise in a warm place until dough has doubled in bulk. Punch down, divide in half and knead each half for about 30 seconds.

Shaped into three loaves and place in greased loaf pans. Cover and let rise again until doubled in bulk about 45 minutes or heat the oven to 200º for 60 seconds, then turn off oven and put in bread and let rise.

Preheat oven to 400º and bake 40 minutes or until done.

Banana Nut Bread
¼ cup soy margarine
1-teaspoon vanilla
½ cup date sugar
1-1/2 cup whole grain flour (whole wheat or a combination)
1 tbsp arrowroot
1-cup bran cereal or oatmeal, uncooked
2 teaspoons baking powder
½ teaspoon baking soda
1-1/2 cups plantain or Bananas mashed
½ cup nuts, chopped

Puree margarine and date sugar until light. Add arrowroot and mix well. Stir in cereal, plantains or bananas and vanilla. Combine the remaining ingredients in a bowl and add to the first mixture, stirring enough to moisten the flour. Oil and flour a loaf pan; pour in batter. Bake at 350º for 1 hour or until done.

Cheese Bread
1-1/2 cups vanilla vegetable milk
2 packages dry yeast
2 tbsp date sugar or honey or fruit juice concentrate
½ cup warm water (105º - 115º)
1 tbsp sea salt.5 cups whole grain flour
2 tbsp soy margarine
2 cups grated rice or poppy, flax or sesame seeds
soy cheese (8 ounces)

Preheat oven to 350º. Heat milk and combine with sweetener, sea salt, margarine and cheese in a large bowl. Let cool until lukewarm. Dissolve yeast in the warm water and add to the cooled milk mixture. Stir. Add flour, while gradually stirring after each addition until fairly stiff dough is formed.

Knead dough approximately 5-8 minutes. Put dough in an oiled bowl, turning to grease top. Let rise in a warm place until doubled in bulk or heat oven to 200º for 60 seconds, then oven off. Then put dough in oven and let rise.

Divide the dough into two equal portions. Roll each piece out into an 11" x 15" rectangle. Cut three equal strips along the 15" side of the rectangle, leaving the strips joined at one end.

Braid the strips loosely. Pinch the three ends together. Place each braided loaf in a well-oiled pan. Cover and let rise until doubled. Bake 40-45 minutes.

Whole Wheat Muffins

1-cup whole-wheat flour
1 tbsp arrowroot powder
¾ cup whole wheat pastry flour
1 cup vegetable milk
¼ cup date sugar or honey
¼ cup vegetable oil
4 teaspoons baking powder

Mix ingredients. Stir until moistened. Batter will be lumpy. Fill oiled muffin tins 2/3 full and bake at 400º for 20-25 minutes. Remove muffins from tins immediately after baking.

Peanut Butter Bread

2 cups whole grain flour (whole wheat or a combination)
¼ cup fruit sweetened jelly or date sugar, honey or concentrated fruit juice
4 teaspoons baking powder
1-1/4 cup vanilla vegetable milk
2/3-cup peanut butter

Lightly mix dry ingredients in a large bowl. If using honey, use a blender to cream it with the peanut butter in a separate bowl. Heat the milk until lukewarm, and then add the peanut butter and blend. Combine the wet and dry ingredients and beat thoroughly.

Bran Muffins
2 cups boiling water
5 cups whole grain flour (whole wheat or a combination)
6 cups 100 percent bran cereal
1-cup vegetable oil or soy margarine
5 teaspoons baking soda
2 cups date sugar or 1-2/3 cups optional additions: dry apples, papaya mango, pineapple, apricots, pears, raisins coconut, peanuts, blueberries, chopped fresh apples or pears, chopped dates, nuts
fruit sweetened jelly, honey or juice concentrate
4 tbsp arrowroot powder
1 quart vanilla vegetable milk
a cube of rice or soy cheese

Preheat oven to 375º. Pour boiling water over 2 cups of the cereal and set aside. Use a blender to cream oil with sweetener, arrowroot, vegetable milk and the moistened bran cereal. Mix. Fold in the remaining dry ingredients. Fill oiled muffin thins ¾ full and bake for 20-25 minutes. Or fill a loaf pan ½ full and bake at 350º or until done.

The proportions called for in this recipe make several quarts. If you want less, cut the recipe in half or 1/3.

Bread Pudding
1 tbsp whole grain flour
4 slices whole grain bread
1 tbsp soy margarine
½ cup fruit sweetened jelly
1-cup hot vegetable milk
1 teaspoon cinnamon
2 tbsp honey
4 tbsp arrowroot

In the top of a double boiler over hot but not boiling water, mix the flour and soy margarine together; gradually add the hot milk, stirring often. In a small bowl, beat together the honey and arrowroot; stir this into the milk mixture and set aside to cool.

Preheat oven to 325º. Oil a glass-baking dish. Lay the bread slices in the bottom of the pan and spread them with the jelly. Pour the custard mixture over the bread slices and bake for 30 to 35 minutes. Sprinkle with powdered coconut if desired. Serves 4 to 6.

Rice Pudding
2 cups cooked brown rice

2 tbsp arrowroot
2 cups vanilla vegetable milk
½ lemon rind, grated
½ cup vegetable protein soy free powder
½ teaspoon vanilla
¼ cup raisins
¼ cup date sugar
breadcrumbs or wheat germ
1 tbsp soy margarine, melted

Mix all ingredients together, except crumbs or wheat germ. Oil a 1-quart casserole dish (or individual custard cups) and sprinkle bottom with some crumbs or wheat germ. Pour in pudding mixture and sprinkle some crumbs on top. Bake at 350º for 20 minutes or until a knife inserted in the center comes out clean.

Hot Corn Cereal

¼ cup yellow cornmeal
¼ cup vegetable protein powder (soy free)
¼ cup cold water
¾ cup boiling water

Mix together cornmeal and cold water. Bring the ¾ cup water to a boil and add the cornmeal mixture and the vegetable protein. Stirring constantly, bring to a boil and let boil about 2 minutes. Cool and serve with any of the following: soy margarine, honey, date sugar, raisins, and fruit sweetened jelly, chopped dates or diced dried fruit.

Granola

4 cups oatmeal, uncooked
1/3 cup vegetable oil
1-1/2 cups wheat germ (raw or toasted
½ cup honey
1 tbsp vanilla
1-cup coconut, grated
½ cups sesame seeds
¼ cup vegetable protein powder
½ cups raw nuts, dried fruits and seeds or raisins
1 tbsp date sugar

In a large bowl, mix dry ingredients. Combine oil, honey and vanilla in a saucepan and warm. Add to the dry ingredients and stir until the particles are coated. Spread this mixture in a canola oiled long, low pan or rimmed baking sheet. Bake at either 250º for 1 hour or 300º for 30 minutes or microwave in a low glass pan for 10-15 minutes on high, stirring mixture approximately every 5 minutes. Turn occasionally with spatula. When finished toasting, add dried fruits. Cool and store in a container.

Serve with vegetable milk to babies and young children who may choke on the ungrounded cereal. If you fear that a child will choke, soak granola in soy or rice milk overnight in the refrigerator.

Breakfast Fruit

- Apricots and soy or rice or vegetable cheese
- Cantaloupe and honeydew slices
- Grapes, apples and other fruit with diced rice or soy cheese
- Mandarin oranges with soy or rice ice cream
- Orange slices cut into circles and mango slices
- Sliced peaches and blueberries
- Strawberries and pineapple chunks

Waffles/Pancake Toppings

Many different types of natural whole grain waffles are sold in health food stores as well as commercial stores. Listed below are a few suggestions for pancake and waffle toppings:

- Soy or rice ice cream
- Apple butter or peach butter
- Cinnamon mix with honey
- Any type of concentrated fruit juice (defrost if frozen) and thicken with arrowroot powder
- Carob powder mixed with honey
- Peanut butter and fruit sweetened jelly
- Applesauce
- Diced or chopped dried fruit (or raisins) soak overnight in the refrigerator before using

French Toast Batters

Listed below are batter recipes for toast:

1 tbsp arrowroot powder
1/3-cup vanilla rice or soymilk
1/8-teaspoon vanilla

Or:

1 tbsp arrowroot powder
4 teaspoons whole grain flour
1/3-cup vanilla rice or soymilk

For both recipes, mix ingredients. Dip bread into the mixture. Fry in a vegetable oiled pan over high heat, brown on both sides. Or, preheat the oven to 500º and bake the dipped bread on a canola-oiled pan, turning after the tops brown. Makes approximately 3 slices each.

Serve with the suggested waffle/pancake toppings.

French Toast Waffles

1 tbsp arrowroot
Whole grain bread slices
¼ cup vegetable milk
½ teaspoon cinnamon
2 tbsp vegetable or olive oil
1 to 2 tbsp date sugar or concentrated fruit juice defrosted or honey

Combine ingredients except bread. Cut the bread to fit the waffle iron. Dip bread into the batter and bake on a hot, canola oiled iron until browned. The top of the waffle iron may have to be held down because bread has more height than waffles.

French Pancakes

1 slice whole grain bread
½ cup vanilla vegetable milk
1 tbsp arrowroot
¼ teaspoon vanilla or maple extract

Combine the ingredients and blend in a blender except the bread. Dip bread in batter and cook the same as pancakes.

Griddle Cakes

1-1/2 cups whole grain flour (whole wheat or a combination)
2 tbsp arrowroot

3 tbsp canola oil
1-3/4 teaspoons baking powder
1 or 1-1/4 cups vanilla vegetable milk
3 tbsp date sugar, honey or defrosted concentrated fruit juice

Combine dry ingredients in a bowl. Add sweetener, oil and vegetable milk. Next add wet ingredients to the dry ingredients and mix until barely moistened. Set covered mixture in a cool place for 6 hours or overnight. Bake on a lightly oiled griddle or frying pan. When bubbles appear on upper surface of the cakes, turn and brown on second side.

Crumpets

3 cups whole grain (whole wheat or a combination)
2 tbsp soy margarine or canola oil
1 tbsp baking powder
1 tbsp arrowroot
2 tbsp date sugar, honey or defrosted fruit juice concentrate
½ to 1/-3/4 cups rice, almond or soymilk

Mix dry ingredients together. Mix wet ingredients together. Combine dry and wet ingredients and stir until moistened. If the batter is too thick to spread when dropped on griddle, add more milk. Drop batter by tablespoons on the hot and oiled griddle. Cook the same as pancakes.

SYRUP AND SAUCES

Fruit Dressing

¼ cup pure creamy peanut butter
½ cup egg less mayonnaise
¼ cup fruit sweetened jelly or honey

In a small bowl, combine all the ingredients and blend thoroughly with a fork. Put on bread, waffles, pancakes or fruit. Makes 1 cup.

Pear Sauce

6 pears
a pinch of ground nutmeg
2 tbsp water
a pinch of ground cinnamon
2 tbsp fruit sweetened jelly

Peel, core and chop the pears. Cook the pears in a pan until soft – about 20 minutes. Stir in the nutmeg, cinnamon and sweetener. Serve either hot or cold. Serves 4.

Honey Sauce

½ cup nut butter (almond, soy, peanut, etc.)
½ cup honey
½ cup water

Blend all ingredients on medium speed for 15 seconds. Serve over vegetable ice cream or as a spread on waffles, pancakes or bread. Makes 1-1/2 cups.

Carob Syrup

2 cups boiling water
1 tbsp arrowroot
½ cup honey or fruit sweetened jelly
Pinch of Sea Salt
6 tbsp carob powder
1-teaspoon pure vanilla

Mix all ingredients together.

COOKED FRUIT

Bananas or Plantain Cream
6 firm bananas or plantain
5 small slices mango, papaya or
2 ounces lemon juice
unsweetened pineapple, cut thinly (to make about 6 tablespoons)
3 teaspoons fruit sweetened jelly or honey

In a bowl, mash the bananas or plantain slightly. Add the lemon, sweetener and pineapple and mix together well. Serve in a cup. Refrigerate for several hours. Serve cold.

Baked Bananas or Plantain
4 bananas or plantain
2 teaspoons lemon juice
4 tbsp fruit sweetened jelly or honey
4 tbsp soy margarine

Preheat oven to 350º. Oil a glass-baking dish. Pell the bananas or plantain and cut them in half lengthwise. Place in the baking dish. Sprinkle sweetener, margarine and lemon juice on the bananas or plantain. Bake for 10 to 15 minutes or until tender but not soft. Serve warm.

Honey Bananas or Plantain
2 medium ripe bananas or plantain
1 tbsp grapefruit or pineapple juice
Add a pinch of ground cinnamon
2 teaspoons soy margarine
2 teaspoons fruit sweetened jelly or honey
1 to 2 ounces lemon juice

Peel the bananas or plantain and slice them lengthwise. In a skillet, slowly melt the margarine in a frying pan and brown the bananas or plantain on both sides. Add the sweetener, cinnamon and lemon juice and baste bananas or plantain with pan juices. Pour the fruit juice over them and heat just before serving.

Bananas or Plantain Sauce

1-8½ ounce can unsweetened crushed pineapple, undrained
2 teaspoons arrowroot
2 tbsp unsweetened shredded coconut
1 tbsp lemon juice
2 tbsp fruit sweetened jelly or honey
1 tbsp soy margarine

Heat the margarine, arrowroot, pineapple and sweetener in a pan. Stir constantly until thickened. Add the coconut and lemon juice. Mix together thoroughly. Serve hot over sliced bananas or plantains. Makes 1 cup.

Broiled Grapefruit

2 grapefruit
2 teaspoons honey

Cut each grapefruit in half and cut into each grapefruit section to loosen it or use seedless. Remove the seeds. Pour ½ teaspoon of the honey in the center of the grapefruit half. Place the grapefruit on a baking sheet and broil for a few minutes until heated but not browned. Serves 4.

Glazed Baked Pears

1 teaspoon lemon juice
1-teaspoon pure vanilla
½ teaspoon ground cinnamon
1-quart vanilla rice or soy ice cream (soften ice cream slightly)
1-teaspoon date sugar
3 pears cut in half, seeds removed
½ cup of water

Preheat oven to 300º. Place pears in a baking dish. Mix together the lemon juice, cinnamon, vanilla, date sugar and ½ cup of the water. Pour this mixture over the pears. Bake for 30 minutes. Brown the tops of the pears under the broiler. Serve with soft ice cream as a sauce. Serves 4 to 6.

COOKIES

Creamy Balls

Combine chopped nuts and soy cream cheese. Roll into balls and serve.

Carob Drop Cookies

1-cup date sugar
2 cups sifted whole grain flour
½ cup soy margarine
½ teaspoon baking soda
1 tbsp arrowroot
Add a pinch of sea salt
6 tbsp carob
2/3 cup chopped nuts
½ cup vanilla vegetable mil
1-1/2 teaspoons pure vanilla

Preheat oven to 350º. Mix all the ingredients in a blender except for the nuts. Beat at medium speed for 4 to 5 minutes. Turn off blender. Stir in the nuts. Drop by the teaspoonfuls onto ungreased baking sheets. Bake for 8 to 10 minutes. Makes 3 to 4 dozen.

Fudge

1-cup honey
1-cup sunflower seeds
1-cup pure peanut butter
½ cup shredded unsweetened coconut
1-cup carob powder
½ cup chopped dates
½ cup sesame butter

Grease two 8-by-8-by-2-inch baking pans. In a saucepan over low heat, heat the honey together with peanut butter and sesame butter. Quickly stir in the carob powder and the seeds, coconut and dates. Pour the mixture into the pans and refrigerate until hardened (about 1 hour). Cut into 1- inch squares. Store, covered with waxed paper, in the refrigerator. Makes 84 pieces.

Carob Coconut Chews

2 tbsp arrowroot
½ cup chopped nuts (walnuts, pecans, etc.)
1- 3 ½ ounce can shredded unsweetened coconut

1 teaspoon pure vanilla
4 ounces carob powder
¾ cup date sugar

Preheat oven to 350º. Oil a baking sheet with canola oil. In a medium bow, mix together all the ingredients. If it is too dry, add enough water to make it thick. Drop by rounded teaspoonfuls about 1 inch apart, onto the baking sheet. Bake for 12 minutes, or until the chews are set. Makes about 2 dozen cookies

PIES AND PIECRUST

Piecrust

Before rolling the crust out, dampen the counter top to prevent the waxed paper from slipping. Then place 4 pieces of waxed paper cut into 12-inch squares onto the counter top.

2 cups whole-wheat pastry
½ cup vanilla vegetable milk
½ teaspoon sea salt
½ cup vegetable oil

In a large bowl, mix together the flour and sea salt. Pour the oil and milk into a separate bowl or large measuring cup but do not stir. Pour all at once into the flour and stir until mixed.
Shape the pastry into a smooth ball. Cut in half. Flatten one half between two pieces of the waxed paper. Roll out the dough thin and gently from the center to the edges of the paper.

Peel off the top paper. The dough may tear, press it back together with your fingers but do not moisten it.
Put the dough with the wax paper side up into a 9-or-10-inch pie pan and peel off the waxed paper. Shape the pastry to fit the pan. Roll out the remaining pastry for the top crust following the directions above. Puncture the top crust with a fork or knife for steam vents. Seal and crimp the edges.

Pineapple Custard

1 piecrust rolled out thin
2 cups vanilla vegetable milk
1-15 ounce can unsweetened
2 tbsp date sugar crushed pineapple, drained
½ teaspoon pure vanilla
2 tbsp arrow root
1 tbsp soy margarine, melted
Add a pinch of nutmeg

Preheat oven to 425º. Use canola oil to oil a n oblong 9-by-13 inch baking pan and line it with the piecrust. Spread the crushed pineapple over the pastry.

In a bowl, mix the remaining ingredients. Pour the mixture over the pineapple. Bake for 10 minutes then reduce the heat to 325º and bake until the custard is set – about another 20 minutes. Serve warm, in slices. Makes 12 slices.

Sweet Potato Pie

Piecrust (use ½ of previous recipe)
½ teaspoon ginger powder
2 cups hot peeled, cooked and mashed sweet yams or potatoes
¼ teaspoon sea salt
½ cup fruit sweetened jelly or concentrated fruit juice
2 tbsp soy margarine, melted
¼ cup lemon juice
3 tbsp arrowroot
1-teaspoon cinnamon powder
1-cup vanilla vegetable milk

Preheat oven to 450º. In a bowl, mix all the ingredients one at a time in the order given until smooth. Place piecrust in a 9-inch pan. Pour the mixture onto the unbaked piecrust shell. Bake for 10 minutes, reduce the heat to 350º and bake for 40 minutes longer or until set (inset a toothpick in the center, it will come out clean).

Pineapple Pie

1 piecrust
2 tbsp arrowroot
2 – 10 ounce cans unsweetened crushed pineapple, drained
½ cup honey, fruit sweetened jelly or concentrated fruit juice
¼ teaspoon sea salt
1 tbsp soy or safflower margarine
1 tbsp lemon juice

Preheat oven to 425º. Line the bottom of a pie pan with one crust. In a saucepan, mix the arrowroot, sweetener, sea salt and pineapple, cook until thick, stirring constantly. Add lemon juice and soy margarine. And stir until well mixed.

Pour the mixture into the piecrust. Put the top piecrust over it and puncture it with a fork or knife at the top and pinch the edges; or cut and wave pastry strips across the top. Bake for 25 to 30 minutes.

MENU

The menu listed below does not follow good Food Combining. It is designed for those in transition from poor food combining to good food combining. Ideally, protein and starch should not be served at the same meal.

In the menu selection, there are many varieties of vegetables meats, cheese and milks to choose from. Therefore, only the choice is not indicated just the word is used for the following:

NUT BUTTER = soy, almond, cashew, peanut, sunflower, pecan, walnut, macadamia, etc.

SOY MEATS = chicken, hotdogs, bacon, sausage, turkey, steak, burgers, fish, sandwich meats

CHEESE = rice, soy

VEGETABLE MILKS = almond, spelt, rice, soy, oats, kamut, etc.

WHOLE GRAINS = rye, millet, kamut, spelt, amaranth, buckwheat, wheat, barley, etc.

SAMPLE BREAKFAST MENUS

1. Grapefruit Juice, Whole Grain Waffles, Vegetable milk

2. Melon, Scrambled Tofu

3. Pear Juice, Vegetable Cheese and Dice Tofu Omelet, Vegetable Milk Whole Grain Waffles

4. Pineapple Juice, Puffed Whole Wheat or Brown Rice Cereal Toast, Vegetable Milk

5. Papaya Juice Hot Oatmeal with Date Sugar or Fruit Sweetened Jelly, Vegetable Milk, Scramble Tofu

6. Melon, Soy Yogurt, Soy Sausage, Cinnamon toast, Vegetable Milk

13. Whole Grain Pancakes with Sweetener, Fruit Juice Soy Bacon

14. Lemonade, French toast with Soy Margarine and Sweetener

15. Pineapple Juice, Grilled Vegetable Cheese Sandwich, Carob Milk

16. Papaya Juice, Granola and Vegetable Milk Vegetable Milk

17. Mango Juice, Granola

18. Sliced Oranges, Pancakes with Sweetener, Vegetable Milk, Soy Sausage

7. Mango Juice, Barley or Rice Cereal, Fruit Sweetener or Honey, Vegetable Milk

8. Sliced Grapefruit, Whole Grain Waffle, Soy Bacon

9. Pear Juice, Vegetable Cheese and Diced Tofu Omelet, Vegetable Milk

10. Sliced Oranges, Baked French toast with Sweetener, Vegetable Milk

11. Pineapple Juice, Soy Sausage, Toast

12. Sliced Grapefruit, Whole Corn Flakes with Vegetable Milk and Sweetener, Toast, Vegetable Milk

19. Orange Juice, Scrambled Tofu with Vegetable, Cheese Toast, Vegetable Milk

20. Grapefruit Juice Scrambled Tofu Bread Vegetable Milk, Soy Bacon

21. Whole Grain Puffed Cereal with toasted Wheat Germ, Banana Toast Vegetable Milk

22. Pineapple Juice, Oatmeal, Vegetable Milk, Soy Sausage

23. Grape Juice Soy, Yogurt on Split Banana Toast with Apple butter, Vegetable Milk

Sample Lunch Menus

1. Soy Meat, Baked Potatoes, Brussels Sprouts, Vegetable Milk

2. Soy Meat Sandwich, Banana, Cookies, Vegetable Milk

3. Whole Corn Chips Raw Carrots Bananas Vegetable Milk

4. Pita Bread filled with ground, cabbage, carrots, lemon juice and Egg less Mayonnaise, Pear Juice, Tossed Salad

5. Veggie Cheese Sandwich, Pineapple Chunks, Dates, Vegetable Milk

6. Soy Meat (hotdogs), Potato Salad, Vegetable Milk

12. Soy Cream Cheese with grated carrot sandwich, Apple Juice, Vegetable Milk

13. Soy Meat, Sandwich Kiwi, Vegetable Milk

14. Nut Loaf Sandwich, Cranberry Juice, Oatmeal Cookies, Vegetable Milk

15. Grilled Cheese Sandwich, Carob Milk, Baked French fries

16. Soy Cottage Cheese with Diced Pineapple, Soy Meats, Corn Chips, Vegetable Milk

17. Peanut Butter and Fruit Sweetened Jelly Sandwich, Black Bean

7. Soy Meat (chicken) with Pita Bread, Carrots, Baked Potato, French fries or Chips, Papaya Juice, Vegetable Milk

8. Soy Meat, Nut Butter on Carrot and Celery Sticks Pear Juice, Vegetable Milk

9. Nut Butter on Pita Bread Baked Potato Chips, Plantain or Banana Chips

10. Melted Cheese on Toast, Cookies, Vegetable Milk

11. Dice Soy Meat mixed with Salad and Mayonnaise put on sandwich Whole Corn Chips, Vegetable Milk

Chips, Banana Chips, Banana, Vegetable Milk

18. Soya Meat Sandwich (Pita Bread), Banana, Kiwi Juice, Cookies

19. Burritos, Carrot and Celery Sticks, Vegetable Milk

20. Soy Meat, Banana, Blue Corn Chips, Vegetable Milk

21. Pita Bread stuffed with shredded carrots and soy cream cheese Pear Juice, Sweet Rice Cakes

Dinner Menus

1. Soy Meat, Baked Potatoes, Brussels Sprouts, Pie

2. Tossed Salad, Soy Meat, Baked Potato, Peas, Broiled Grapefruit

3. Tossed Salad with Zucchini, Diced Cheese Noodles and Soy Meat, String beans, Oatmeal Cookies, Vegetable Milk

4. Soy Meat, Biscuit, Mashed Potatoes, Green Beans, Vegetable Ice Cream, Vegetable Milk

5. Salad with Spinach and Soy Yogurt, Soy Meat, Biscuit, Baked French fries, Cookies

6. Salad with Diced Avocado, Soy

12. Soy Meat Basmati Rice, Zucchini Cookies Lemonade

13. Tossed Salad Soy Meat Carrots Mashed Potatoes

14. Salad, Soy Meat, Black Bean Chips, Vegetable Milk, Snacks

15. Nut Loaf, Tossed Salad, Scallop Potatoes, Broccoli, Bread, Vegetable Milk

16. Spinach and Bean Sprouts add to Toss Salad Macaroni and Vegetable Cheese Cauliflower Vegetable Milk, Cake

17. Tossed Salad, add Bean Sprouts,

Meat, Vegetable Milk, Pie

7. Mashed Potatoes, Brussels Sprouts, Bread, Vegetable Milk, Snacks

8. Spinach Salad with Lemon and Olive Oil Soy Meat Basmati Rice Bread Vegetable Milk

9. Vegetable Salad Soy Meat Carrots Pudding Snacks

10. Baked Beans, Soy Meat, Carrots and Celery Sticks, Vegetable Ice Cream, Vegetable Milk

11. Taco Salad, Brown Rice, Pudding, Vegetable Milk, Sweet Potato Pie

Lemon and Olive Oil Dressing, Soy Meat Peas, Yams, Vegetable Ice Cream

18. Toss Salad add Zucchini and Sliced Cucumbers Baked Potato Asparagus with melted cheese Snacks

19. Coleslaw(use lemon juice instead of vinegar) Soy Meat Brown Rice Broccoli Vegetable Milk

20. Carrot – Zucchini add to Coleslaw Spaghetti and Tomato Sauce Soy Meat Vegetable Milk, Pineapple Slices

21. Carrot and Cauliflower add to Coleslaw Soy Meat, Peas Brown Rice Baked Apples

22. Avocado and Grapefruit add to Coleslaw Soy Meat Basmati Rice Vegetable Milk

CHAPTER 11 HEALTH, DISEASES, REMEDIES

"No White American (Caucasians) ever thinks that any other race (Black Folks) is wholly civilized until he wears the white man's clothes, eats the white man's food, speaks the white man's language, and professes the white man's religion."

Booker T. Washington

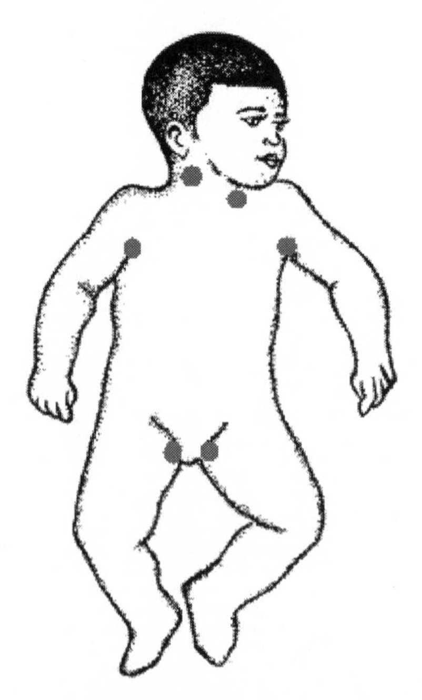

The Lymph Glands Absorb Impurities And Protection From Disease. When There Is An Infection, They Swell And Become Tender And Hot. They Can Be Felt With Your Fingertips.

Common Diseases

When treating children with diseases, it is best to get liquid supplements and/or herbs. The health food stores have many formulas with the name of the diseases they treat on the label also homeopathic remedies have the name of the diseases on the label. Use liquid herbal extracts in vegetable glycerin (non-alcohol, non-vinegar based). If they are not the children's type, get the adult type and follow the label dosage. If the children's dosage is not indicated, use 1/3 to ½ the adult dosage based upon the weight of the child (usually 1/3 amount). The herbs can be used singularly or in combinations of twos or threes. You will find that most infant problems can be treated with catnip and peppermint.

ASTHMA

Spasm of the lungs (bronchial tubes) and/or swelling of lung tissue (mucous membrane). Usually, an over stimulated nervous system and an allergic reaction causes attacks.

SEASON: Varies.

MOST SUSCEPTIBLE: Children, young adults.

SYMPTOMS:

1) Shortness of breath
2) Panting, Wheezing
3) Difficulty breathing – may hunch over to get air

TREATMENT: Elecampane and Pleurisy, Lobelia, Mullein, Avoid junk foods, white sugar, dairy, white rice, etc.

CAUSES: Allergens such as dust, pollen, eggs, shellfish, chocolate, drugs, stress, fatigue and emotions.

DEVELOPS: Varies from a few moments to a few days.

DURATION: Attacks vary.

BRONCHIOLITIS

(Inflammation of the smaller branches of the bronchial tree leading to the lungs).

SEASON: For respiratory type winter and spring; for para influenza type, summer and fall.

MOST SUSCEPTIBLE: Those under 2 years (especially under 6 months); those with an allergy.

SYMPTOMS:

1) Cold symptoms
2) A few days later: Rapid, shallow breathing; wheezing on breathing out; 3 days with a low-grade fever.
3) Sometimes: Chest expansion, difficult on breathing, loss of appetite, dehydration, bluish fingertips and nails.

TREATMENT: Supplements for cough/cold/flu, Herbal cough/cold formula, Herbs – Elecampane, Pleurisy, Coltsfoot, Rosehip, Mullein, Horehound, White Pine, Peppermint, Lemon Grass, Elderberry, Hyssop, Lobelia, Catnip, Echinacea and Goldenseal (infection), Red Clover.

Inflammation and Fever Herbs: Cat's Claw and Feverfew.

CAUSES: Mucous congestion, dairy, junk foods, cellular waste.
TRANSMISSION: Usually via respiratory secretions, person-to-person contact, or by contact with contaminated household objects.
DEVELOPS In: 2 to 8 days.
Duration: Acute phase may last only 3 days, cough from 1 to 3 weeks or more.

BRONCHITIS

(Inflammation of the bronchial tree and often the trachea, or windpipe).
SEASON: Varies.
Most susceptible: Children under 4 years.
SYMPTOMS:
1) Usually: Cold symptoms.
2) Abrupt onset of: Fever, about 102ºF (38.9ºC); harsh cough, worse at night, wheezing, bluish lips and fingernails, greenish or yellowish sputum, whistling on breathing out and periodic coughing episodes.

TREATMENT: See Bronchiolitis
CAUSE: See Bronchiolitis
DURATION: Fever lasts 2 or 3 days; cough 1 to 2 weeks or more.

CAT SCRATCH DISEASE

SEASON: More frequent in fall and winter.
Most susceptible: Anyone, but 80% of cases occurs in those under 20.
SYMPTOMS: Usually: Swollen lymph glands under arms or in the jaw or neck 1 to 4 weeks after contact. The glands may be tender, warm, red, hard (sometimes) and can discharge pus.
Sometimes: Fever (100.4ºF to 102.2ºF, or 38ºC to 39ºC); also, malaise, fatigue.
Occasionally: Loss of appetite, vomiting, headache. Only fever with no apparent cause and possibly abdominal pain. Rash and red pimple at site of scratches or bite, 1 or 2 weeks before other symptoms.
TREATMENT: Red Clover, Burdock, Comfrey, Thuja, Dandelion, Vitamin A, Lysine, Vitamin C, Apply Vitamin A, Comfrey salve and Lysine crème.
Transmission: Usually, kitten scratch, bite or lick; sometimes, older cat or other animal; rarely no contact.
DEVELOPS in: 7 to 12 days from scratch to skin lesion (rash); then 5 to 50 days (a median of 12) to swollen glands.
DURATION: Usually 2 to 4 months; fever about 2 weeks; gland tenderness, 4 to 6 weeks; swelling, several months can last a year.
Prevention: Keep children away from cats, declawing the cat.

CHICKENPOX, (Varicella)

SEASON: Late winter and early spring in temperate zones.
Most susceptible: Anyone.
SYMPTOMS: Slight fever, malaise and loss of appetite. Flat red spots turn into pimples, then blister, crust and scab and continue to develop for 3 or 4 days. Itching is usually intense.

TREATMENT: Goldenseal, Bayberry, Burdock, Origanum, Mugwort and Chickweed.
Poultice: Raw carrot (pulp or puree) Lobelia, Clay.
Transmission: Person-to-person; and airborne droplets from respiratory secretions. Very contagious from 1 to 2 days before onset until sores get a scab (about 6 days).
DEVELOPS in: 11 to 20 days most often 14 to 16 days.
DURATION: First vesicles crust in 6 to 8 hours, scab in 24 to 48 hours; scabs last 5 to 20 days.

COLDS

(See Bronchiolitis)

CONJUNCTIVITIS

(Pinkeye)
Inflammation of the conjunctiva, the membrane lining the eyelids and the eyes.
Season: Not seasonal.
Most susceptible: Anyone.
SYMPTOMS: Can include: Bloodshot eyes; tearing; eye discharge (lids may be crusted after sleep), burning, itching; light sensitivity. Usually begins in one eye and can go to the other.
TREATMENT: Feverfew, Cat's Claw, Eyebright, Vitamin A, Beta Carotene and Lysine.
Cause: Many, including bacteria, chlamydia, parasites, fungi, allergens, irritants, chemicals.
TRANSMISSION: For infectious organisms, eye-hand-eye, towels, bed linens.
DEVELOPS: Quickly.
DURATION: Varies with cause; viral, 2 days to 3 weeks (can become chronic); bacterial, about 2 weeks; others, until allergen or irritant is removed.

CROUP

TREATMENT: Use Cold remedies

DIARRHEA

TREATMENT: Arrowroot, Slippery Elm Powder and Alum Root.

EAR INFECTION

TREATMENT: Echinacea and Goldenseal, antioxidants, Vitamin A, C, and E, Lysine.

ENCEPHALITIS

(Inflammation of the brain).
SEASON: Depends on cause.

MOST SUSCEPTIBLE: Depends on cause.
SYMPTOMS: Fever, drowsiness and headache. Sometimes: Neurological impairment (confusion, moody, swimmy head, altered consciousness, muscle weakness), progression to coma at a late stage. In late stages, can cause a coma.
TREATMENT: Cat's Claw, Feverfew, Echinacea and Goldenseal, Red Clover and MSM.
CAUSE: Bacteria usually a complication of another disease.
TRANSMISSION: Depends on cause.
DEVELOPMENT: Depends on cause.
DURATION: Varies.

EPIGLOTTITIS

(Inflammation of the tongue – the upper part of the larynx, or voice box)
SEASON: Winter months in temperate climates.
Most susceptible: children 2 to 4 years old.
SYMPTOMS: Sudden onset of fever over 102ºF or 38.9ºC (lower I tots under 2); drooling, difficulty swallowing, hoarse cough (croupy in under 2's); noisy breathing (stridor) and sore throat. Sometimes: Protruding tongue, retractions, bluish nails and lips. Symptoms worsen rapidly. Child seems ill, restless, agitated and irritable and wants to sit upright, will lean forward with mouth open in order to get air. The tongue usually is extremely red and swollen.
TREATMENT: Cat's Claw, Feverfew, and MSM
CAUSE: Bacteria most often, hemophilus influenzae (Hib); sometimes group A Streptococcus. See Bronchiolitis.
TRANSMISSION: Can be person-to-person, or the inhalation of respiratory droplets (remote possibility).
How it develops: Uncertain.
DURATION: 4 to 7 days or longer.

FIFTH DISEASE

(Erythema Infectiosum)
SEASON: Early Spring.
MOST SUSCEPTIBLE: Children 2 to 12 years old.
SYMPTOMS: Sometimes: Fever. Rarely: Joint Pain.

1) Intense flush on face (slapped-cheek look).
2) Next day: Lacy rash on arms and legs.
3) 3 days later: Rash on inner surfaces, fingers, toes, trunk and/or buttocks.
4) Rash may reappear on and off with exposure to heat (bath water, sun) for 2 to 3 weeks, even months.

TREATMENT: Red Clover, Echinacea and Goldenseal, Chaparral, Vitamin, A, C, E and Lysine.
CAUSE: Cellular waste, mucus congestion.
TRANSMISSION: Probably, respiratory secretions and blood; can be contagious before onset of illness.
Develops in about: 4 to 14 days but as long as 20 days.

DURATION: Initial rash, several days to a week; rash can continue to recur for weeks or months.

GASTROENTERITIS

(See Diarrhea)

TREATMENT: MSM, Cat's Claw and Feverfew.

GERMAN MEASLES

(Rubella)

SEASON: Late winter and early spring.

Most susceptible: Any person.

SYMPTOMS: In 25% to 50% of cases – no symptoms.

1) Sometimes: Slight fever and swollen glands.
2) Small (1/10 inch) flat, reddish pink spots on face.
3) Rash spreads to body and sometimes, roof of mouth.

TREATMENT: See Chickenpox.

Cause: Cellular waste, mucus congestion.

TRANSMISSION: Can be contact or droplets from respiratory secretions. Usually contagious from a few days before 5 to 7 days after rash appears.

Develops in: 14 to 21 days, most often 16 to 18 days.

DURATION: A few hours to 4 or 5 days.

HAND-FOOT-MOUTH DISEASE

(Vesicular stomatitis)

SEASON: Summer and fall in temperature climates.

Most susceptible: Babies and young children.

SYMPTOMS:

1) Fever; loss of appetite. Difficulty swallowing, sore throat and mouth.
2) In 2 or 3 days: Sores in mouth (which can blister).
3) Then, sores on fingers; sometimes, buttocks, feet, legs, arms, less often on face.

Treatment: See Fifth Disease.

Cause: Cellular waste, mucus congestion.

TRANSMISSION: Mouth-to-mouth, feces-to-hand-to-mouth.

Develops in: 3 to 6 days.

DURATION: About 1 week.

HERPANGIA

(Mild herpes bumps)

SEASON: Mostly summer and fall in temperate climates; any time in tropical regions.

Most susceptible: Babies and young children.

SYMPTOMS:

1) Fever: 100ºF to 104ºF, occasionally to 106ºF; (7.8ºC to 40ºC or 41.1ºC), sore throat. A seizure caused by a fever in the beginning.

2) Painful swallowing. Sometimes: Diarrhea, loss of appetite, lethargy, abdominal pain and vomiting.
3) Distinct grayish white papules in back of mouth or throat (5 to 10 in number) that blister and ulcerate.

TREATMENT: See Fifth Disease – also use Lysine crème and Herbal salve.
Cause: Cellular waste.
TRANSMISSION: Mouth-to-mouth, feces-to-hand-mouth.
Develops in: 3 to 6 days.
DURATION: 4 to 7 days but healing can take 2 to 3 weeks.

HYDROPHOBIA

(Fear of water)
TREATMENT: St. John's Wort, Skullcap, GABA, B6 and Glutamine.

IMPETIGO

(Skin inflammation)
(See Encephalitis)

INFLUENZA

(See Bronchiolitis)

KAWASAKI DISEASE

(Mucocutaneous lymph node syndrome, MLNS – swollen glands)
Season: Any.
Most susceptible: Infants and children under 5; more boys than girls, more children of Asian (especially Japanese) than of other origin.
SYMPTOMS:

1) Fever, usually last 7 days but can be between 5 to 39 days.
2) Within 3 days of onset of fever: Skin of nose, mouth and/or throat gets red can have cracked lips, swollen neck gland, throat swollen, strawberry colored tongue, conjunctivitis in both eyes, with no discharge.
3) Flat red rash on body; redness and/or swelling or hardening of palms of hands and soles of feet.
4) Palms and sores may peel during second to third week.

TREATMENT: See Cat Scratch Disease.
Cause: Cellular waste, mucus congestion, junk food, dairy.
Transmission: Unknown.
DEVELOPMENT: Unknown.
DURATION: Without treatment, fever lasts about 12 days; appetite lass and irritability can last 2 or 3 weeks. Complications last longer.

LYME DISEASE

(Borrelia burgdoferi)
Season: May 1 to November 30, with most cases in June and July.

Most susceptible: Anyone
SYMPTOMS:
1) Usually a bull's-eye-shaped red rash (erythema migrans) where tick bite occurred; it usually spreads in a few days and expands over days to weeks to form larger red rash.
2) Sometimes: Multiple rashes develop when it spreads. Often: After the rash, there is aching, headache, fever, malaise, and mild neck stiffness. Sometimes as disease spreads: pains, fatigue, aches, problems with nervous system involvement and headaches. If untreated: Chronic arthritis, central nervous system damage and painful knees, rarely, heart damage.
3) Weeks to years later, if untreated: Deformed joints. None of these symptoms alone, however, is diagnostic; see under Rash.

TREATMENT: See Cat Scratch Disease.
Cause: A spirochete, borrelia burgdorferi.
TRANSMISSION: Spread by the bite of a pinhead-size deer tick (carried by deer, mice and other animals) can be caused by other ticks and flying insects. It takes 24 to 48 hours for an attached tick to transmit Lyme disease.
Develops in: 3 to 32 days, typically 7 to 10 days.
DURATION: Without treatment, possibly years.

MENINGITIS

(Inflammation of the membranes around the brain and/or the spinal cord)
Season: Varies.
Most susceptible: Mostly infants and children under 3, usually city dwellers, African Americans and children in day-care centers.
SYMPTOMS: Fever, bulging soft spot on head (fontanel), high-pitched cry; vomiting, drowsiness, loss of appetite and irritability. In older children: sensitivity to light blurred vision and neurological problems and/or stiff neck.
TREATMENT: Cat's Claw, Feverfew, Skullcap, Eyebright, Peppermint, Catnip and MSM.
Cause: Bacteria, cellular waste.
TRANSMISSION: Can be person-to-person, possibility of direct contact through inhalation of droplets from respiratory secretions.
Develops in: Less than 10 days.
DURATION: Varies.

MENINGOENCEPHALITIS

(Combined meningitis and encephalitis) See Meningitis.

MUMPS

Season: Late winter and spring.
Most susceptible: Anyone.
SYMPTOMS:
1) Sometimes: Vague pain, loss of appetite and fever.

2) Usually: Swelling of parotid (salivary) glands on one or both sides of jaw, below and in front of ear; pain on chewing; ear pain; swelling of the salivary glands. No symptoms in about 30% of cases.

TREATMENT: Echinacea and Goldenseal, Witch Hazel, Shepherd's Purse. Do not drink sodas or eat anything with vinegar in it.
Cause: Junk food.
TRANSMISSION: Can be direct contact with respiratory secretions from 1 or 2 (but as long as 7) days prior to onset until 9 days after.
Develops in: 16 to 18 days may be as few as 12 or as many as 25 days.
DURATION: 5 to 7 days.

NONSPECIFIC VIRAL (NSV) ILLNESSES

SEASON: Mostly summer.
Most susceptible: Young children.
SYMPTOMS: Can vary and may include: loss of appetite, diarrhea and fever. Different types of rashes.
TREATMENT: Fever: Cat's Claw, Feverfew; Diarrhea: Arrowroot, Wild Alum Root; Skin Problems: See Cat Scratch Disease.
Cause: Cellular waste.
TRANSMISSION: Feces-to-hand-to-mouth, possibly, mouth-to-mouth.
Develops in: 3 to 6 days.
DURATION: Usually a few days.

PERTUSSIS

(Whooping Cough)
Season: Late winter, early spring.
Most susceptible: Infants and young children.
SYMPTOMS:

1) Catarrhal stage: Cold symptoms with dry cough, irritability, and low-grade fever.
2) Paroxysmal stage 1 0 2 weeks later: Thick mucus, coughing in explosive bursts with no breaths between. Often: Vomiting, bulging eyes and protruding tongue, exhaustion, pale or reddened skin, sweating. Sometimes; Hernia, from coughing.
3) Recovery stage: Whooping and vomiting stops, reduced coughing, less moodiness and improved appetite.

TREATMENT: See Bronchiolitis.
CAUSE: Bacteria.
TRANSMISSION: Can be respiratory droplets, most communicable during catarrhal stage.
Develops **in: 7 to 10 days, rarely more than 2 weeks.**
DURATION: Usually 6 weeks or longer.

PHARYNGITIS

See Sore Throat.

PINWORM INFECTION

(Enterobiasis)

SEASON: Not seasonal.

Most susceptible: Preschool and school age children and their mothers. Anyone that eats junk food, meat, uses wrong food combining, dairy, or suffers from constipation or gas.

SYMPTOMS:

1. Pinworms enter and live in lower digestive tract; females lay eggs around anus and on buttocks. They can crawl out of the rectum at night or during the day to lay eggs. The eggs cannot hatch inside the body.
2. Itching begins around the anus. Children may cry at night; be irritable; restless and fatigued. Check for eggs with flashlight in the middle of night or before your child wakes up. You will see a little dark spot inside the egg. Anal area can be raw and red.
3. Occasionally, in girls, itching of the vulva. If worms enter the vagina, they can cause vaginitis and a slight vaginal discharge.

TREATMENT: Wormwood, Black Walnut leaf or hulls, Quassia, Clove bud, Male Fern, Pomegranate Juice.

CAUSE: A tiny (1/4 to ½ inch) grayish, thread-like parasitic worm, Enterobius vermicularis.

TRANSMISSION: Letting animals lick you in the face, walking bare foot in dirt where dogs or cats had bowel movements, hand-to-mouth, thumb sucking after scratching or wiping or using an unclean toilet seat. If swallowed, eggs hatch and worms move down to rectum. You can have worms and give them to others as long as the females are laying eggs; eggs remain infective for 2 to 3 weeks.

DURATION: If you do not treat it, you can keep worms forever.

PNEUMONIA

(Inflammation of the lungs)

SEASON: Varies.

Most susceptible: Anyone.

SYMPTOMS: A child with a cold or other illness that seems to suddenly get worse. There can be increased fever; pain; heavy mucus low; productive cough; shortness of breath; wheezy, raspy and/or difficult breathing; chest retractions, abdominal bloating and rapid breathing.

TREATMENT: See Bronchiolitis.

Cause: Protozoa, fungus, mycoplasmas, allergens, inhalation of a chemical.

TRANSMISSION: Varies.

DEVELOPMENT: Varies.

DURATION: Varies.

RESPIRATORY

SYNCTIAL VIRUS

(RSV) ILLNESSES

(Includes pneumonia; bronchiolitis and the common cold.
SEASON: Winter and early spring in temperate climates; rainy season in the tropics.
Most susceptible: Anyone, most cases occur before age 3.
SYMPTOMS: Can be like a mild cold, pneumonia or bronchiolitis. There can be a cough; sore throat; painful breathing; inflammation of the nose and throat, malaise, and wheezing. Sometimes: A long pause between breathes (apnea), mostly in premature infants.
TREATMENT: See Bronchiolitis.
Cause: Cellular waste.
TRANSMISSION: Direct or close contact with respiratory secretions (fluids of others) or contaminated articles, it takes from 3 days to 4 weeks for it to begin.
DEVELOPS in: Usually 5 to 8 days.
DURATION: Varies.

REYE SYNDROME

SEASON: Not seasonal.
Most susceptible: Children who are given aspirin during illness.
SYMPTOMS:

1) 1 to 7 days following an upper respiratory infection: Persistent vomiting every hour or two, all day; lethargy; irritability, rapid heartbeat, confusion, and delirium.
2) Can have seizures if untreated.

TREATMENT: See Bronchiolitis.
Cause: Unknown, can be related to a reaction to aspirin.
TRANSMISSION: Unknown.
DEVELOPS In: Unknown, it seems to develop within 6 days or onset of viral infection.
DURATION: Varies.

ROCKY MOUNTAIN SPOTTED FEVER

(RMSF)
SEASON: Spring and summer.
Most susceptible: Anyone and children under 15 years old.
SYMPTOMS:

1) Fever; nausea, vomiting, muscle pain and weakness; headache. Sometimes: Abdominal pain, cough.
2) Usually before the sixth day: Flat red sports or splotches appear on the soles of the feet and palms, spreads to wrists, arms, legs, ankles and then the trunk.
3) Later bumps can develop. Occasionally: No rash or late-developing rash.

TREATMENT: See Encephalitis.
CAUSE: Rickettsia rickettsii.
TRANSMISSION: The bite of a tick.

Develops in: 1 to 14 days, usually 1 week.
Duration: Up to 3 weeks.

SORE THROAT

(See Bronhiolitis).

TETANUS

(Lockjaw)
Season: More frequent in warmer climates and months.
Most susceptible: Anyone.
Symptoms: Localized: Spasm and increased muscle tone near the entry wound. Generalized: Uncontrollable muscle contractions, which can arch the back, twist the neck and lock the jaw; convulsions; children have difficulty sucking the breast and the nipple on the bottle; profuse sweating; low-grade fever; rapid heartbeat.
Treatment: Cramp Bark, Catnip, Skullcap, Peppermint, Feverfew, MSM, Echinacea and Goldenseal, Lysine.
Cause: Cellular waste toxins, junk food, dairy.
Transmission: Infection or contamination of a cut, scrape, puncture, burn, open skin or wound.
Develops in: 3 days to 3 weeks but an average of 8 days.
Duration: Several weeks.

TONSILLITIS

(See Bronchiolitis).

UPPER RESPIRATORY INFECTION (URI)

(See Bronchiolitis).

URINARY TRACT INFECTION (UTI)

Treatment: Cranberry Juice, Uva Ursi.

WHOOPING COUGH

(See Bronchiolitis).

DISEASE CHARTS

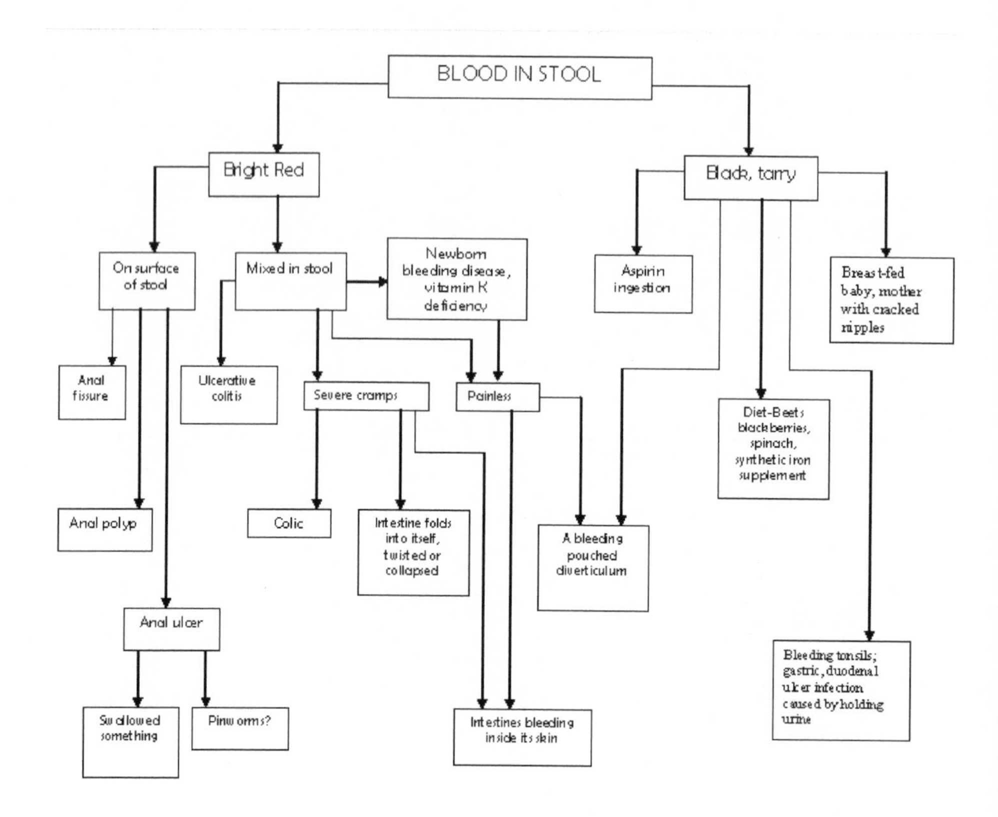

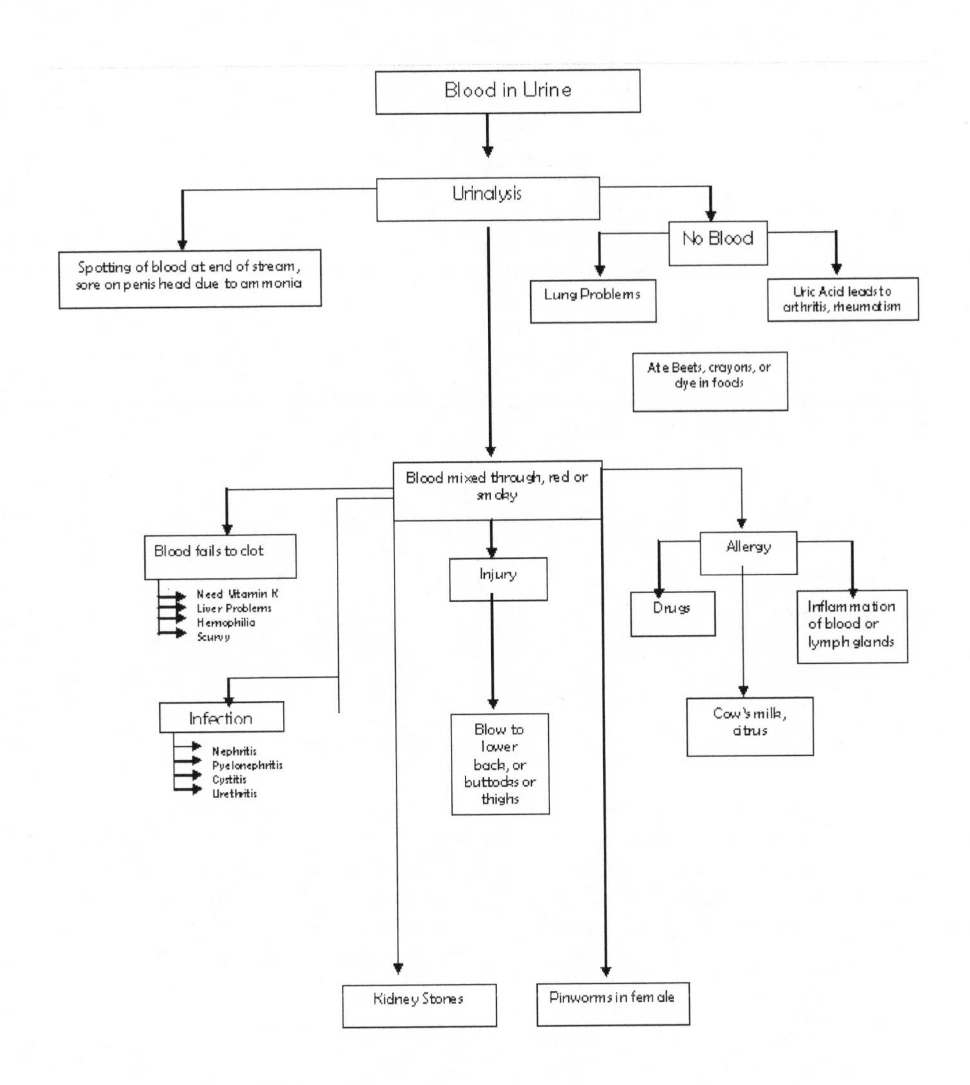

Blood in Urine
Urinalysis
Spotting of blood at end of stream, sore on penis head due to ammonia
No Blood
Lung Problems
Uric Acid leads to arthritis, rheumatism
Ate Beets, crayons, or dye in foods
Blood mixed through, red or smoky
Blood fails to clot
Need Vitamin K
Liver Problems
Hemophilia
Scurvy
Injury
Allergy
Drugs
Inflammation of blood or lymph glands
Infection
Nephritis
Pyelonephritis
Cystitis
Urethritis
Blow to lower back, or buttocks or thighs
Cow's milk, citrus
Kidney Stones
Pinworms in female

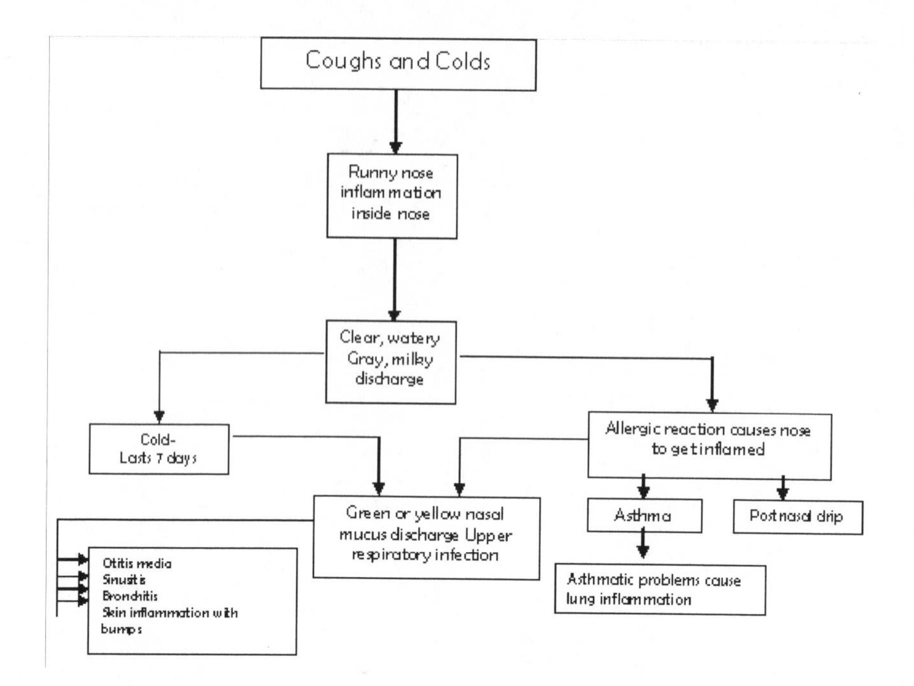

A Cough:

▲ that lasts more than 2 weeks; take elecampane and pleurisy

▲ that disturbs sleep at night; take catnip or chamomile with mullein

▲ that brings up blood-tinged phlegm; take witch hazel, Alum root, mullein, vitamin K, comfrey

A Cough accompanied by:

▲ difficulty breathing; lobelia, catnip, peppermint
▲ chest pain; white willow, hawthorn, elecampane
▲ wheezing (a whistling sound on breathing out, as in asthma); catnip, mullein
▲ retractions (the skin between the ribs appears to be sucked in with each breath); cramp bark, catnip, mullein
▲ rapid breathing; catnip mullein, lobelia

Sore Throat:

▲ following exposure to someone with diagnosed strep infection; Echinacea and goldenseal, chaparral, mullein
▲ in a child with a history of chronic lung disease, rheumatic fever, kidney disease; same as above

Sore Throat accompanied by:

▲ fever over 102°F (39°C); cat's claw, feverfew, mullein
▲ discomfort when swallowing; witch hazel, sage, hyssop, catnip, mullein
▲ severe difficulty swallowing, drooling; digestive enzyme, catnip, chamomile, mullein, lobelia
▲ white spots or blisters on reddened throat; witch hazel, burdock, chickweed
▲ swollen, or tender glands in the neck; Echinacea, witch hazel, shepherd's purse

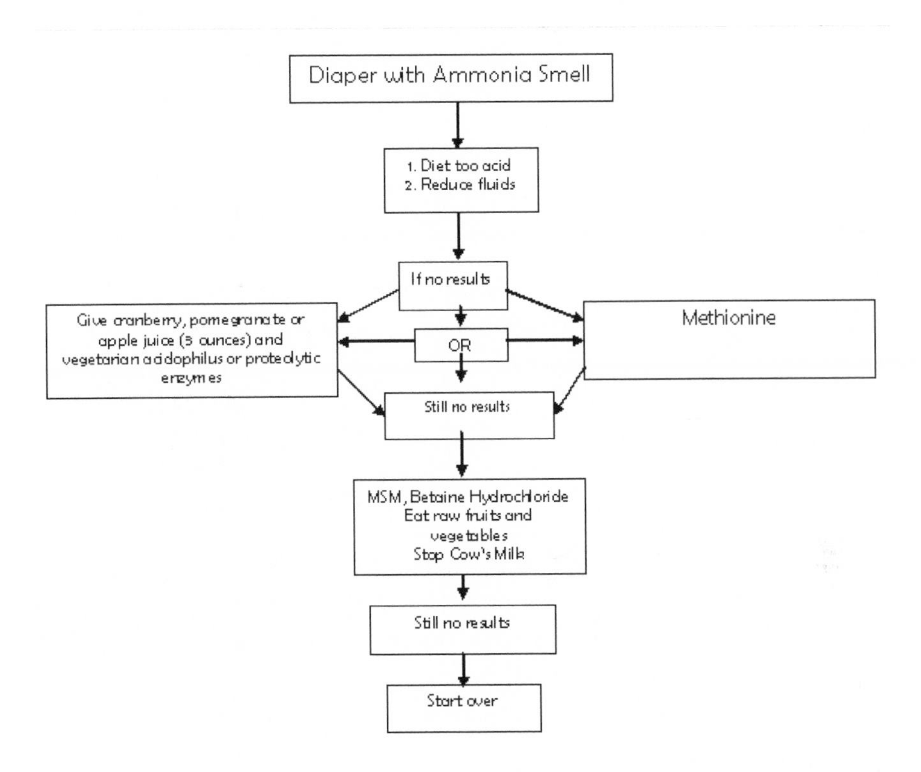
Diaper with Ammonia Smell
1. Diet too acid
2. Reduce fluids
If no results
Give cranberry, pomegranate or apple juice (3 ounces) and vegetarian acidophilus or proteolytic enzymes
OR
Methionine
Still no results
MSM, Betaine Hydrochloride
Eat raw fruits and vegetables
Stop Cow's Milk
Still no results
Start over

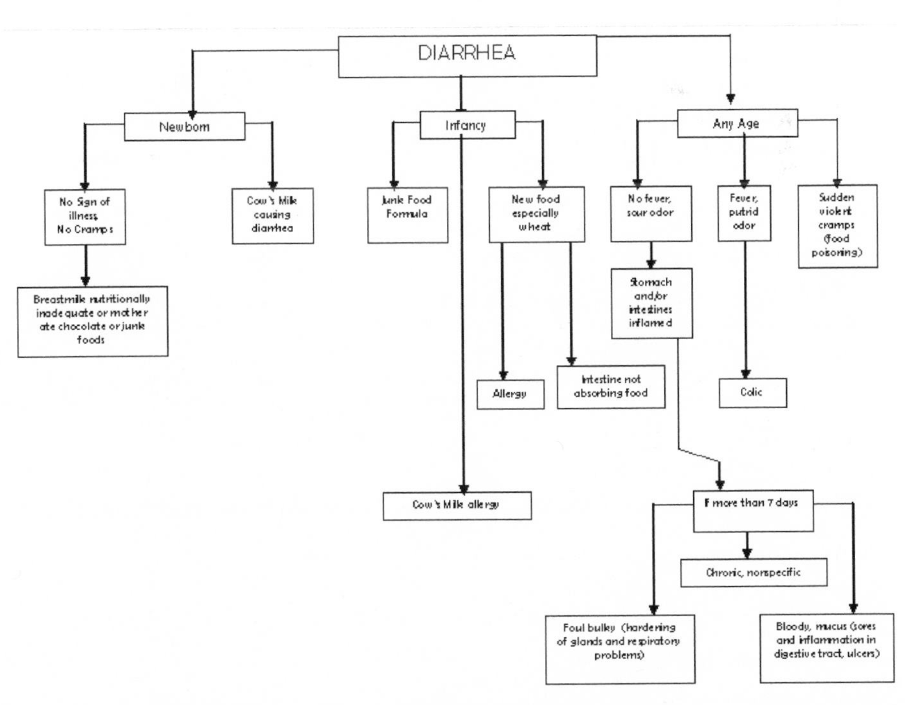
DIARRHEA
Newborn
No Sign of illness
No Cramps
Breastmilk nutritionally inadequate or mother ate chocolate or junk foods
Cow's Milk causing diarrhea
Infancy
Junk Food
Formula
New food especially wheat
Allergy
Intestine not absorbing food
Cow's Milk allergy
Any Age
No fever, sour odor
Stomach and/or intestines inflamed
If more than 7 days
Chronic, nonspecific
Foul bulky (hardening of glands and respiratory problems)
Bloody, mucus (sores and inflammation in digestive tract, ulcers)
Fever, putrid odor
Colic
Sudden violent cramps (food poisoning)

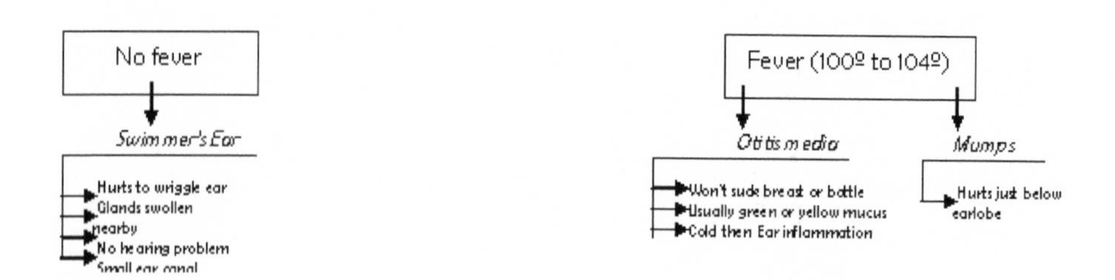
Earache
No fever
Swimmer's Ear
Hurts to wriggle ear
Glands swollen nearby
No hearing problem
Fever (100º to 104º)
Otitis media
Won't suck breast or bottle
Usually green or yellow mucus
Cold then Ear inflammation
Mumps
Hurts just below earlobe

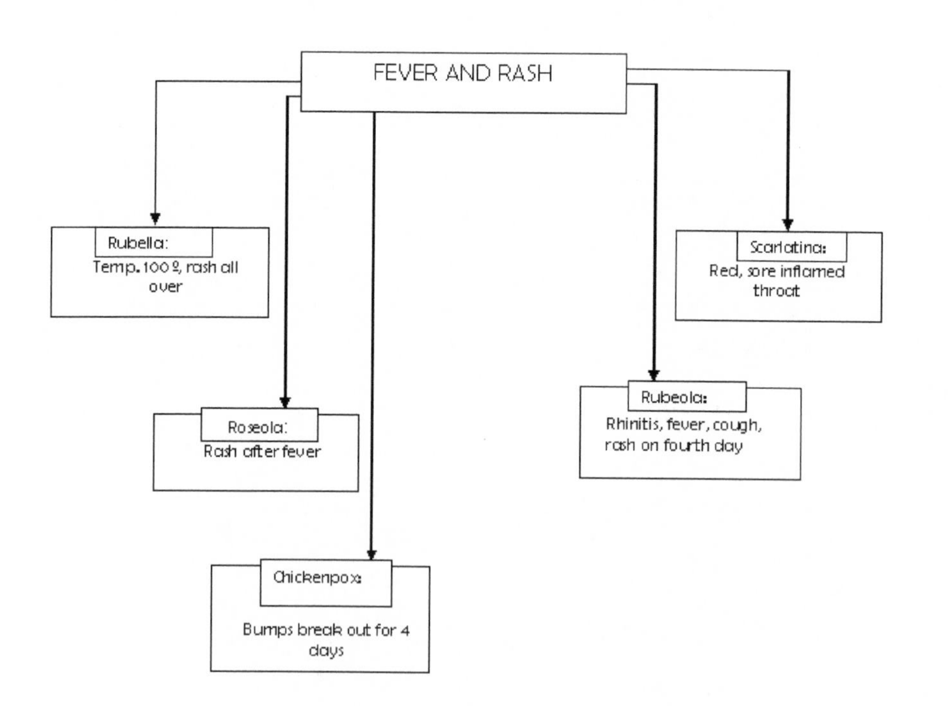
FEVER AND RASH
Rubella:
Temp. 100º, rash all over
Scarlatina:
Red, sore inflamed throat
Roseola:
Rash after fever
Rubeola:
Rhinitis, fever, cough, rash on fourth day
Chickenpox:
Bumps break out for 4 days

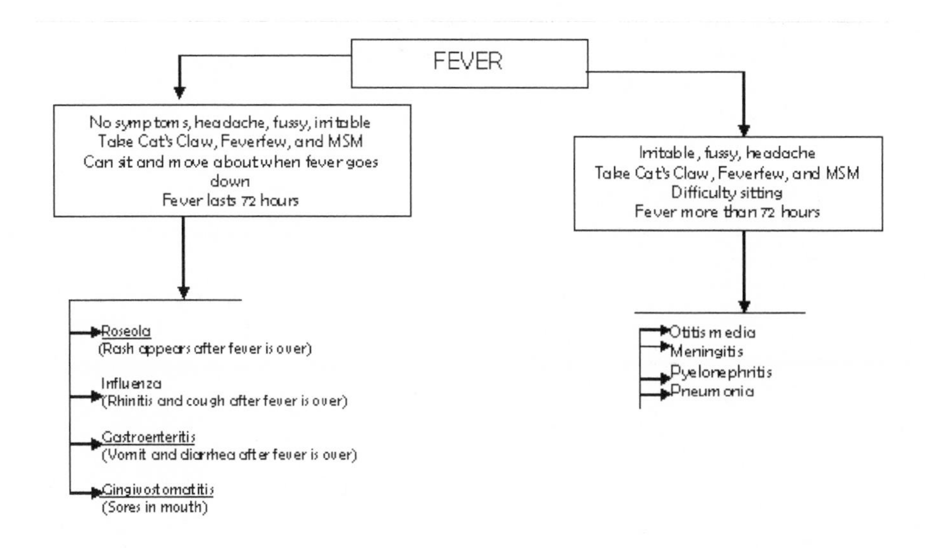
FEVER
No symptoms, headache, fussy, irritable
Take Cat's Claw, Feverfew, and MSM
Can sit and move about when fever goes down
Fever lasts 72 hours
Roseola
(Rash appears after fever is over)
Influenza
(Rhinitis and cough after fever is over)
Gastroenteritis
(Vomit and diarrhea after fever is over)
Gingivostomatitis
(Sores in mouth)
Irritable, fussy, headache
Take Cat's Claw, Feverfew, and MSM
Difficulty sitting
Fever more than 72 hours
Otitis media
Meningitis
Pyelonephritis
Pneum onia

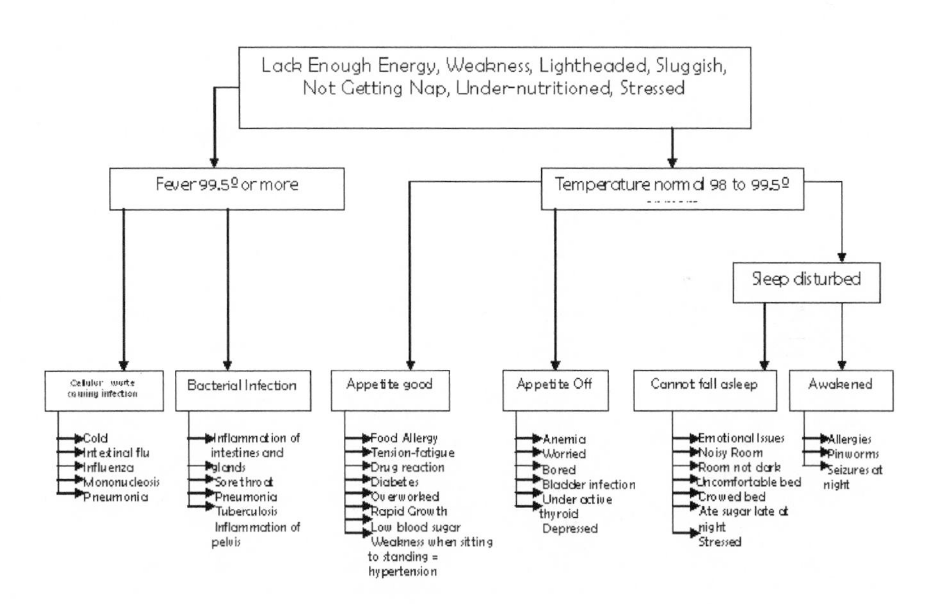
Lack Enough Energy, Weakness, Lightheaded, Sluggish,
Not Getting Nap, Under-nutritioned, Stressed
Fever 99.5º or more
Temperature normal 98 to 99.5º
Sleep disturbed
Bacterial Infection
Appetite good
Appetite Off
Cannot fall asleep
Awakened
Cold
Intestinal flu
Influenza
Mononucleosis
Pneumonia
Inflammation of intestines and glands
Sore throat
Pneumonia
Tuberculosis
Inflammation of pelvis
Food Allergy
Tension-fatigue
Drug reaction
Diabetes
Overworked
Rapid Growth
Low blood sugar
Weakness when sitting to standing = hypertension
Anemia
Worried
Bored
Bladder infection
Under active thyroid
Depressed
Emotional Issues
Noisy Room
Room not dark
Uncomfortable bed
Crowed bed
Ate sugar late at night
Stressed
Allergies
Pinworms
Seizures at night

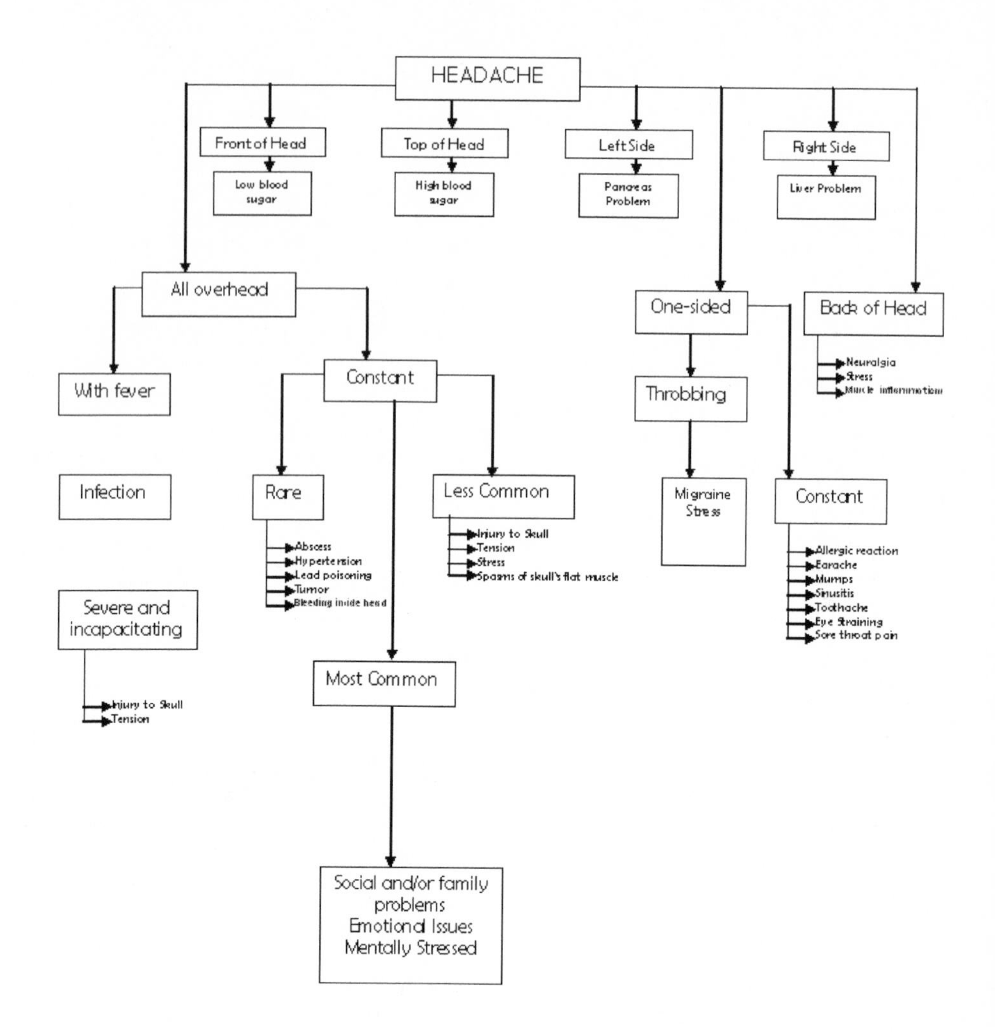
HEADACHE
Front of Head
Low blood sugar
Top of Head
High blood sugar
Left Side
Pancreas Problem
Right Side
Liver Problem
All overhead
With fever
Infection
Severe and incapacitating
Injury to Skull
Tension
Constant
Rare
Abscess
Hypertension
Lead poisoning
Tumor
Bleeding inside head
Less Common
Injury to Skull
Tension
Stress
Spasms of skull's flat muscle
Most Common
Social and/or family problems
Emotional Issues
Mentally Stressed
One-sided
Throbbing
Migraine
Stress
Constant
Allergic reaction
Earache
Mumps
Sinusitis
Toothache
Eye Straining
Sore throat pain
Back of Head
Neuralgia
Stress
Muscle inflammation

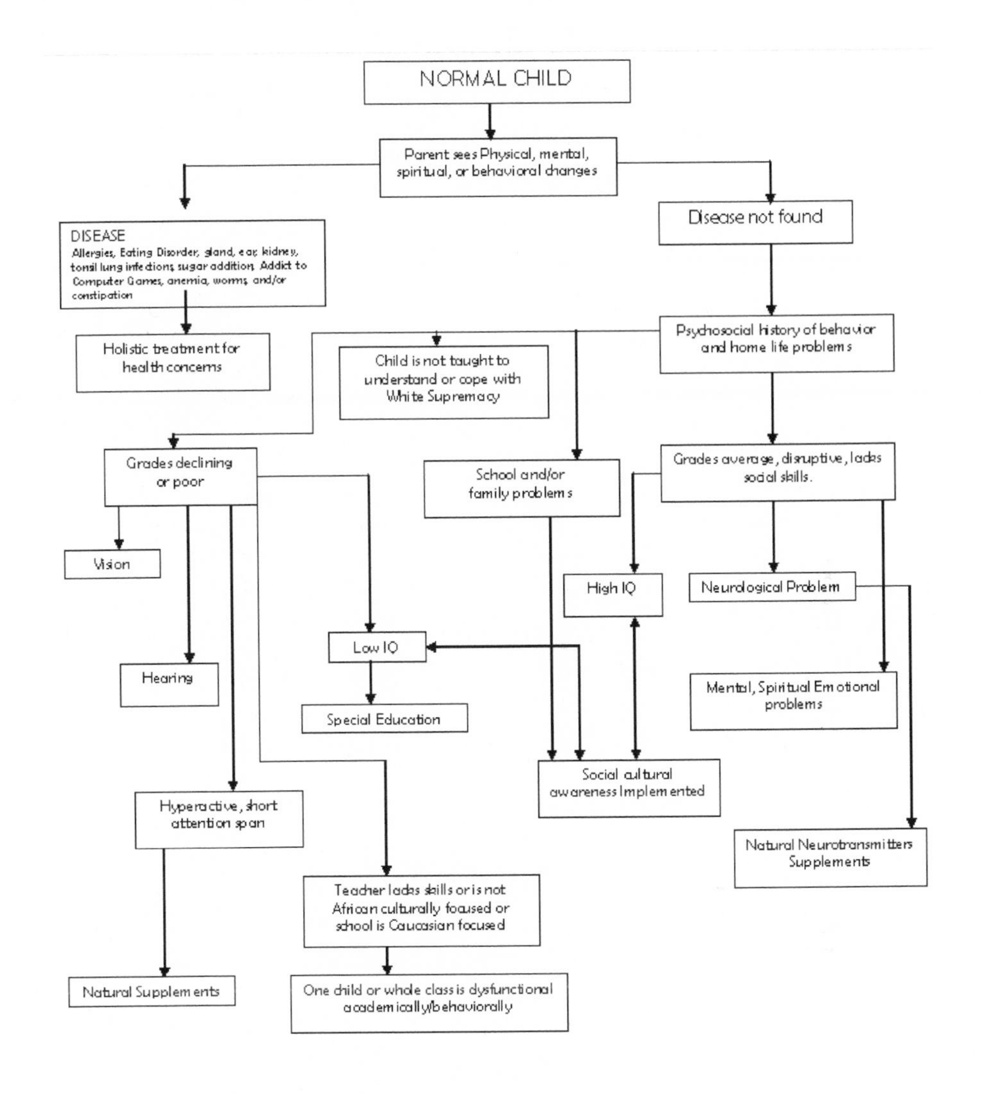
NORMAL CHILD
Parent sees Physical, mental, spiritual, or behavioral changes
DISEASE
Allergies, Eating Disorder, gland, ear, kidney, tonsil lung infections, sugar addition, Addict to Computer Games, anemia, worms, and/or constipation
Holistic treatment for health concerns
Disease not found
Psychosocial history of behavior and home life problems
Child is not taught to understand or cope with White Supremacy
Grades declining or poor
School and/or family problems
Grades average, disruptive, lacks social skills.
Vision
High IQ
Neurological Problem
Low IQ
Hearing
Mental, Spiritual Emotional problems
Special Education
Social cultural awareness Implemented
Hyperactive, short attention span
Natural Neurotransmitters Supplements
Teacher lacks skills or is not African culturally focused or school is Caucasian focused
Natural Supplements
One child or whole class is dysfunctional academically/behaviorally

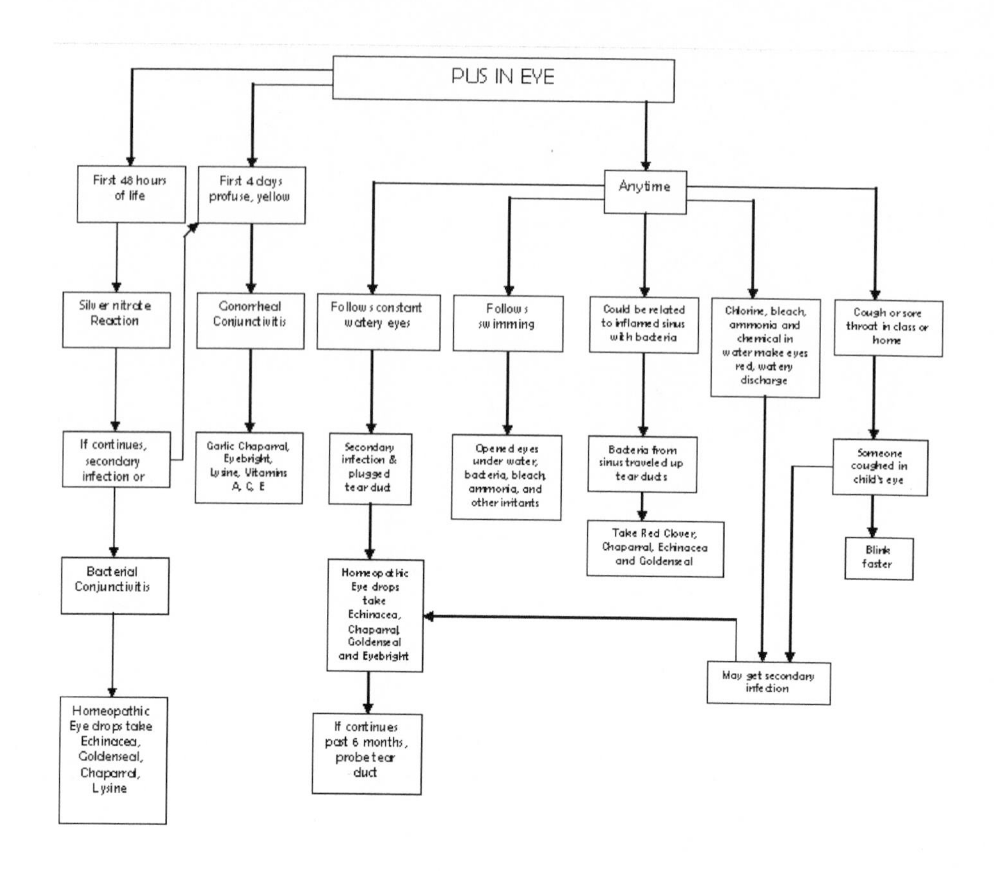

PUS IN EYE
First 48 hours of life
First 4 days profuse, yellow
Anytime
Silver nitrate Reaction
Gonorrheal Conjunctivitis
Follows constant watery eyes
Follows swimming
Could be related to inflamed sinus with bacteria
Chlorine, bleach, ammonia and chemical in water make eyes red, watery discharge
Cough or sore throat in class or home
If continues, secondary infection or
Garlic Chaparral, Eyebright, Lysine, Vitamins A, C, E
Secondary infection & plugged tear duct
Opened eyes under water, bacteria, bleach, ammonia, and other irritants
Bacteria from sinus traveled up tear ducts
Someone coughed in child's eye
Take Red Clover, Chaparral, Echinacea and Goldenseal
Blink faster
Bacterial Conjunctivitis
Homeopathic Eye drops take Echinacea, Chaparral, Goldenseal and Eyebright
May get secondary infection
Homeopathic Eye drops take Echinacea, Goldenseal, Chaparral, Lysine
If continues past 6 months, probe tear duct

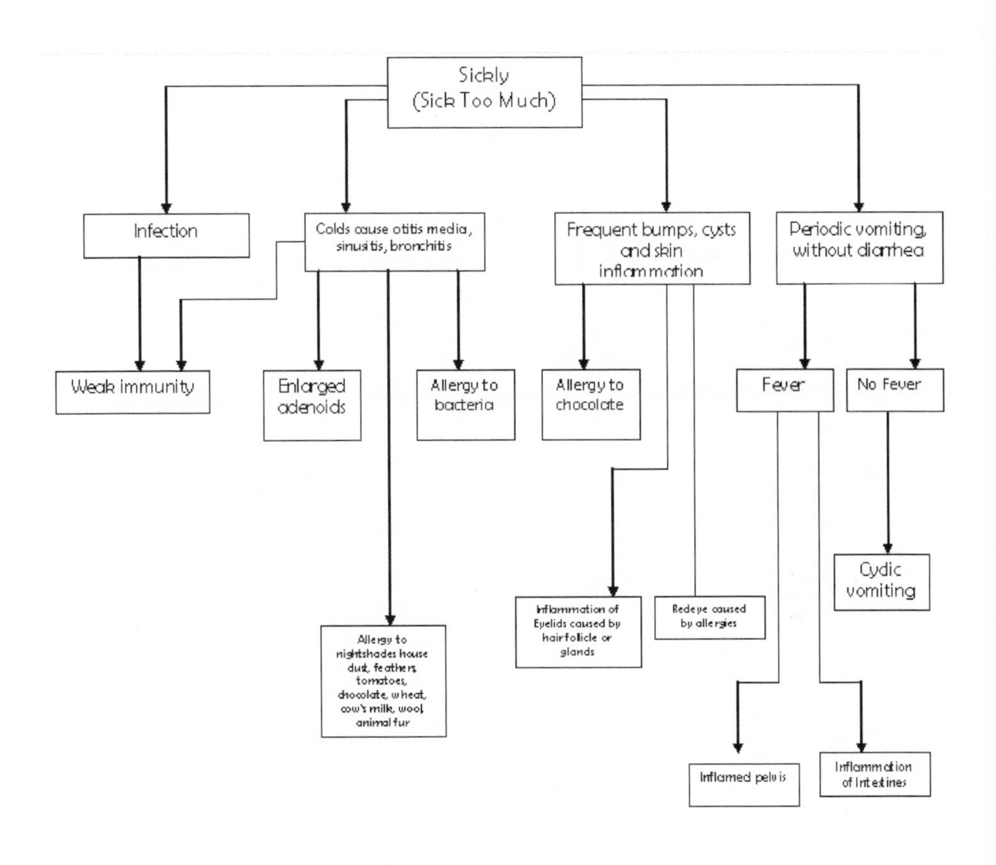
Sickly
(Sick Too Much)
Infection
Colds cause otitis media, sinusitis, bronchitis
Frequent bumps, cysts and skin inflammation
Periodic vomiting, without diarrhea
Weak immunity
Enlarged adenoids
Allergy to bacteria
Allergy to chocolate
Fever
No Fever
Cyclic vomiting
Inflammation of Eyelids caused by hairfollicle or glands
Redeye caused by allergies
Allergy to nightshades house dust, feathers, tomatoes, chocolate, wheat, cow's milk, wool, animal fur
Inflamed pelvis
Inflammation of Intestines

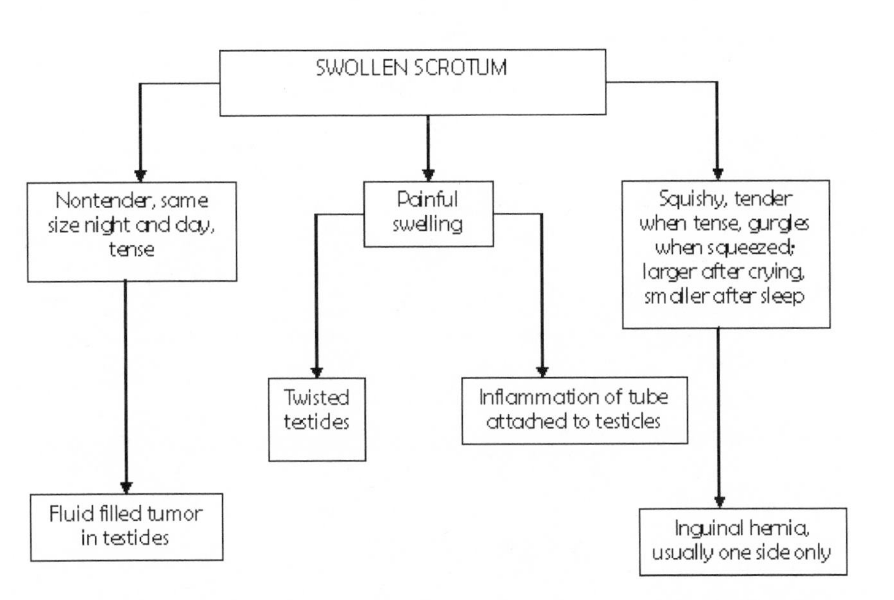
SWOLLEN SCROTUM
Nontender, same size night and day, tense
Painful swelling
Squishy, tender when tense, gurgles when squeezed; larger after crying, smaller after sleep
Twisted testicles
Inflammation of tube attached to testicles
Fluid filled tumor in testicles
Inguinal hernia, usually one side only

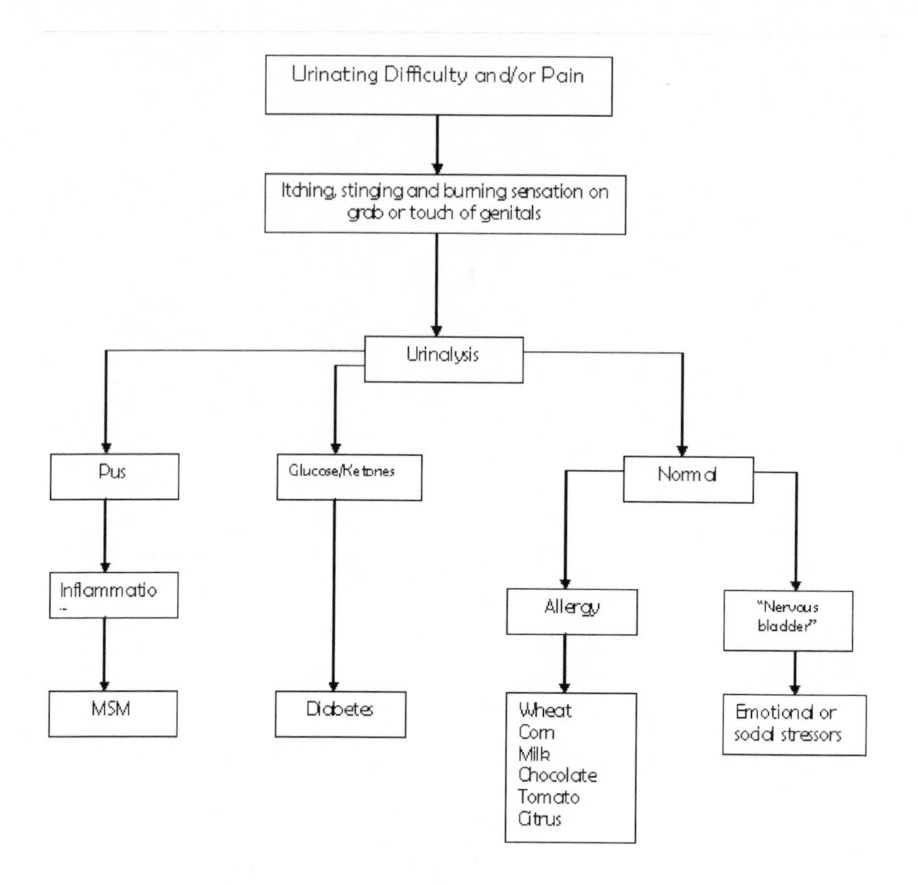

Urinating Difficulty and/or Pain
Itching, stinging and burning sensation on grab or touch of genitals
Urinalysis
Pus
Glucose/Ketones
Normal
Inflammatio
Allergy
"Nervous bladder"
MSM
Diabetes
Wheat
Corn
Milk
Chocolate
Tomato
Citrus
Emotional or social stressors

BOYS WEIGHT CHART

BOYS HEIGHT CHART

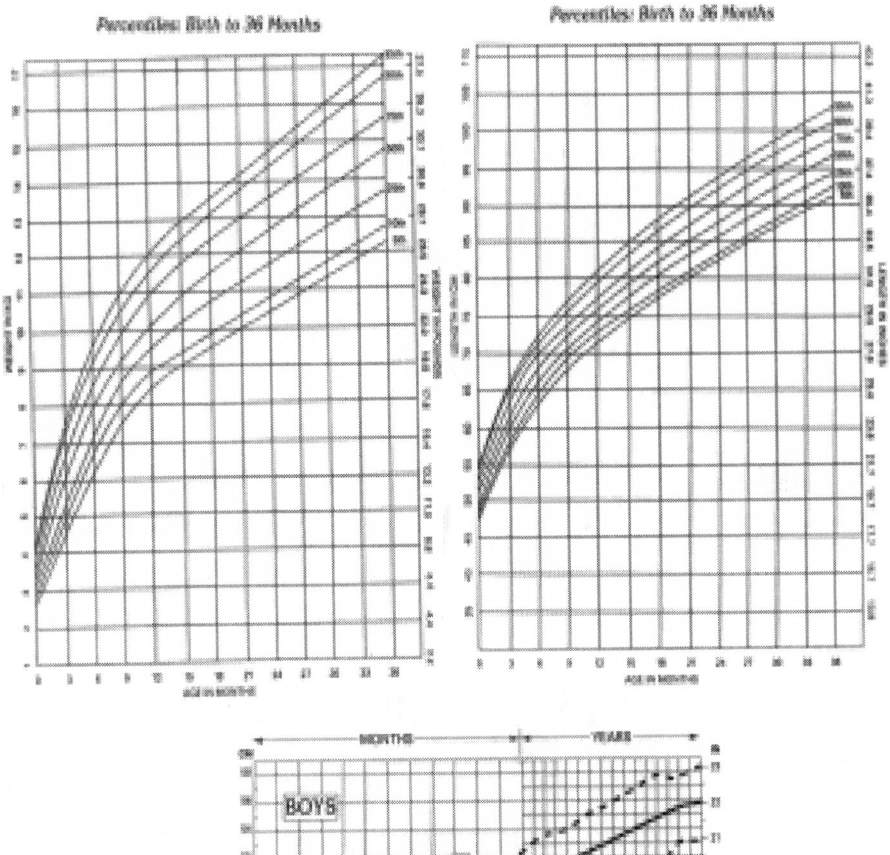

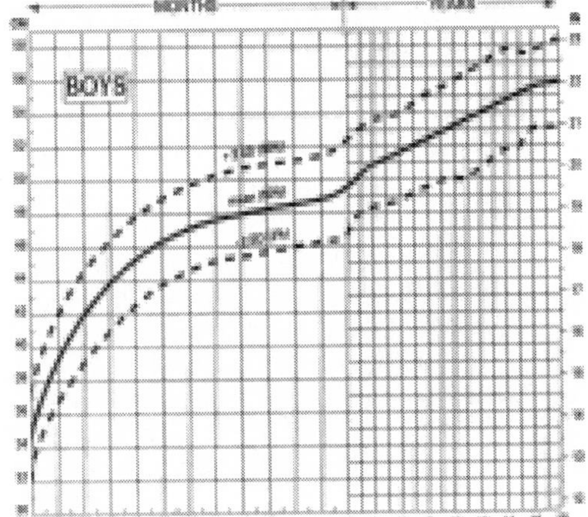

Source: *Pediatrics*

HEALTH CONCERNS
SKIN ERUPTIONS
(Bumps, Rashes)

Disease	Symptoms	Skin Characteristics	Duration
ENTEROVIRA EXANTHEMAS	Temperature 101º to103ºF, pharyngitis, gastrointestinal symptoms.	Rash starts with the fever or after fever drops; non itchy bumps on the chest and face and can be on the palms and soles.	Five days or less
ERYTHEMA INFECTIOSUM	Low grade fever, pharyngitis, head ache.	Flushed cheeks; reticulated erythema on extremities(often itch) exacerbated by sunlight, pressure, heat.	Two to Five weeks
INFECTIOUS MONONUCLEOSIS	Temperature to 101º F, malaise, sore throat enlarged lymph nodes, enlarged spleen, upper pharyngitis	Rash occurs in less than 15% of the cases. Small dark red bumps or papules on trunk and arms. Tonsillitis, enlarged spleen.	One to Two days
ROSEOLA	High fever for three to four days resolving by crisis, convulsions can be caused by fever.	When fever drops, dark, red-dish bumps appear on trunk spread to neck and behind ears and may not appear on face or extremities. Swollen lymph nodes at the back of neck. (95% in children under 3 yrs)	Three days or less
RUBEOLA	Temperature	Temperature is	Five days or more

(MEASLES)	103º to104ºF, inflammation conjunctivitis, cough small red spots with bluish center on the mouth.	usually highest on the 4th day. Bumps develop on forehead and neck, spread to face and trunk and by the third day appear on the feet. Rash becomes brownish and patchy.	
RUBELLA	Low grade fever, eye and throat inflammation, lymph nodes behind ears are sensitive.	Pink-red macules around mouth spreading to trunk.	Less than five days
SCARLET FEVER	Temperature 101º to103ºF, for 3 to 4 days, headache, tonsillitis vomiting and sore throat.	Rash develops one to two days after the fever begins starts on neck, underarm and chest; rapidly spreads. Skin on hands and feet peel.	Five to Seven days
WARTS	Raised, indented lesions and bumps	Common warts: Brownish, rough, raised lesions, often including genitals (common warts are not sexually transmitted). Flat warts: Multiple small, slightly raised lesions, flesh-colored to tan, on face, neck arms, legs. Plantar warts: Speckled raised, or indented sores, often painful. Genital warts:	Without treatment, warts resolve in 6 months to 3 years

Soft, flesh-colored bumps on genitalia.

DIAPER RASHES

TYPE	SIGNS AND SYMPTOMS	CAUSE
Atopic Dermatitis	Itching with redness	Allergy or sensitivity
Candidal (fungal) Dermatitis	Bright red, tender rash increases between abdomen and thighs, bumps spreading uncomfortable	Candi ccandida albicans (a fungus); Candida often infects a skin rash usually last 3 days or longer
Chafing Dermatitis	Redness where there is the Most friction, no discomfort	Moisture rubbing
Impetigo		Bacteria
Intertrigo	Poorly defined reddened areas where skin rubs together, can ooze white to yellowish pus, can burn when in contact with urine	Rubbing of skin on skin
Seborrheic Dermatitis	Deep red rash, can have yellow scales; may start on or spread to scalp; no discomfort	Cellular waste, mucus waste, dairy, junk food

SLEEPING DISORDER

(Wakeful at night, problems falling asleep)
Possible Causes

Age	Won't go to sleep	Awakens after going to sleep
BIRTH TO 6 MONTHS	Colic, Over-stimulated, Hunger	Colic, hunger, sickness, lost pacifier, bed too small, urinary infection, cutting teeth, earache, urine contacting open sores
6 MONTHS TO15 MONTHS	Fear of separation Use to staying up late Naps too long Low calcium Overstimulated	Croup, ear infection, pinworms, fever, diaper rash, gas, low calcium, allergic to blanket or pillow or toy
15 MONTHS TO3 YEARS	Playing a "game" Fear of separation Naps too long Anxiety	Sickness, pinworms, teething, refused to have a bowel movement during the day, relaxes and has it at night, bed too small, diaper rash
3 TO 5 YEARS	Naps too long Fears ghosts in room, Family arguments or sex in next room Overstimulated	Pinworms, sickness, fell out of bed
5 YEARS ON	House too noisy Doesn't need much sleep Parents fighting Use to staying up late	Pinworms, seizure, sickness, full bladder

FEVERS

COMMON CAUSES OF FEVER & SORE THROAT

Smallpox
Syphilis
Chickenpox
Coxsackie virus
Enterovirus
Gingivostomatitis
Toxoplasmosis
Typhoid fever
Herpes simplex
Herpangina
Infectious mononucleosis
Influenza
Scarlet fever
Tonsillitis

RARE CAUSES OF FEVER & SORE THROAT

Diphtheria
Hand, foot & mouth disease
Infectious lymphocytois
Peritonsillar abscess
Retropharyngeal abscess

COMMON CAUSES OF FEVER & RASH

Chickenpox
Enterovirus
Erythema infectiosum
Exanthems chart
Infectious mononucleosis
Measles
Roseola
Rubella
Rubeola
Scarlet fever

FEVER & SKIN SORES

Cat-scratch disease
Mycotic infection
Polyarteritis nodosa
Rat-bite fever

RARE CAUSES OF FEVER

Brucellosis (Bang's disease)
Bubonic plague
Hemolytic-uremic syndrome
Kawasaki disease
Malaria
Mycotic infection
Tuberculosis Typhoid Fever

RARE CAUSES OF FEVER & RASH

Erythema nodosum
Leptospirosis
Listeria monocytogenes
Lupus erythematosus
Polyarteritis nodosa
Rat-bite fever Rickettsial diseases
Septicemia

CAUSES OF FEVER & SEVERE HEADACHE

Cavernous sinus thrombosis
Encephalitis
Viral
Herpes
Mump
Mononucleosis
Ethmoiditis
Meningitis
Poliomyelitis
Reye's disease

FEVER & JOINT PAIN

Arthritis

EYESIGHT PROBLEMS

Children usually are not aware that they have vision problems. Keep in mind that a two years old vision is usually 20/60 and gradually improves to 20/20 when they are near ten years old. Eating junk food diet and/or white sugar and/or products with white sugar in it as well as undetected and detected diabetes usually causes eyesight problems. The parent through observations and alertness can identify a problem using the following suggestions:

- Frowning when doing a visual task or frequent squinting (unrelated to bright lights or sunlight).
- Squinting when a light is turned on in a dimly lit room. Frequently starring at lights.
- Undue sensitivity to light.
- Crusting, frequent bumps on eyelid, redness or swelling of the eyelids. Eyelids may be crusted shut in the morning. A yellowish white or green fluid may leak from the eyes.
- Tilting the head to one side in an attempt to avoid using the weakest eye.
- Continuously shutting or covering one eye.
- Avoiding visual activities such as looking at books.
- Unequal pupils (black center in eye) or pupils that seem a little grayish. Normal pupils both get large in dim light and small in bright lights.
- Looking at videos, computer monitors or TV, often causes frequent headaches, nausea, double vision and/or dizziness.
- Tends not to be able to recognize people or objects.
- More than normal toddler bumping into things, stumbling and/or clumsiness.
- Often rubs eyes, which can mean the eyes, are burning, scratchy or itchy. Eye rubbing due to sleepiness is normal.
- Eyes are watery and tearful.
- Eyes that bulge or jump up and down, dance or bounce rapidly.
- When looking away or at a distance, the child tends to hold their body rigid or at an angle.
- Always sitting too close to the TV but this can be the child's desire to see things bigger.
- Holding toys, objects and books close to their face.
- Eyes that do not move together at the same time (unison) or look mismatched or crossed.
- Problems distinguishing colors. Keep in mind that children usually cannot identify colors.

APPENDICITIS SYMPTOMS

Appendicitis symptoms are usually the same as an upset stomach. The discomfort and pain starts around the navel and gradually moves to the lower right abdomen. If the appendix is located in a different area of the intestines, the pain can be in the wrong place such as the back. The area of pain is tender when touched and can cause the child to walk bent over or limp. There is usually loss of appetite, irritability and the child is easily upset. After the pain starts there can be vomiting. Vomiting before the pain starts is usually caused by a stomachache or inflammation of the stomach and/or intestines. There can be scant, non-watery diarrhea, gas and a low-grade fever of 100ºF to 101ºF (38ºC to 38.5ºC). If the pain stops after several hours, it could mean a burst appendix. The best cure is prevention; avoid junk foods, cheese, dairy, meats, and sodas, eating late, wrong food combinations, worms and constipation. If appendicitis is suspected, use Cat's Claw, Feverfew, MSM, Witch Hazel, Shepherd's Purse, Echinacea and Goldenseal.

BOWEL MOVEMENT

SIZE AND SHAPE

- A raw food and/or high fiber diet usually has bulkier stools, stools that can float which may be somewhat mushy. Hard firm stools can indicate a lack of fiber and inadequate water consumption. Worm-like, narrow, or ribbon shaped stools can indicate a blockage in the colon or hemorrhoids, especially if there is abdominal upset or distress or a lot of groaning or moaning.

- Change in bowel regularity or habits can be a sign of emotional stress, a change in diet, depression, unsteady eating schedule, constipation, low to high fiber or stomach distress. It is associated as a warning sign of cancer.

CONSISTENCY

- If stools are hard and dry, the transient time is too slow or the digestive enzymes are too weak or the system is too alkaline. If the stools are watery and loose, the transient time is too fast or the system is too acidic or there is stress.

COLOR

- Medium brown stools are normal. Vegetarians' stools are lighter and smell like vegetables. Meat eaters' stools are darker and have a foul, sulfur like smell. Black tarry looking stools indicate bleeding in the digestive tract. Yellowish stools indicate problems digesting fats. Gray or chalky stools indicate a medical problem.

HEARING PROBLEMS

Children tend to be inattentive, lack auditory attentiveness, listen to their imagination or a song, they hum while playing, listen to the food they are chewing and have selective listening. In other words, they sometimes only hear half of what their parents are saying. Children tend to play music, TV and videos too loud. Most will damage their ears before they are eighteen years old if their parents do not insist that they "turn it down" (lower the volume) all the time. The child with a hearing problem can be detected by using the following:

- When not facing the speaker directly they tend to miss what's being spoken. Children instinctively learn how to lip read so they can understand what is being said when facing the speaker. If the speaker talks to them from the rear or the side, the child misses part of what is spoken.

- Seems to miss auditory and verbal cues.

- Use a limited vocabulary because they miss a lot of things said. This may cause the child to be labeled as a "slow learner" (See Infant to Toddler Learning).

- Problems or lack of ability to hear low pitched sounds (i.e. clock ticking).

- Complains about their ears ringing or ear pain.

- During pregnancy, the mother was exposed to Rubella or Cytomegalvirus (CMV) during the first trimester.

- Has difficulty telling the difference between tonal nuances – a sad, angry or joking tone to your voice.

- Problems distinguishing the differences between similar sounding words (blue and you, door and store, cake, lake, fake and shake or sue and shoe). The words that begin with "s", "sh", or "f" give them problems.

- They were born with facial or ear abnormalities or diagnosed as having Franconi Syndrome.

- They had an illness that could have damaged the ear (i.e. Meningitis) or were given drugs that damaged the ear (i.e. Gentamicin).

- Tends to miss what others are saying.

- Does not answer if you talk softly.

- Inability to follow directions.

- Favors an ear when turning towards a sound.

- The child tends to have problems singing along, clapping or moving in rhythm to sounds or music.

- Does not notice or respond to timer buzzer, birds singing, telephone or doorbell ringing, or outside noise (sirens, howling wind, lightning).

- Gives an inappropriate answer to questions, "Do you want the book?" "No, I do not want to look."

CHOKING

Children may have a full set of teeth (usually in the third year). However, chewing and swallowing is a developmental task. They have not completely mastered it and tend to choke because their mind wanders, they have not coordinated tongue and teeth movements, have bitten their tongue and chew to avoid it, gulp their food down, swallow air while chewing, eat and run, rush to chew, do not chew the food completely and try to swallow without chewing. Listed below are a few suggestions to eliminate choking:

- Make your child sit down to eat.
- Slice soy hotdogs lengthwise.
- Peel and remove pits or seeds of cherries or grapes.
- Cut raw apples or carrots into strips or thin slices.
- Do not let them eat a spoonful of nut butters (peanut butter will clog the throat).
- Squash chickpeas or beans or soak hard raisins (best to buy the moist soft ones).

- Do not allow laughing, singing, giggling or talking with a mouth full of food. The parent should follow this rule in order for the child to follow it.
- Avoid marshmallows, hard candies, nuts, firm biscuits, hard cookies, popcorn, etc.
- Do not let the child stuff their mouth full of food.
- Do not allow the child to eat a food that can be choked on while in the car.

GENITAL PROBLEMS AND BOYS

The most common problem is the undescended testicles (Cryptorchidism). A testicle or testicles that fails to descend down into the scrotum, it cannot be felt in the scrotum. This condition usually occurs with premature births. It is usually the right testicle. If it does not descend by the time the child is one year old, then it may require surgery or hormone treatment.

It may appear as though there is an undescended testicle when it is a retractile one (moves up and down). The best time to observe whether the testicle is retractile is during a warm bath. The warmth will cause the testicle to descend while cold water (room or weather) causes the testicles to ascend. If the testicle comes down into the scrotum during a warm bath, it is okay. Retractile testicles settle permanently in the scrotum after puberty and do not need treatment.

Another problem is the blockage or impeded urinary flow (Meatalstenosis). It is common in boys who are circumcised. It usually causes urinating difficulties, repeated urinary tract infections, a narrow urinary stream and/or dribbling or slow urination. During circumcision, the tip of the penis can get irritated and develop scar tissue that blocks or impedes urination.

VACCINATIONS/IMMUNIZATIONS

Vaccinations are harmful and cause many diseases. If you are requested by an agency or institution to take a vaccination and you refuse; you must give them a declaration of vaccination exemption. Make copies of the Vaccination Exemption form and give it to them.

AFFIDAVIT
DECLARATION OF VACCINATION EXEMPTION

"EXEMPTION FROM IMMUNIZATION", I hereby declare that I as guardian/parent/adult having responsibility for myself/child named herein

withhold my consent and let it be known that said adult/minor is exempted from any and all vaccinations on the grounds that such is contrary to my personal beliefs.

Immunizations Of A Person Shall Not Be Required For Employment, Admission To A School Or Other Institution...If The Guardian, Parent, Or Adult Who Has Assumed Responsibility For His Or Her Custody And Care In The Case Of A Minor, The Person Must File With The Government Authority, A Letter Or Affidavit Stating That Such Vaccination Is Contrary To His/Her Beliefs...

Any institution, school or medical authority which tries to enforce vaccination on children or anyone else is in violation of the laws of the United States and may be subject to prosecution.

Amendment 14 of the United States Constitution:
"No state shall make or impose any law which shall abridge the privileges or immunities of the citizens of the United States, nor shall any state deprive any person of life, liberty or property."

Amendment 4 of the United States Constitution:
"The right of the people to be secure in their persons shall not be violated."

INTERNATIONAL VACCINATION EXEMPTION (Can use for travel)
Exemption has been ratified and approved by all United Nations members under WORLD HEALTH ORGANIZATION International Sanitary Regulations Article 83, Chapter IV; "Each individual has the right of vaccination exemption."

Subscribed And Affirmed To And Before Me On This _____ Day Of
______________________________, 20_____.

SIGNATURE AND DATE

____

NOTARY PUBLIC
COMMISSION EXPRIES

____

CHAPTER 12
ONCE UPON A TIME

"Our children are our future and as such they are the most valuable resource of our culture."

Dr. Gloria Peace

HARMFUL EFFECTS OF WHITE FAIRY TALES ON BLACK CHILDREN

Caucasians fairy tales/children's stories and nursery rhymes were written for Caucasians by Caucasians. The purpose of the fairy tales is to emotionally attach the child to Caucasian culture. Fairy tales program the child with Caucasian logic, morals, rituals and ceremonies, values, standards, ethics, social and sexual behaviors and violence. A Black child with a White Mental program cannot access their Black intelligence. Once the child is psychologically hardwired, a new program (African culture) will be hard to understand, difficult to accept, be questioned and given less respect and distorted. The first program, (Caucasian thought and behavior program) will be the norm standard and used to understand and measure the validity of the African program (African culture).

The fairy tales are a method to program the Black child into having a White consciousness and subconsciousness. They "seasonin" the child into a Caucasian mindset. Fairy tales and nursery rhymes are derived from ancient Greek and Roman myths and folklore. Instead of Latin names the characters have English and German names. The Black child learns the Caucasian worldview (cosmology), rituals, ceremonies, rewards, punishments, how to act and react and begins to distort and modify their African character logic so that it will fit into a Caucasian culture's character logic. Thus, they gradually become programmed with a dysfunctional African personality and functional Caucasian personality.

The fairy tales and nursery rhymes are written oral stories that were originally told amongst ancient primitive Caucasian ethnic groups, clans and tribes. Their folklore scientists (social engineers), philologists and mythologists collected various nursery rhymes and fairy tales and put them in books. Jakob Ludwig Grimm (1785-1863) and Wilhelm Karl Grimm (1786-1859) collected stories that ancient Caucasians told to each other. They compiled the book Grimms Fairy Tales. The author, Basil (1637 in Italy) compiled various ancient Caucasian stories and named them Mother Goose. Mother Goose was transliterated by Charles Perault (1697, France). These stories have many versions, which have been revised, modified and changed and put into the English language in 1729. The Three Bears (1834) by Robert Southey is another ancient Caucasian story that subliminally (subconscious awareness) engineers the Black Children's mind and behavior. The stories teach the child Caucasian culture and how to manipulate others, to steal, be disobedient, how to dream, be superstitious, to do Caucasian rituals, to value winning above morality, use inappropriate parenting skills, to be a liar, to want and eat junk food and sweets, that killing animals is sport and to run away from home.

The fairy tales have a story pattern and subconsciously the child learns to act out their life according to the life of the fairy tale characters. If you have ever wondered why some adults act like they are immature or don't want to grow up and be responsible, look at the fairy tales. This type of dysfunctional adult has the Peter Pan Syndrome or the Alice In Wonderland Syndrome (never, never, never-land, never grow up). The patterns of the stories are:

1) FALL OF CHARACTER –character has a problem that has caused an obstacle or a change and/or failure in their life.

2) ATONEMENT-character seeks a solution to the problem and has to overcome or to defeat an enemy.

3) NEED SUPERNATURAL MIRACLE-character seeks special person, superhero, genie, savior or item, magic, good fairy or witch and/or magic to become happy, successful, rich and normal.

The fairy tales have common ingredients such as:

- Single women have children
- Magic (words, coins, etc.) will save you (i.e. lottery, talk shows, psychic hotline)
- Poor people/poor elves live to serve the rich
- Have sex with someone if they dress good (i.e. prince or princess that wears designer clothes and expensive shoes)
- Married couples are miserable and usually childless (it is best to be single)
- Women want men for their money (king's gold, gold diggers)
- Stay in bad relationships (widower married to stepmother who abuses his children)
- No extended families
- Black is evil, White is good
- God does not exit for happy people (stories never mention God)
- Spirits are evil (spirituality is bad = African culture is bad)
- Sex symbolism
- Evil is successful without magic and goodness, good needs magic to be successful
- Marry a stranger for money or power not character
- Candy, cake and sweets are rewards and make you happy
- Meat eating is normal

- Man's deceased first wife subconscious is resurrected as evil stepmother (true nature of women is evil)
- Sacrifice children for wealth (successful career)
- Men are sexually wolves (sex predators)
- Child abuse is normal
- Poor parenting skills are normal
- Thieves and liars are successful
- Ancestors are not part of the family
- Straight hair and Caucasian facial features are beautiful
- Beautiful people are good and ugly people are evil (buy expensive jewelry and clothes to make yourself beautiful = good)
- Women are not interested in sex = men always want sex because women have charm and beauty
- Dysfunctional families are normal
- Violence is normal
- No wisdom given by the elderly relatives

Fairy tales use a story form (pattern) called "The Chase." In "The Chase," the character is chasing after success or the perfect life (self-actualization). The cartoons (animated fairy tales) such as The Road Runner and Wally Coyote, Tom and Jerry (cat and mouse), Flintstones, Bugs Bunny, Woody the Woodpecker, Scooby Doo, Butt Head and Beavis and Daffy Duck (represents a stupid Black person) use the chase; while Batman, Superman and Spiderman focus on a prophet who will save you. Chase themes are in movies such as: Men In Black, Star Wars, Tarzan, Titanic, Malcolm X and The Wild Wild West. "The Chase" theme is the format for Talk Shows (Jerry Springer, Oprah, Montel, etc.), Music videos, professional wrestling, Soap Operas and Commercials such as: Ronald McDonald and the Breakfast cereal commercials. The Talk show host helps a guest to overcome a problem or chase after a solution to problems (hunger, money, stressors, bad behavior, negative emotions, sex problems, social problems, etc.). "The Chase" theme is fairy tale based.

The breakfast and fast food commercials use clowns and fairy tale type characters, which appeal to infantilism (Peter Pan Syndrome). They emotionally take you down memory lane (back to your past life as a child) and subliminally satisfy the need to be nurtured or escape adult life. The commercials subliminally cause consumers to emotionally live a fantasy life of happiness with the fairy tale type characters. Fairy tales are a propaganda (political and social) tool and used in a 'military logic' fashion to reinforce and maintain Caucasian cultural values and White Supremacy.

The Caucasian civilization spends more dollars on media (fantasy commercial fairy tale characters) than on its military. The military maintains its power and attacks (makes wars to maintain peace) those who they classify as a terrorist or are classified as operating against their peaceful economic interest. However, the new weapon of the Caucasians is subliminal fairy tale fantasy propaganda, which is used to seize the mind of Black children and adults. Caucasians spend 3 to 4 times more money on the media of television shows (make believe-fantasy), commercials and movies that use exclusively fairy tale themes. They have invaded Africa with fantasy characters (fairy tales, movies, commercials). Their fairy tale fantasy invades the mind while the military invades the country. Media (fantasy) is the new military of Caucasians. An examination of the overt and hidden subliminal messages communicated to Black children in these fantasy stories can reveal their true effect on the mind.

The Africans in Africa, Africans in America and the Diaspora have African centered children's stories (fairy tales) that teach the child Maat (truth, justice, balance, reciprocity, righteousness, the real from the unreal, right from wrong, respect, etc.). They teach respect for the privilege to love God and the importance of culture and family as well as respect for the ancestors and Mother Earth (nature's balance = ecology). The stories present a variety of problems and a variety of the African Maat solutions.

The African children's stories usually have major themes:

1) A message gets changed and a character has to seek the true message
2) Rebirth (Rites of Passage) of a character teaches various solutions to problems
3) A mixture of 1 and 2
4) The use of Maat will solve problems (i.e., Ashanti Spider Stories, Aesop's Fables)

An African ethnic group called the Hottentots has many stories. One story is about the moon (unseen heavenly power) giving a message to a rabbit to tell Adam (Osiris) and Eve (Isis). The rabbit forgets the correct message and tells them a lie. The moon learns of the error and throws a stick (Rod of Righteousness) at the rabbit and splits its lip. Therefore, the child is told not to seek wisdom from those who lie.

The Maasai of Botswana, Kalahari Desert and Southern Rhodesia have a children's story about a turtle and rabbit that were told by God to tell man he will live forever. The fast moving rabbit runs to man and reaches him before the turtle. The rabbit with his bad memory forgets part of the message and tells man a lie instead of the truth. The turtle with the correct message gets to man after the rabbit. This caused man to lose his immortality. Therefore, man became doomed to solve his earthly problems by himself.

Ancient Greek and Roman myths and Caucasian fairy tales are distorted versions of the series of African Egyptian mythological stories about the children, Osiris and Seth, who are brothers and their sisters, Isis and Nepthys. The brothers and sisters represent attributes of God. It is a long story about how and why these brothers and sisters maintain Maat, family and Godly values in the face of negative forces outside and inside the family. It also contains the African spirituality construct.

The Africans in America that live on the Carolina Sea Islands, Upotos of the Congo and Gallas of East Africa have stories about a bird bringing mortal life and immortal life to man. The stories are built upon the Egyptian Osirian stories. African stories have a common connection and that is to demonstrate what is Maat, how to use Maat in social life and how to use Maat to solve problems. The stories are designed to emotionally bond African children to African culture.

The Caucasian culture's children stories are totally different, culturally abrasive and can be psychologically and emotionally harmful to Black children. They can addict children to white culture and sugary sweets. They do not reflect a Godly relationship with one's spirit and soul. For example, in Little Red Riding Hood, the little girl's mother abuses her by sending her into the woods where predatory, man-eating wolves live. The little girl is disobedient to her mother. She goes off the trail, which her mother told her to stay on. Little Red Riding Hood talks to the wolf (a total stranger) and tells the wolf she is going to her sick grandmother's house. She should not talk to strangers, but does. She wears a red hood. The hood symbolically represents deceit and the hiding of something. Red in Caucasian culture means fertile – sexually active. Consequently, Caucasian women wear red lipstick, red nail polish, red underwear, red shoes (Dorothy in "Wizard of Oz"), the areas of prostitution in cities where sex is sold is called the red light (sex) districts, etc.

The grandmother in the story is obviously senile as she leaves the door to her house open and has forgotten that wild wolves roam live in the forest and can come in the open door. The grandmother has poor hearing and cannot distinguish a wolf's voice from that of Little Red Riding Hood. When Little Red Riding Hood arrives at her grandmother's with a basket of food and sweets and a bottle of wine, she cannot recognize (poor eyesight) the difference between a wolf and her grandmother.

The story does not seem to make sense to the conscious mind because it is emotional and aimed at the subconscious mind. The wolf is symbolic of men. Men are wolves that seek sex. Men are dogs and want to rape virgin young girls. Girls want a man to be virile and a sexually aggressive stud. However, when a man is sexually aggressive towards them, they are insulted and call the man a dog (wolf). If a man is kind and gentle like a sheep, then he is a wolf in sheep's clothing. This means that men are deceitful. If a man whistles at an attractive lady, then he is acting a like a wolf – it's a wolf's whistle.

A hunter appears in the story with a rifle. The rifle is symbolically a man's penis. This means that a man's penis will save Little Red Riding Hood from her whore – like sexual urges. Therefore, the idea is promoted that the next man is always better than the last man and that females are trapped into sexual relationships by sexually aggressive dogs (men). The wolf dresses up like a drag queen to protect his virginity from hot (red – hot = red hood) Little Red Riding Hood. The hunter impregnates the drag queen (wolf) and the wolf drag queen has rocks (symbolic baby). The rock symbolizes a baby born by a woman. The woman (Eve) gave birth to the loss of man's immortality (eating the Apple in the Garden of Eden). The hunter skins the wolf and takes his fur (virility). Skinning or scalping people such as the American Indians symbolically means that their virility and soul are stolen because of an evil woman. After the murder of the wolf, the grandmother gets drunk (alcohol is called spirits). The wine bottle is symbolically a penis that gives the grandmother her true spirit (sexual awakening).

This story programs Black boys to be promiscuous wolves and Black girls to want to be in competition with other females and in conflict with their mothers. It can subconsciously cause girls to want the latest fashion in order to be sexy hunters of the penis that will save them from the evilness of being a woman with sinful menstruating vagina (means false hole).

The story Cinderella has many mixed messages and emotional themes. It symbolically suggests that dirt (cinder is black ash dirt from burnt wood) poor people can be saved from poverty by the rich, money, expensive clothes, shoes, magic (prophet, lottery), sex and that women are naturally dirty (evil) etc. Cinderella is a story about child abuse. The father is obsessed with love for his wife's sexuality and lets her abuse his child. It teaches the child that the woman's vagina will get her anything because Cinderella can only be saved from this parental abuse by being dressed in the latest, expensive clothes in order to sell her sexuality.

In the story, the personality and character development of the prince is never discussed. Therefore, the story implies that if a man dresses nice (expensive clothes, shoes) and has money, he can have sex with women. The fairy godmother in the story did not try to correct the father's behavior or put the mother and father in marriage counseling so that they would be better parents to Cinderella. The story projects the idea that being wealthy will save you from abuse and solve your problems. The story makes ugly people evil with dark hair (Black). The prince picks a wife as if she is an object or commodity. The story indicates that women are valued the same as a slave, horse or ornament and are sex candy for men. It also implies that women should not trust other women (stepmother, female friend or a sister). The stepmother and daughters ask for forgiveness for being abusive to Cinderella. It is denied, this subconsciously means that women must be punished for their sins and menstruation (bleeding) is the punishment for her original sin. The story implies that people should not be rehabilitated but punished. This culturally justifies prisons and prisoners.

The stories and rhymes can use a variation of the Adam and Eve in the Garden of Eden theme. One interpretation has it that Adam desired the same knowledge as God. Therefore, he ate the apple that Eve gave. This caused Adam to fall from the grace of God and lose his immortality. In the children's rhyme, Jack (Adam) and Jill (Eve) climbed up a hill (symbolic of Eden, Mountain where the gods lived = Mount Olympus) and got water (symbolic apple, Ambrosia/Elixir of Life = Fountain of Youth water) from the well, then Jack fell down and burst his head and lost his immortality. His head wound as bandaged by Dame Nog (noggin = head). Eggnog is an alcoholic drink symbolic of the Fountain of Youth/Ambrosia water = youthful sexual ability.

The Fountain of Youth (Apple = young forever/immortality) is subliminally associated with a rise in sex hormones (puberty), which causes the sex drive and the need to have sex (sew your oats). The early Caucasian explorers were searching for the Fountain of Youth (i.e. Ponce de Leon). Drugs were originally sold because they promised youthful sex abilities. For example, chocolate was sold because it contains the sex stimulating theobromine drug, cocaine was sold because it was believed to cause hypersex, heroin was believed to increase sexual stamina and drinking alcohol was believed to make having sexual conquest easier because it causes the loss of self-control and the loss of inhibitions and morals. The cosmetic facial crèmes, exercise gyms and equipment and hair dyes are sold because they are symbolic of maintaining youthful sexual ability. Youthful sexual ability is promised by herbs, vitamins, crèmes and drugs. The children's stories and rhymes are usually the child's first introduction to the subliminal concept that youthfulness is sexy and gets you sex, success and wealth.

The stories and rhymes have characters seeking magic and/or wealth (apple, golden eggs, Midas touch, etc.). The 3 Bears, 3 pigs and the Wizard of Oz three characters (Lion, Straw man and Tin man) are associated with a hero that possesses power of some type. The emotional message is that power can give you youthfulness. Youthfulness gives you a license to have promiscuous sex (sew your oats).

Shoes are usually associated with women and sex. For example, the Wizard of Oz's, Dorothy's Rites of Passage (Yellow Brick Road adventure) to womanhood (sexually fertile) = red shoe, Cinderella seeking a prince to marry and have sex with = glass shoe and the hypersex single woman that lived in a shoe could not stop having sex and children. These stories cause women to emotionally associate sexual ability with shoes; they often own an excessive amount of shoes. This demonstrates the subliminal effect of the stories.

The stories and rhymes are advertisements for Caucasian culture. They sell the Caucasian culture to the Black child. Advertisements work; that is why businesses use them. They spend more money on advertising than the worth of their product. Countries advertise their power by using war. Their ability to win wars attracts other countries businesses (wealth). An example of the power of advertisement is the story about a man who had a business. He said advertisement was an unnecessary business expense and he refused to advertise. He eventually had to go out of business because of a lack of enough customers, so he advertised in the newspaper "Business for Sale." Caucasian culture uses children stories as advertisements for their culture. They use media, computer games, sex movies, text books, religions, school and children's stories to sell their culture.

The earlier you condition a Black child's conscious and subconscious mind and emotions with a fairy tale and nursery rhyme program the better. The earlier the stories are told the more tightly bound the emotional, junk food diet, physical image and behaviors of the Caucasian characters are imprinted on the mind. The more the stories are repeated the stronger the Caucasian cultural impression. The adult story teller's voice quality, inflection, voice tone, tension and facial expressions emotionally attach the child to the fairy tale so completely that they will mimic the story teller's voice tones used when expressing anger or talking about sex, joy, stealing, deceit and lies. The child will subliminally copy the fairy tale characters culture. The fairy tales become hard wired to the electrical circuit of the child's brain and any aggressive attempt to free the child from the Caucasian culture's ideals (cosmology) further bonds them to it. The fairy tales sell them emotional stocks in Caucasian culture that makes them bond to the Caucasian culture = livestock (slaves) in bondage (chains) = stocks and bonds. Fairy tale jingles, rhymes and songs are repeatedly hummed and sung by Black children, which makes a negative subconscious impression and gives the child an emotionally soothing cultural effect. Along with the effect, comes the Caucasian mindset. The child becomes possessed by the spirit of the themes of the stories and the characters. They become alienated from African culture and aliens. Aliens only serve aliens. The child is created into an Afropean (Black skin with a white culture's mind).

The Caucasian fairy tales and children's poems, songs and rhymes subliminally program the future adult behavior of the child. When the child matures, they become Black women that meet Black men who are either sex hunters, wolves (dogs), Prince Charmings, Peter Pan, men that think they possess magical words (good rappers), rapist (Frog Prince) men that allow themselves to be dominated (like the husband in Hansel and Gretel or Cinderella), homosexuals, and some men become homosexuals or drag queens that are wolves for other men. Conversely, Black men will meet Black women who are Cinderellas, that are looking for Prince Charmings, or the Princesses type (dress nicely), submissive (allow men to choose them = Goldilocks), woman who want to rescue the man from his childishness and raise the man (Little Red Riding Hood Syndrome), gold diggers types (marry men because they have a good job not because the man is a good person), or subconsciously choose to be a single female parent that has had a series of bad relationships that have left her with a series of abortions or children (Old Lady That Lives In A Shoe), etc.

The Caucasian fairy tale programmed Black adults will live a life that follows the fairy tale themes and characters. The unreal fairy tale story and their real life story become one and the same. They dress for sexual intercourse like fairy tale characters. The women may wear red (Little Red Riding Hood). This Caucasian culture's fairy tale cultural program emotionally influences their sexual positions and erotic sexually arousing areas of the body.

Fairy tales consistently show pictures of white sugary sweets, talk about sweets and use sweets to reward good behavior. The child is subconsciously programmed to associate white sugar with fun, happiness, family, sex and love. White sugar, candy, cookies, pies and cakes are in numerous stories such as Hansel and Gretel, Christmas, Halloween and Thanksgiving stories, the Ginger Bread Boy, etc. Sugar addiction is created by the stories. The only solution to Black folks having Fairy Tale

Syndrome is not to tell Caucasian fairy tales to Black children. The stories subliminally and emotionally will cause an aspect of the child's mind, behaviors, feelings and life to be dysfunctional. "Once Upon A Time" Black folks only told African stories to African children. Now, is the time to return back to that "Once Upon a Time" so that we can save our children in this time.

CHAPTER 13
HEALTHY BONDING

The way you bring up a child is the way it grows up.

Swahili proverb

HEALTHY BONDING

Bonding for the child is biochemical, hormonal, cultural and has a cyclic task like motion. An example of healthy bonding and good parenting protocols are as follows:

1. When talking to the child or listening to the child, be calm, hold (embrace) the child or look the child in the eyes and smile.
2. When you talk to the child, ask the child to listen.
3. Give the child instructions in action words. ("Put on your shoes, please," or "Let's go see the lion")
4. Then ask the child to repeat instructions with you. Saying instructions together assists bonding.
5. Model the task or perform the task with the child until they master it unsupervised.
6. Thank the child for his/her good actions.

In the bonding process, the thought process of a child causes them to see words as properties of a behavior, to a child words are a picture, words are a living actuality and words are abstract symbols. They understand that word and action are combined as one task and one motion. Thoughts are synonymous with action. This helps the child to conceptualize the bond of words with life. The child conceptualizes that words and action are one. In other words, learning and doing are one task.

The child's thought process should be used as the standard for communicating with and understanding the child. Their body goes through obvious changes. In some cases the legs, arms, torso, hands, feet, toes, fingers, nose, internal organs, ears, eyes and bone structure as well as emotions and intellect may grow out of proportion or sporadically or in synchronized harmony. Growth is physically while mental and spiritual development may not be apparent. However, emotional growth, spiritual growth, intellectual growth and physical growth influence the parent/child bond.

Mental, emotional and spiritual Africentric growth is not given importance by parents suffering from a Caucasian mis-education. Bonding is made dysfunctional by junk foods, the absence of breastfeeding poor parenting skills, absence of African culture, and a poor relationship between the mother and father. Junk foods cause nutritional restraints, which nutritionally limit the range of thoughts and behaviors. The bond restraining junk food diet makes the child's growth and development dysfunctional. The child's brain function is altered.

Junk food and cow's milk causes sub-clinical malnutrition and reduces the brain's ability to function. This makes the child dysfunctional.

BONDING REPAIR REMEDIES

Bond Damage is a dis-ease and, as such, it can be treated. The accumulation of damaged thoughts, words, behaviors, moods, spirituality, and parental relationship is imprinted in the emotions,subconscious and conscious personality. This personality distortion can be changed by a healing. A bonding-healing crisis has the signs and symptoms of a dis-ease. A dis-ease is the body's attempt to be well. Dis-ease is merely the spirit, mind and body's attempt to rid itself of a harmful toxin, such as a Bonding Disease. The healing crisis may cause the child to have anger towards the parents or parenting, or the child may reject African centered activities, they may withdraw from parent/child activities, or have episodes of confusion, emotional instability, or act lost or become disturbed during nurturing and parental loving behavior.

The bond damaged child must go through a redefinition of self, parents, culture, and spirit. The child has to become accustomed to new feelings and concepts. The following bond healing protocol will help to develop an acceptance of healing by the Bond-damaged parent, adult, family and/or child. Added to this, the Bond-damaged child or adult must learn to defend themselves from the constant reinforcement of Bond Damage that is built into their Europeanized social lifestyle, entertainment medias and male/female relationships. The bond damaged parent, child and affected individuals must be nurtured while they go through healing.

REMEDY AND PREVENTION LIST

- Ideally a bond damaged infant should be carried close to the naked breast whenever possible. Use a sling to carry the child. Do not use strollers.

- Do not bottle feed; Breast Feeding is a must.

- Do not use Caucasian culture's dolls, toys or games. Do not use cages such as playpens or cribs. (The Black child is made a prisoner by cribs and playpens. They emotionally cause the child to easily accept caged schools with metal detectors, iron bars at windows, jails and police patrols in the building.) They restrict thoughts, emotions and the crawling activity of the child.

- Do not use leashes or body harness to walk the child. (This is how animals or trained dogs are treated.)

- Use natural foods, vegetable milk substitutes and a vegetarian diet.

- Avoid Caucasian culturally focused nursery school, preschool, day care and other baby-sitting services until Bonding has been established. Use African culturally oriented services and people.

- Avoid hospital delivery. Use natural home birth. Do not sexually abuse the child by playing sexual and/or violent music, music videos, computer games, television programs or movies in the child's presence.

- Engage in storytelling. (Read African centered stories) Play cultural music, put African (includes African American) artwork and pictures in the home.

- No acts of physical, verbal or spiritual violence or cursing at the child or in the child's presence.

- Do not call the child bad, stupid, dumb, hardheaded, or a liar.

- Sing African songs to the child.

- Allow the family to bond with family activities. In some African cultures, after birth the bonding mother and child are alone for up to two weeks and during that period the mother is the only one allowed to handle the child. If the child is handled, it is by an adult, parent or child family member. Usually a female family member will assist the mother of a newborn. A family member, as well as the family, are essentials for the bonding remedy process.

The remedies and preventive measures chosen from the list vary according to whether the adult has European culturally centered family/friends or dysfunctional family/friends or is a single adult parent. The bond damage remedies can be used for children, prisoners, recovering addicts, teenagers, etc. They can be used one on one or in a group healing process or family healing process. It should be noted that burial of the dead according to African cultures' ceremonies and rituals helps the person see and feel the bonding imperative in their life. A Bond-Damaged Black child is dysfunctional and grows up to become a dysfunctional adult.

BONDING DISEASE SYMPTOMS

There are major and minor signs and symptoms of Bonding Disease. The following are a few generalized symptoms that can help identify the need for Bonding Remedies.

ACUTE BONDING DAMAGED DISEASE PERSON:

- mistakes ancestral spirits for dangerous ghosts
- is easily agitated about dressing in African clothing or hearing negative remarks about whites or lacks African cultural social skills
- has mood swings
- fails to complete cyclic task in time
- fails to have a working rhythm

SUB-ACUTE BOND DAMAGED DISEASE PERSON:

- has opposite sex relationship problems
- is under-reactive or has no emotional connection to African culture or Africentricity
- is under-reactive to White Racism
- all of Acute symptoms

CHRONIC BOND DAMAGED DISEASE PERSON:

- mixes African culture with Caucasian (celebrates White holidays and Kwanzaa)
- confuses spirituality with religion
- speaks excessively logical and concrete and does not use spiritual terms
- lacks improvisational skills
- straightens their hair and men cut their hair very short so kinks won't be apparent – this is called a neat haircut
- all of the Acute and Sub-acute symptoms
- they believe all races think alike
- they believe all races are the same

DEGENERATIVE BOND DAMAGED PERSON

- believes they are one with all races; excuses the Caucasian race's behavior

- lacks rhythm

- gets angry and upset when negative words are said about White folks or prefers to protest truthful statements about the White Supremacy behavior of White folks (defends White folks)
- dates White folks and socializes with them in preference to own race
- all of Acute, Sub-Acute, and Chronic symptoms

AFRICAN FAMILY RELATIONSHIP

The African family serves Maat. A few of the principles of Maat are: I shall not pollute myself with junk food and I will be balanced. Junk foods are synthetic and have chemicals that pollute the body and cause biochemical imbalance resulting in disease and death. The family that is free of disease is a viable technology. Everything in the African family focuses on Maat and transmits and translates culture.

ARE YOU NORMAL?

A normal child has been bonded with their culture and mother and their father fully participates in raising the child. When the child is not securely bonded to the parents and African centered culture, some area of their personality becomes dysfunctional. The incomplete or partially banded child has abnormal electrical activity in Frontal and/or Temporal area of the brain. An MRI (a type of x-ray) indicated that in the dysfunctional child the brain cells have altered (defective) electrical activity and the brain tends to be slightly smaller. An abandoned or spiritual, emotional, mental and physically abused and/or insecurely bonded child has abnormal electrical activity in the Hippocampus (long term memory, etc) area of the brain. The brain's Frontal Lobe (area) reacts when the unborn baby has been stressed or the pregnant woman is stressed (i.e., insecurely bonded) stress causes the child to have feelings of fear, distress, anxiety and social withdrawal behavior and a decrease in feelings of affection, feeling good, joy, etc. These emotions contribute to the child's personality and temperament. Emotions become dysfunctional to some degree when the child is not securely bonded or is raised by dysfunctional parents or raised in a negative social atmosphere or raised without its culture's rituals and ceremonies.

A parent will have a normal child when the laws of nature are followed. When nature's laws are violated in the child's life then a type of dysfunction will occur in some area of the child's emotional, social, mental, spiritual or sexual personality and/or physiology (i.e., biochemistry, hormones). A normal child grows up to become a normal adult and a normal parent. Are you normal?

A normal person's mother and father both ate organic food and they were breastfed. A normal person's parents said prayers to God before they had sexual intercourse and conceived a child. A normal parent is able to practice their culture at all times and in all situations. Normal parents and adults in African centered cultures went through a Rites of Passage to become an adult. A "Rites of Passage" is a study course (training) that a child must take before they are allowed to become an adult. Upon completing the training the child becomes an adult that parents all children in the village. The child finishes its Rites of Passage and becomes a father or mother to each child in the community. In other words, in African culture there are no teenagers – a child becomes an adult parent to each child in the community. Consequently, a normal adult sees each female as a mother and each male as a father. In Caucasian culture each female is first seen as a possible wife, girlfriend or sex item and then is seen as a mother. In African culture the female is seen first as a mother then as a possible wife or friend. Normal Black people are raised with African Maat rituals and ceremonies and parented by their mother, father, relatives, and village. They have a natural diet and they are breastfed.

A child raised on organic foods and breast milk is biochemically, hormonally balanced and well nourished. Malnourishment or an under nutrition junk (processed) food diet causes chronic fatigue, behavioral problems, attention deficit, behavioral problems, attention deficit, irritability, listlessness, mood swings, brittle nails, darkness under the eyes, dry skin, wax-like skin, skin disease, an abdomen that bulges, flabby muscles, underweight, overweight, laziness, round shoulders, finicky about food, defective teeth, poor eye sight, anemia, weak immunity, allergies, childhood diseases and/or lack of social, emotional and intellectual development.

A normal child's brain is stimulated and they develop to be normal adults. However, a child's brain cells do not grow adequately when the child is constantly restricted in social activities. Decreased brain stimulation occurs when the child is constantly told "no", "stop", "don't do that", "shut up", "keep still" or when the child is left alone in a playpen. Loud music, noise and/or television increase social problems and decrease the child's language skills. The child's toys and books should not be limited or restricted to the same toys and books because this under stimulates the brain. Toys and books should be rotated and/or traded periodically with other parents. Aside from this, the child can be made dysfunctional before it is born.

The unborn child can develop dysfunction when the pregnant woman is stressed. The stress can be social, emotional, a disease, spiritual, under nutrition (i.e., junk food), sexual intercourse, mental and/or a relationship. Stress causes the sympathetic nervous system to respond by using hormones to help the mother fight the stress (i.e, epinepherine) or run away from the stress (norepinepherine). The sympathetic nervous system hormones cause reduced blood (i.e., nutrients, air) to the digestive, reproductive and immune systems. Reduced blood (air, nutrients) to the reproductive system (i.e., uterus, prostate) makes it weak and prone to disease. The stressed unborn child reacts by activating its sympathetic nervous system and this decreases nutrients to its digestive, immune and reproductive systems. This causes the child to have eczema, psoriasis, respiratory problems, ulcers, pancreas (diabetes) and liver problems, ear infections, childhood diseases, neonatal death, Sudden Infant Death Syndrome, low birth weight, stomach problems, heart problems and can result in the mother having a premature birth and/or miscarriages. A stressed unborn child will have emotional, mental and social problems or some type of dysfunction when it is born.

A dysfunctional child will have abnormal mental, emotional, spiritual, social, relationship and sexual problems. Dysfunction can be caused by poor quality sperm and eggs. A stressed female or male adult have reduced nourishment (blood, air, etc.) to the reproductive system (eggs and sperm). This deprives the sperm and egg of vital nutrients resulting in a dysfunctional child being born.

A stressed pregnant woman can cause an unborn girl's brain to be inadequately feminized and the unborn boy's brain will be inadequately masculinized. A section of the brain called the hypothalamus is responsible for manhood, fatherhood and maleness as well as womanhood, motherhood and femaleness. In boys a small region near the front of the hypothalamus has twice as many nerves as girls. Unborn boys around the fourth month or second trimester have a rise in testosterone sex hormone. This testosterone surge of sex hormone helps to stimulate the region of the hypothalamus with extra nerves and masculinizes the boy's brain. In girls the region is not stimulated by testosterone and their brain remains feminized. An abnormal (dysfunctional) child is created when the mother is stressed. Stressors cause the mother to have a sympathetic nervous system reaction (i.e., adrenaline – fight hormone for a crisis or noradrenaline hormone makes you run away from a crisis) which interferes with the natural feminization or masculinization of the unborn child. This can result in gender confusion, tomboyish girls, bisexual and/or homosexual tendencies, androgen insensitivity syndrome in boys (girlish boys), or some type of sexual problems or dysfunction.

A normal child is birthed using the natural birth rituals and ceremonies of their culture. This means the pregnant woman was in a squatting position when delivering the child. If the pregnant woman delivered the baby on her back or her legs were in stirrups then the child did not get adequate blood to the brain. A normal child is born in the presence of friends and/or relatives of the parents. Friends and/or relatives and midwives would have sang, said prayers, danced, play drums, recited poems or gave the mother and child a cleansing bath. The relatives and friends give emotional, spiritual and physical support to the mother before, during and after the birth. The holistic support could be done in an informal or formal ritual. Their nurturing support reinforces Maat and transmits cultural values and norms to the child.

The child's intelligence is decreased and dysfunctions will develop if the pregnant woman gains over 30 pounds or does not gain at least 20 pounds (the size and bone structure of women determines weight gain). The birth order can affect a child's intelligence. The first born child can have an Intelligence Quotient (IQ) from 1/2 to 3 points higher than children born later because more bonding time is usually spent with the first born. The space between pregnancies affects the IQ. Children that are born between 2 to 4 years apart tend to have a higher IQ than children born one year or less than two years apart. This birth space allows the mother to adequately breastfeed a child, limits the number of children she births, acts as a natural birth control and allows the mother's body time to regenerate. A normal mother does not have sex while pregnant or breastfeeding because it alters the nutrient level and hormones of the breast milk and alters the normal hormone balance of the child. If she does it results in a type of dysfunction in the child and affects the child's IQ. If the natural laws are not obeyed the child pays for it with lower intelligence.

If laws of nature are not obeyed then a child will be abnormal. The question is – Are You Normal? If your parents did not follow an ethnocentric, natural foods diet, were not breastfed for 2 to 4 years, did not use African Centered sex rituals and ceremonies and were not African culturally centered, then you have some type of dysfunction. This is the price nature makes the child pay for parents disobeying the natural rules. If you are now on a holistic diet and African centered you still had to pay the emotional, spiritual and mental price for disobedience to nature's rules. Nature does not forgive or forget. For example, if you eat junk food and get a tooth cavity, nature will not take away the cavity because you are currently eating organic raw foods. An oppressed people are made dysfunctional. Oppression means your normal behavior is made abnormal. Black folks are oppressed and suffer from white supremacy. The challenge for dysfunctional (i.e., oppressed) Black Folks is to learn how to function holistically healthy despite their dysfunction. The challenge is to raise children to be the technology to solve the problems of oppression and white supremacy.

BIRTHING

Bonding is interrupted by the birth techniques of Caucasians. Labor is induced by synthetic drugs causing the contraction to be out of rhythm and violently forceful. This results in too much pressure on the child's head. This increased pressure decreases the air, blood and nutrient supply to the child's brain. The skull is squeezed together too hard causing the bones to collide resulting in a fluid-filled bruise on the top of the head. Drugs (prescriptions or illegal or over the counter) can cause bone malformation and the bones to collide together. This can result in dimples in the chin or improper growth such as cleft tongues and lips or dimples in the ear or knock knees.

Hospital deliveries use a pair of pliers (forceps) to clamp and squeeze the head so they can pull the baby out of the womb. This decreases the air, blood and nutrient supply to the brain. Hospitals use a vacuum pump, which they clamp on the baby's head so they can forcefully suction the baby out of womb. This drains rhythm, electromagnetic energy and nutrients out of the brain and can stop nutrients from getting to the brain. Forceps and vacuum suction are a shock to the baby, which is beyond any criminal assault and battery. The typical hospital birth with drugs, forceps and vacuum suction when classified according to the United Nations Human Rights Charter's definition is an assault and battery that mains, mutilates, and harms the child spiritually, physically, emotionally and mentally.

Hospital births interrupt the proper rhythmic biochemical rites of passage of the child by cutting the umbilical cord before it stops pulsating. This deprives the baby of air, nutrients, and blood and shocks the baby's entire system. Often, in the typical hospital birth they will turn the baby upside down and slap the baby's behind for no other reason than to follow a primitive Caucasian ritual based superstition. This should only be done in an extreme emergency. A junk food diet and/or drugs cause the amniotic fluid to be full of mucus and cellular waste instead of healthy, nourishing amniotic fluid which is a light weight clear liquid. The diseased amniotic fluid of today's mother is thick, has an offensive odor, and is sticky. This is caused by synthetic junk foods, drugs and constipation. This unhealthy amniotic fluid slime is what babies are forced to live in while in the womb instead of the natural electromagnetic melaninated amniotic fluid. The newborn baby may have a white rancid crusty sticky slime over the face caused by the man ejaculating into the uterus during the woman's pregnancy. Sex, during pregnancy is erroneously promoted by Caucasian medical science as being ideal for couples and the baby. The total of poor prenatal nutrition, sex during pregnancy, ignorant superstitious medical techniques, birthing violence, and the junk food diet harms the child forever. Added to this, proper natural bonding does not occur between mother and child. The newborn baby should be placed on the mother's breast after being born to stimulate bonding and placenta release. Bonding for the baby, mother and father starts before conception and prenatal growth. The placing of the baby on the mother's stomach near the breast is an extension of bonding.

STARCH AND CHILDREN

African infants, babies and children under 2 or 3 years of age cannot eat starches. Carbohydrates (starches) such as wheat, corn, rice and oat breakfast cereals cannot be digested by the child. The breakfast jelly sandwiches called pop tarts and breakfast candy bars are illogical food combinations and indigestible. Refined carbohydrates such as a white sugar, candy, cake, potato chips, pizzas, jelly sandwiches, waffles and pancakes with syrup, pretzels and teething biscuits should not be given to the child. The child does not have the enzyme (ptyalin) that allows starches to be eaten. Starches eaten by children become a type of liquid mucus manure slime that floats in the blood resulting in childhood diseases. When a child eats starches the immune system gets weak and the kidney, liver, pineal, adrenals and spleen get exhausted. Breakfast cereals (starches) are usually combined totally improperly, so if they could be digested it could not occur. Starches should not be combined with goat or cow's milk, or fruits and/or refined sugar because they cause starches to ferment and spoil. Improperly combined starches are absorbed in the intestine and create toxins, gases and an acidic body. Fruit and cereals combined and eaten in the same meal cause toxins and a biochemistry that weakens all cells, tissues, organs and bones. Animal milks should not be combined with fruits or sugar or starch. This combination causes toxins and an acidic biochemistry that deteriorates the heart, bones, tissues and organs. Starches can only be combined with green vegetables or a vegetable milk such as almond, rice, soya, oat, spelt, or sesame milks. Bread should not be combined with jelly or grease (butter) and other constipating combinations such as wheat, milk, eggs and grease. Bacon (pig's ass) and eggs (chicken fetus) should not be combined. Eggs combined with bacon or drank with a glass of mucus-forming cooked, plastic pus called cow's milk should only be eaten with a protein such as eggs. Protein should be eaten between 10 am and 2 pm when they are easily metabolized. Starch protein cereals in the morning are extremely taxing on the digestive system of the body. Cooked starches require fermentation in the intestines and should be eaten alone or with vegetables. Breakfast should be of cleansing fruits. Ideally food should be eaten between the hours of 12 noon and 7 pm, as this is the ingestion cyclic phase of the body's rhythm. The food is utilized by the body (assimilated) between the hours of 7 pm and 4 am. Digested food is ideally cleansed from the body from 4 am to 12 noon. Therefore, breakfast should be cleansing fruits. Starches should not be eaten until the child has developed a full set of teeth and is capable of fully chewing and mixing the food with saliva. The junk food breakfast and wrong food combinations contribute to eating disorders (food addiction mental illness).

Caucasians stuff their babies as if the Ice Age is still going to freeze the food supply. They force their babies to eat as often as possible or every two hours and in between meals or suck on an amputated breast's rubber nipple (pacifier). Sucking on a milk-less, amputated nipple (pacifier) is subconsciously and emotionally negative. The babies try to reject the overfeeding of food by drooling, vomiting, burping, having hiccups, diarrhea, stomach gas and childhood diseases. Finally, the babies that are overfed become bloated with fat. Fat babies resemble any of McDonald's or Burger King's or Wendy's or Huddle House's fat pigs or fat cows that they buy for sandwich meat. Fat babies like fat pigs are only fit to be led to a feeding trough and slaughtered so their fat can be used to fill a can of lard to use to fry burgers. Babies are forced to be overfed by well meaning nutritionally ignorant parents.

The Caucasian Eating Disorder (mental illness) with food becomes another means for the dairy, junk food, drug and medical industries to make large profits. The industries create food addiction and use the "break-fast" to reinforce the eating disorders. The junk food and snack food industries create a stable profitable food addicted consumer. Children are trained food addicts that are experimental laboratory animals that eat junk food garbage and their food addiction makes them beg for more. The Black child is the only experimental animal specimen that buys their own food. They are paying for their own nutritional suicide with a rotten tooth smile on their faces.

The Black child eats an under-nutritious junk food breakfast. Their diseased body is used for drug chemicals and surgical medical sacrifices. If breakfast cereal is not available to destroy them, then the destructive jelly (or syrup) sandwiches in the form of bread, waffles, pancakes, or pop tarts are eaten. It is a hypoglycemic mucus forming breakfast that degenerates health. It causes obesity and a sudden energy drop while in school called Attention Deficit. This energy drop causes the child to feel bored or disinterested in schoolwork. The sugary breakfast sets the child up to have trouble with school work, fail and/or dislike school. The white sugar energy collapses in the morning hours of school resulting in low energy, fatigue, depression, inability to concentrate and learning problems. The child becomes overweight from eating junk foods. An obese child is a sign of a diseased spirit, mind and body. An infant or young child that constantly eats becomes fat and bloated. The fat gets into the digestive system and builds up plaque in the cells, tissues, organs, glands and brain. A fat baby is a sick baby. A natural whole foods diet, vegetable milks and breast milk are the only defense against fat bloat and childhood diseases. Breast milk regulates feeding intervals and is biochemically balanced, is spiritual, cyclic and has the electromagnetic charge of melanin. Denying the Black child the melanin stimulating milk is denying the child the gift of Blackness (Africanity). When a Black child is given a bottle of white milk instead of breast milk there is the negative psychological imprint. This subconsciously causes the Black baby to associate the color white with nurturing, affection and love. When the baby gets ill it is taken to a hospital where all the medical supplies are wrapped in white and the doctor wears a white laboratory jacket. The Black baby associates being helped, saved and rescued with the White race. The Black baby associates normal and health with the White race. The custom of fattening the child and feeding them breakfast cereal concoctions along with denying the child breast milk presents a bonding, nutritional and mental illness problem. When babies are not breastfed they begin to be mentally or emotionally dysfunctional and feel that nature denied them milk and that nature cannot be trusted to nurture and love them. This stems from the complete interruption of the breastfeeding "rights of passage" and the natural bonding process of mother and child.

Parents should fit the child to the food instead of fitting the food to the child. In other words, it is not proper to put sugar, fruit and milk on a cereal in order to get a child to eat it. Feed the child simple food combinations. It is not correct for the parents to let children eat (past 7 pm) at night, or when the child is overheated, feels bad, is tired, stressed, excited, chilled, upset, in pain or is angry. Help the child work through negative emotions or to relax so that the food will get digested properly.

The cereals are usually not chewed but swallowed, and this ultimately causes disease. Stuffing the child with cereal, milk, sugar as if it is a turkey or pig can lead to flu, tonsillitis, colds, learning problems, gastritis, personality problems, mood swings, hypertension and a melanin deficiency. The majority of childhood diseases can be treated with herbs and supplements.

The childhood diseases are the body's attempt to be well (healthy). Childhood diseases are not the illness, they are a reaction to an illness. For example, **Chicken pox** is toxins released through the skin with pimples that ooze fluid and form a crust in 3-to7-day cycle. The child's fingernails should be cut, as the skin is very itchy. **Measles** is a cleansing through the lungs and skin. Usually the child has bumps, a furry tongue, white spots in the mouth and throat and is sensitive to light. **Mumps** are usually swollen parotid lymph glands in the back of the jaw between the ears. The Lymph glands swell with mucus from toxic acidic, over-cooked food and impurities. The glands swell with toxins in an attempt to defend the child from the mucus waste. It can be contagious 48 hours before the swelling and up to 6 days after. **Tonsillitis** is the inflammation of the tonsils caused by constipating food combinations and cereals. The tonsils get sore, swell and there may be an earache, coated tongue and bad breath. **Rheumatic Fever** is an arthritis type condition of the heart caused by crystallized waste and liquid manure mucus. **Flu (influenza)** is similar to the mucus congestion called a "cold." It is characterized by a dry cough and dry throat. The body tries to defend itself by putting the mucus waste into the lungs and nasal cavities and then coughing to loosen it and then spitting it out. **Asthma** is a type of muscle spasm in the lungs that can be caused by waste in the body and muscles. The muscles around the lungs tighten the chest, which results in wheezing, coughing and difficulty breathing. It is believed you get energy from breakfast. This is a physiological impossibility; as it takes 3 hours for food to leave the stomach and another 4 hours for the food energy to be processed in the intestines. The false sense of energy is caused by the stimulating effect of the sugar. The energy stored (glycogen) in the liver sustains bodily functions, not the high-energy from sugar. It is assumed the body gets energy at the hour of breakfast. If the constipating junk food diet is eaten, then the energy from irritating food toxins eaten 1 to 7 days previous to breakfast is the energy felt at breakfast. In this case, the child is using liquid manure (constipation), synthetic chemicals, sugar, hormones and steroids in junk foods, drugs and toxins for energy. The starchy constipating cereal breakfast concoctions cause disease and the body's attempt to fight the disease is mistakenly called breakfast energy.

The food eaten requires energy to be utilized and this energy is diverted from other organs, organ systems and immunity so that an increase of blood can go to the stomach in order to transport nutrients and process the food. Often the child will have energy and then feel sleepy or fatigued after eating stimulants such as sugar, dairy, starches, caffeine, condiments, sex hormones, steroids, bleached white flour, etc. Spicy condiments, irritants such as mustard, pepper, chocolate, nutmeg, cinnamon are stimulants used to overcome the energy drain of a breakfast or meal of sugars, lard, grease, dairy, meat, hormones, steroids, white flour, synthetic toxic chemicals, refined carbohydrates, etc.

A child addicted to junk food breakfasts will have degenerative diseases such as arthritis, cardiovascular problems, varicose veins, weak eyes, fertility problems, senility, weak bones, learning disorders, mood swings, cancer, AIDS, venereal diseases, etc. Added to this, the child rushes to eat, does not chew the food properly and erroneously drinks and eats simultaneously. Breakfast should be of whole foods, spring or distilled water and/or cleansing fruit, or fruit drank one hour before or after the meal. The meal should be eaten in a calm unhurried state, without talking.

Fasting at night while asleep and melatonin secretion helps to create the morning energy felt, not "breaking the fast" so-called "break-fast." The body gets accustomed to food weight in the stomach and small intestines and the weight of impacted manure in the colon. An absence of food weight and the sensation of impacted food and manure causes the child to feel the need to eat. In other words, the child mistakens constipation for energy. It is not true instinct hunger but the absence of constipation and sugar addiction that creates a craving for the starchy breakfast. The energy from food eaten at a 9 am breakfast will not be nutritionally available to the body until 3 pm. If the child eats late at night the body's circadian clock is in the assimilation/melatonin phase. The pace of assimilation is slow at night. The body will be constipated and store much of the energy and will not completely use the energy from breakfast until the next day.

GROWTH AND DEVELOPMENT THROUGH A CHILD'S EYES

The Black child's spirit, mind and body's growth and development have noticeable changes at different ages. If these changes at different ages are interpreted and defined by adult logic then it causes a negative effect upon truly helping to bond with the child. The child has to be accepted on its own terms, in its own language and logic and by its own holistic feelings. Children do not conceptualize or feel abrupt changes at each stage of holistic growth and development because nature has had over a billion years to smoothly perfect the continuous transitions of growth. Abrupt growth spurts in anatomy, spirit or mind are usually caused by junk food diets, hormone imbalances, vaccinations, physical traumas, disease, drugs and/or damaged Bonding between Parent and Child.

The child comes from a spirit world where energy is energy and can freely transform into different forms. For example, the chromosome of the male is Y and is carried to the uterus upon ejaculating sperm, which fertilizes the egg in the fallopian tube. The chromosome of the woman is X. If the XY chromosomes unite, a boy will be conceived. If the XX chromosomes unite, a girl is conceived. However, these chromosomes are simply energy and do not possess a gender or sexuality of their own.

In about 6 to 8 weeks during fetal life, the XY chromosome can change to an XX pair. In other words, the slow moving, long living Y chromosome with a missing leg grows another leg and becomes an X chromosome. A change of this sort causes the girl to be born with emotional and mental imbalances and to have sexual confusion (not homosexuality).

Energy is energy and free to transform. The child comes from an undifferentiated energy state called spirit (egg). Consequently, the child's spirit must adjust to a differentiated world, a world where energy is concrete and fixed in a state of existence. For example, an apple (energy) is an apple and different from a grape. The child tends to touch, hear, smell, taste and see objects, events and people in a concrete (unchangeable) manner. The child understands that the doctor's bill is simply a doctor whose name is Bill. This is concrete thinking. An adult understands the doctor bill to mean a financial charge for services. This is abstract thinking. Once the child has fixed or associates a concrete property to an object, event or person, it then can abstract (change) it. Then after the child makes changes and variations (improvises), it can conceptualize and fit it into its vocabulary. The child identifies and conceptualizes all things that enter its mind. This allows the child to see activities, tasks or an event in time (rhythm) rather than on time (non-rhythm). The African child performs tasks in time (in rhythm) while the adult may come to social events in time (non-rhythm). This is negatively called "Colored People" (C.P.) time. Time (in time) is the movement of the spirit, mind and body while "on time" is the movement of the body only.

The black child's mind is spiritual, physical and mental and a product of culture. The brain is a physical structure that operates with water, magnetic, hormonal, chemical and electrical energy. It has electromagnetic melanin centers (clusters), acupuncture points and is melanin saturated within all its cells. The brain's ventricles (open spaces) are filled with fluid that is continuously moving. It is electromagnetic cerebral spinal fluid (holy waters).

The brain has a force field that physically resembles a galaxy (sometimes called the Third Eye = Heru). This galaxy looks like a cloud and hovers (floats) above the pineal gland and hypothalamus in the third ventricle. Historically, the ancient Africans called the fluid-filled ventricles "holy waters" to denote their spirituality. The brain stem's 12 melanin centers have properties similar to the 12 signs of the zodiac. Information, ideas, data and energy are processed through the brain and translated by the mind. The mind is electromagnetic and a physical object. When the mind needs past, present or future information, it gets it from melanin and processes it through the water, neurotransmitters, magnetic and electrical reactions of brain cells and calls it intelligence. Melanin bonds all Black Folks in the seen and unseen worlds. They are genetically bonded to ancestors and unborn children, and aware of the slightest changes in the present and future of the galaxy, plants, waters, earth, animals, weather and climates. Africans are spiritualized and are united with the Earth's intelligence (Mother Nature).

Melanin allows the child's spirit, body and mind to be in unity and harmoniously synchronized. The Black child should have parents that are African centered and have a whole foods diet and had been breastfed and bonded with their parents. If this is not possible, then the child must have parents who have taken Bonding Remedies. Bonding would help to eliminate dysfunction and confusion on how and why the mind functions. Melanin makes the brain one functioning unit. There is no split in the brain, only areas that may have specialized functions. For example, the human eyes have a specialized function (sight) but are not split or separate from the body. Without the body the eyes have no purpose. The mind sees, while he eyes merely absorb visual stimulation.

The mind is one. There is only consciousness. In Caucasian culture the mind is based upon an unloved, abandoned, Greek fairytale child called

Oedipus and the mind is fragmented into small parts called id, ego, superego, subconscious, pre-conscious, super-conscious and unconscious. The Black mind is not divided and it has functions that are communal like a family of relatives, it is melaninated, cyclic and rhythmic. It takes rhythm to understand and operate the Black mind. It is a total mistake to refer to or rely upon Caucasian psychology. Caucasian psychology transmits and translates Caucasian culture. Blacks that use Caucasian psychology are bond damaged, dysfunctional and de-Africanized.

The Black child's spiritualized thinking does not depend on memory or the content of ideas. The mind has its own thought, growth and development. It is a synchronized unit with the emotions, spirit, feelings, ideas, dreams, and ancestral thoughts. A Bonded Black child's growth and development schedule is ignored and the Caucasian child's standards for growth and development have been forced upon the Black child. This has caused the child to be dysfunctional, bond damaged, de-Africanized and holistically retarded.

Black folks must follow their ethno-medical standard of growth and development in order to create an African centered child. The Black child is a technology and a change agent for Black people. The Black child should not compromise freedom or African centered learning. Learning is a cyclic process. There are basically three "progressions to learning." The first stage: a new idea is introduced to the child. The child translates the idea from adult logic to children's logic. During the second stage: the new idea is experimentally learned. In the third stage the child transposes an idea and treats the idea as if it were a toy and uses variations on the new idea either in play or in fantasy (improvises). The child uses its own language to coordinate, define and redefine a new idea similar to the use of sight to coordinate the senses. The child sees all of life as a symbolic property of energy. All of the child's use of symbolism is merged with self, spirit, the concrete word, fantasy, play and the Parents' bond. It is important to remember that words are symbols, just as letters, music, dance, fantasy, play and Bonding are symbols of energy that the senses detect. The holistic mind interprets energy for the child.

An adult or child that is dysfunctional because of a damaged Bond can be in the acute, sub-acute, chronic or degenerative stages of Bonding Disease. The essential way to understand Bonding and Bonding disease is through a child's eye. It is the child's world as seen by the child that causes the child to understand an adult world. The child's holistic "vision" advances to "supervision." Children must be respected as little "people" not little "children." For example, a child given the freedom to eat any type of natural food will nutritionally balance their diet within a week. A dysfunctional adult needs to read cultural books and read ethnonutrition (race specific) books in order to eat a nutritionally balanced diet. A child forced to see the world with adult abstracts and adult intellectual concepts will eat themselves into poor health and disease. The Black child has the all-seeing and all-knowing Eye of Heru within them. The adult has to use African-centered parenting skills in order to have a healthy Parent and Child Bond.

COMPUTER TRAINED DOGS = AFRICAN CHILDREN

The African child watches excessive amounts of European culturally focused television and plays computer games for entertainment. However, the mental and emotional effect of these activities are dangerous. It may be that the computer games are subconsciously playing (conditioning) the child instead of the child playing the games. The games play the child (social engineer, Europeanize).

The computer games' synthetic action sounds and synthetic music sounds are associated with violence, sex, food and the Caucasian culture and thinking processes. It has been proven by Caucasian physiologist, Ivan Petrovich Pavlov (1849-1936) that the repeated ringing of a bell while giving a dog food will cause the dog to salivate and associate food with the bell. Eventually when Pavlov rang the bell and did not give the dog food, the dog would salivate. The conditioning of the dog with the bell will enable him to get any type of behavior he desired from the dog. People can be conditioned to get desired behavior . Therefore, computer sounds can condition the child and enable you to get desired mental and physical behaviors (program the child). Pavlov, in his later experiments, used his technique to condition people. Therefore, the synthetic sounds and pictures of the computer games and programs can cause dysfunctional thoughts, feelings, emotions and physical behaviors, violence, sex, desire for Caucasian culture and/or junk food, and train the child to use Caucasian linear logic.

The computer's linear logic computer conditions the African child to think like a Caucasian. Eventually, the African child will hear the synthetic sounds of musical instruments, synthetic action sounds, and associate it with violence, sex, people and food. The child will apply Caucasian culture's values, thinking and behaviors to Black people. The

Caucasian cultural themes and racism are a part of computer programs and games (music videos and television). The games have Caucasian rituals, superstitions, group sex, ceremonies, social customs and culture.

The computer logic trains the Black child and adult to view life in terms of inferior versus superior, rule or ruin, win/lose, crime/police, war/peace, "African, poor, powerless" White, rich, powerful", kill or be killed, live/die, violence wins/peace loses, master/slave, bad guy/good guy, White is beautiful/Black is ugly, etc. In this one-dimensional linear thought process, the child's feelings get mixed-up inappropriately. Dysfunctional thoughts combine feelings together inappropriately. For example, sex, violence, junk food, conflict, love or harmony are mixed together as one feeling. In other words, the normal feeling of love may cause a feeling of violence or a violent reaction or a feeling of love can be mixed with anger and result in conflict. This is the primary reason why Blacks that act lovingly or non-violently towards White folks get a reaction of conflict and violence. The Caucasian has mixed lie and truth, love and violence together as a material thing, a material thing to use to control and manipulate.

This same diseased psychosis is programmed; in computer logic, put in computer games, and in synthetic computer action sounds. Ironically, the Black musicians use synthetic sounds in their music but use a Maat cultural approach of harmony. Synthetic sounds do not resemble any sound in nature. A computerized synthetic sound is used to alienate the person from themselves (psychological divides the personality). Synthetic sounds train the ear to make an association with violence, junk food, sex, and cause physical reflex behaviors. The natural sounds of non-electric instruments associated with African culture become alien, unpleasant, unreal and dysfunctional.

Computer games, music videos, movies, cartoons and television programs are used to entertain, to escape financial, emotional, spiritual, mental or physical problems. However, they cause Black folks to escape African culture. Music videos and computer games cause difficulty in relating to others, boredom, irritability, mood swings, personality problems and dysfunction. They drain energy from the African American community. The energy spent on computer games, surfing the Web, chat rooms, e-mail and music videos could be used to do positive things for the Black family, community. Instead, the energy is spent on mindless, repetitive computer beat up and attack games.

The learning process used for instructional computer programs and entertainment games is the same learning method used in schools. School learning requires the child to repeat information over and over until it is memorized. Learning by repetition is call "rote" learning. Rote learning is based upon the research done to teach rats, pigeons and monkeys. It was made popular in 1922 by Edward Thorndike. Rote learning does not teach understanding, it teaches what to think, not how to think. Children that learn by "rote" have problems thinking logically. They become adults that have problems understanding ideas and tend to cling to immature behaviors and emotions. Rote learners mimic words and numbers like a parrot. The child trained with "rote" does not understand that written words and written numbers (symbols) are not reality. For example, written musical notes are not sounds of music. Words and numbers are abstract symbols that represent reality (life). In other words, nature is living words and numerosities (i.e., arithmetic, mathematics). Symbols (words, numbers) are an attempt to explain life and nature.

The "rote" learning method used by computer games and instructional aides was proven to be a way to dumb people. In 1928 William Brownell's book The Development of Children's Numbers Ideas in Primary Grades proved the stupidity of rote. Computers train children to learn like rats (rote) and behave like dogs (Pavlov and B.F. Skinner behavior conditioning systems).

Learning in order to be relevant and effective has to use the child's cultural heritage. Learning requires the wisdom of the culture's ancestors. The ancestors developed techniques, ideas, language games, number games (board games), songs and stories (contain logic and reasoning) that are part of the child's cultural heritage. The child's cultural heritage contains knowledge that helps them to use language and mathematics in meaningful and familiar situations. This is called "street knowledge (situational learning)" while school knowledge is called "Formal Learning". When a child is allowed to use their culture (i.e., street knowledge) in the classroom, the school learning becomes easy to understand and apply. However, the schools and computers' "rote" learning techniques separate the child from their cultural heritage. In school the class work is the "slave master", the teacher is "the overseer" and child is the "seasonin slave" that memorizes and performs academic task.

Computer learning aides control, thought, reasoning, and limits and restricts knowledge. For example, when the Encyclopedia Britannica was put on CD-ROM approximately 30% of the information was omitted so that the encyclopedia could fit into the CD-ROM format. The elimination of the information was done according to the bias and cultural norm values of the Caucasian editors. This means thoughts were censored and omitted. Therefore, parents have to add African centered information to the computer learning process. When the parent does not include culture in the learning process, their child becomes a dog with a white (culture) bone that thinks like a rat (rote).

Clinically depressed children view more music videos, television programs, eat more junk food, and are the most overweight and undernourished. The children have a melanin deficiency. Black children watch 25 hours more television than white children and spend more time with computer games. The computer games, music videos, and television programs are used to escape oppression and the side effects of racism. Unfortunately, they cause the same problems. This makes being an African child twice as painful and dysfunctional. This makes the child more prone to disease and more undernourished than the white child. The National Institute of Mental Health conducted a 13-year study using 1,200 people. The study validated the many mental, emotional and behavioral problems caused by excessive television viewing. It was found that viewing television causes reduced social ability, poor ability to interact and negative moods. This has been revealed in the book Television and the Quality of Life: How Viewing Shapes Everyday Experiences, by Lawrence Earlbaum Associates. Computer games are basically structured similar to the arcade games of the 18th century. Black children become addicted to computer games and the Caucasian culture's behaviors, dysfunctionality and cosmology (worldview). The child's skin identifies them as Africans while their mind, moods, personality, self-centeredness, behavior and thinking process are totally Caucasian. The games can help in problem solving of space and movement, sequence in logic, but are carriers of Caucasian cultural values, thinking, and dysfunctionality. The child becomes devoted to fantasy, solo-play and develops an unreal idea of their competence. The child's competence is based upon winning against a computer opponent.

The child develops competitive behavior instead of the communal, family-centered thinking and cooperative sharing of knowledge of African culture and resources. Selfishness is rewarded by a selfish, competitive way of life. In the real world, the Black child loses the holistic African centered ability to interact with real Black people, African cultural artifacts, cosmology and objects. The child gains a low tolerance of human failure, rejection and compromise. The Black child (and computer games-addicted adult) have increased aggressive behavior. They are conditioned to associate synthetic action sounds and visual image with real life and real people. The child uses mindless amusement as fun. This increases the potential for doing mindless activities for excitement. The child fully develops the Caucasian mental illness that mixes lies with truth, violence with sex or love. Caucasian thoughts cultivate a need to ruin or destroy others. In books such as Playing with Power in Movies, Television and Video, by Marsha Kinder, it is estimated that well over 1 out of 3 African American children own computerized games and play the games.

The Black child that uses computer games and watches music videos loses responsiveness to Maat, African culture and the natural cycles of nature, subtle weather changes, natural sunlight variations, slight changes in the taste of natural foods as well as changes in other people, parents, music, moods and thoughts. Black children become dysfunctional and react only to mindless synthetic sounds. The sound of rivers, the wind, African music, African drum rhythm (language), and wild life become meaningless and unreal. Electronic sounds become real.

The result of computers and computer games is that children do not emotionally get attached to African culture. They become attached to the Caucasian culture. The Caucasian behaviors of violence, sex and destruction are copied by the computer games. The games are playing them--conditioning the child playing them. The child becomes alienated from African family centeredness, Cultural Virtues, African natural diets, African centered thinking and themselves. Black adults, teenagers and children are thinking like rats (rote learners) and behave like Pavlov's dog that associates computer logic and sounds with Caucasian culture. They are becoming computer-trained rats and dogs that behave like African humanoids. African humanoids are computer -generated slaves that serve Caucasian culture and civilization. They are computerized slaves.

WAKE UP, EAT BREAKFAST AND DIE

Refined carbohydrates (cereals, bleached white flour, etc.) cause over consumption of starches. Starches are isolated and separated from the vitamins, minerals, moisture and the fiber of whole grains during refinement. Unrefined whole grain carbohydrates (cereals) have fiber, which is filling and limits the amount of starch consumed. Excess starch turns into fatty acids and is stored as ascetic acid (vinegar), lactic acid (fermented sugar), and cholesterol. These types of fats cause the body to be acidic. Acid causes the veins, arteries, bones, nerves and muscles to deteriorate, weaken and rust (oxidize). These acidic fats, especially cholesterol will stick together (coagulate, clot) and clog or block veins, arteries, thicken the blood with waste and fatten the heart. These fats can block arteries causing senility, strokes, heart attacks, poor vision and hearing and they can result in amputation of feet and legs. Excessive starch causes unstable moods and emotional problems as well as fatigue, memory problems and sluggishness. A diet high in refined starches (grains, cereals, flour) can cause kidney stones. The stones can cause kidney malfunction and kidney failure. Aside from this, processed cereals can cause yeast infection. The processed starch of cereals and grains can cause diabetes and the excess fats that they create can cause diabetes.

HEALTH FOOD AND SCHOOL CHILDREN

The junk food diet has replaced the natural whole foods diet with cosmetic foods that look and taste like food but are synthetic foods (non-food = Pica) that are nutritionally valueless (junk food). This junk food is processed "food"' that is dyed, saturated with sex hormones and steroids, bleached, salted and sugared. White sugar and concentrated sweeteners harm the pancreas, while artificial sweeteners harm the liver. Feeding the child under-nutritional synthetic non-food (Pica) depraves the brain of the nutrients it needs to function normally. An undernourished brain causes learning problems, depression, violence and fatigue. A child that consumes large amounts of white sugar and concentrated sweeteners develops irritability, schizophrenia, uncontrolled emotional explosions, confusion and addiction. The consumption of Pica such as table salt or sea salt causes waste to stay in the body, hardens arteries and veins and causes kidney stress, high blood pressure, depression and mood swings. Junk "foods" are low in vitamins, which can cause paranoia, suicide, mood swings and personality problems. Junk (processed) foods are non-food Pica make the child dysfunctional. Children that eat natural whole foods do not have mental, emotional and behavioral problems. There have been studies that verify this.

In New York City, a ten-year study was conducted on 803,000 children (over 60% Black) by the University of California, at Berkeley, School of Nutrition. This research was presented at The International Conference on Nutrient Brain Functions hosted by the American College of Nutrition at Scottsdale, Arizona. In the study, the school children that ate at school a natural, whole foods breakfast and lunch got the highest Achievement Test scores at all grade levels and had the highest intelligence gain in United States history. The natural foods diet caused disruptive behaviors and dropout rates to decrease dramatically. Additionally violence, learning problems, short attention spans, suicides, rape and drug addiction had a 45% decrease in 25 studies with over 20,000 juvenile prison inmates (over 70% Black) in 7 different states. Virginia Wesley University, Southern Mississippi University, Johns Hopkins University and California State University conducted the research. Basically, the nutritional research returned Black children to the natural foods diet of pre-colonial ancient Africa. These studies made three basic changes in the children's diet. Bleached white flour (Pica) was taken out of the diet, white sugar (Pica) in food was reduced by 3 to 5% and all preservatives (Pica) were removed (including dyes, flavorings, etc.) Sodas were eliminated and fruit juices were substituted for sodas. Ironically, private schools in Connecticut and New Jersey saw the results and started buying natural foods from the New York Public Schools.

The profit-motivated junk food (Pica) industry, politically and economically have forced New York Public Schools to return to a destructive junk food diet and are allowed to cover up the nutritional, mental, emotional and behavioral problems that junk food causes. The junk food industry has no moral concern for children; their concern is profit only. Added to this, the National Academy of Sciences has lowered the Recommended Daily Allowance (RDA) of vitamins, minerals and other nutrients. The lowering of the RDA can be used to decrease the amount of money spent on Public Schools' lunch program, federally sponsored food programs, and food stamps. The lowering of the RDA causes the deterioration of children and senior citizens' health and increases diseases. This is done at a time when the number of children and adults with physical impairments (handicaps) and birth defects has been increasing steadily at 10% per year because of junk foods, vaccines, and drugs (World Health Organization Survey).

If Black children eat their natural whole foods diet learning and behavioral problems would stop. A holistic Black family --a family built on the foundations of spiritual, physical and mental unity will always seek whole (holistic) foods to nourish their children.

PSYCHIATRIC TERMS/MEANINGS

These psychology terms are commonly used to define a child or adult's behavior, thoughts and moods. Psychological terms are political and social tools used to manipulate and control thoughts and behaviors. Failure to conform to Caucasian standards of normal means a person is abnormal. An abnormal child is reacting to the failure of the school system to provide African centered and relevant academic information. The child can be reacting to under-nutrition caused by eating Pica (junk foods) as well as a dysfunctional home life and/or dysfunctional parents. The terms or labels given the child punish the child for society's failures.

AGGRESSIVE TANTRUM = aimless, thrashing, flailing limbs, wiggles legs

ATTENTION DEFICIT = easily distracted, loses things, fails to finish task, doesn't listen, doesn't stay on task

DEMENTIA = forgetful, memory problems

DEVELOPMENTAL ARITHMETIC DISORDER = difficulty understanding and solving arithmetic problems

DRAPETOMANIA = a mental illness which causes a slave to think about running away from the plantation ; a slave that attempts to escape from slavery

DYSAETHESIA AETHIOPS = a mental illness which causes a slave to be disrespectful or disobedient to the Slave Master

DYSLEXIA = fails literacy test, misspells words, cannot read words correctly, puts letters backwards

HEREDITARY VIOLENT GENETIC DISEASE = protesting, acting militant or confronting White Supremacy, expressing doubt about White authorities, at risk social conditions (ghetto, poor education) which genetically makes you inferior can cause this so called genetic disease.

HYPERACTIVITY = impulsive, constantly moving, excessive talking, impatient, makes excessive mistakes, excessive running and/or climbing

HYPOACTIVITY = withdrawn, passive, plays alone, talks very little, seems lost

OPPOSITIONAL DEFIANCE DISORDER = acting independent, having self identity

PAIN DISORDER = having headaches, backaches or unexplained aches and pains

PASSIVE TANTRUM = frown, cries, grimaces, beats on objects/furniture, throws and/or breaks objects

PERSECUTION COMPLEX = getting into confrontations with others and/or authorities, getting into fights

GREASE

The oils, lotions, cremes, mineral oils, moisturizers, softeners, powders (perfumed dirt), bleaching cremes, rejuvenators, sheep fat (lanolin), and other assorted concoctions contain poisonous synthetic chemicals that damage living cells and do not allow the skin to breath and clog the pores. They are cancer causing and harmful for babies, children and adults. The toxic chemicals are absorbed into the blood. Cosmetic chemical companies are interested in profit and deliberately promote the greasing and oiling of the baby's skin. A greased baby becomes an adult that greases their body. The grease concoctions feel smooth when touched because the hand slides over the oiled skin. The skin beneath the top skin layer remains unchanged because skin is nourished and made smooth because of what is eaten not what is put on the skin. The upper layer of skin is dead and cannot utilize the grease concoction that is applied. The chemicals can be fabric softeners, cancerous hydrocarbons, alcohol, bleach, hydrogenated fats that destroy bodily functions and destroy nutrients and weaken immunity.

The Caucasian custom of greasing their skin has nothing to do with health. It is an ancient superstition. During the many plagues in Europe, it was believed that open skin pores allowed diseases to enter the body. Consequently, Caucasians stopped bathing with water and started using animal grease to bathe their skin. They used cooked sheep fat, which was believed to make limp Caucasian hair curly because sheep have curly fur and pig grease was believe to make you violent and a better fighter. Lanolin (sheep grease) is found in many skin car products based on the ancient belief system of Caucasians. Other skin care products are based upon superstitious ignorance.

In the 1600's Europeans used protective alcohol spirit water (cologne) to bath babies and protect them from evil diseases. Cologne inflamed the eyes and skin of babies and caused severe pain. Many concoctions were used including blood (human blood, menstrual blood and/or animal blood) combined with pagan rituals and superstitious ceremonies. Remnants of the rituals still exist. For example a grease cleansing (cleansing crème) is followed by an ancient spirit mask (clay facial or mask), this is usually followed with a holy spirit protection water (astringent skin cologne) rinse or a skin peel (evil of facemasks removal) and another greasing (skin lotion). The ancient Greeks used salt on the skin to protect them, the biblical Hebrews used salt, and Soranus of Ephesus used salt and honey on the skin. The Ice Age Caucasian as well as the Britons, Scythians, Germans, Russians, and Greenlanders used ice or snow as a spiritual protection bath for newborn babies. The bath would kill unhealthy or weak babies and damaged the baby's skin and was an emotionally and mentally abusive for healthy babies. Soap did not become popular until the 1600's and then it was usually used once a week. It was usually too acid and damaged the skin. This made Caucasians scared of soap (cleanliness).

In ancient Africa, babies were bathed in warm water (not cold), such as the Natives of Pitcairn's Island or the Araucanian Natives of South America. Modern baby lotions and creams have harmful synthetic chemicals, antiseptics, hydrocarbons and dyes in the baby grease. When grease is mixed with water, it is called a lotion. Lotions are emulsified grease floating in water. The antiseptic lotions kill germs and irritate the sensitive skin of the baby. Fossil oils (mineral oil) applied to the skin dry it and destroy oil-soluble nutrients such as vitamins A, D, E and K. Grease concoctions cause the skin to peel and chafe and rob it of air, sunlight and nutrients. The oil and grease concoctions are absorbed into the blood and travel to the organs and brain. The hospitals grease babies because they do not have time to constantly change diapers. Baby lotion is a labor saving convenience for mothers and hospitals. A gentle massage of the baby's body would help the skin to release its natural oils and eliminate the need for grease concoctions. Aside from this, massages increase the baby's intelligence and emotional well being. Good hygiene is all the baby or an adult needs for skin care—keep the skin clean. In the case of fat-bloated babies, the layers of fat and folded fat should be kept clean. Greasing the baby as if they are an automobile or metal motor is a way to avoid keeping the baby clean. It is a chemical solution for bad parenting skills and uncleanliness.

In African culture, there is no need for greasing because the mother is trained to sense when the child has to urinate. When the child needs to urinate, the mother lowers the child to a squatted position and the child urinates. By the parent constantly repeating the lowering of the child to a squat, the child learns to squat when it needs to urinate. The mother makes a sound when they are lowering the child to a squat for urinating and bowel movements. The child imitates the sound and uses it to signal the need to defecate or urinate. Therefore, the mother does not need diapers and does not need to grease the baby. A child on a raw food diet would not have slimy-paste gooey-manure (bowel movements). Therefore, toilet paper would not be needed. Greasing, toilet paper and diapers are associated only with the Caucasian race. They have destroyed the intricate communication between the mother and child. This ultimately contributes to dysfunctional emotions, thoughts, and feelings. The Caucasian's dysfunctionality and abnormal mother and child relationship, feelings and practices are forced upon Africans as normal.

Caucasians superstitiously have a fear of the weather. This is understandable considering their Ice Age heritage with earthquakes, loud thunder, floods, landslides, huge boulders moving, animals constantly running, food shortages, starvation, diseases, cannibalism, heterosexual and homosexual rape, dysfunctional families, lack of educational systems and fresh water, resulted in a distorted (dysfunctional) relationship with mother nature and mothering. They fear nature, fear mothering, fear the weather, fear God, and fear each other. Therefore, all Caucasian countries have armies to protect themselves from each other.

In fear of mother nature and mother nature's weather, they overdress babies. Babies should be dressed for the type of weather; in the summer, lightweight and light colored clothes. In the winter, the temperature in the home is usually between 70 and 80 degrees. In the winter, summer clothes should be put on the baby while indoors. If going outside in the winter cold, then winter clothes should be worn. Skin rashes are usually caused by putting too much clothing on babies. Excessive or overly heavy clothes cause sweating. The wearing of synthetic clothes (should wear cotton) can stop air circulation to the body resulting in sweating and rashes.

Tight underwear and underwear made of synthetic material (i.e., nylon) can cause sweating and fungus growth. Cotton underwear should be worn. It must be noted that the long cotton gowns and full-length cotton clothing of African woman and men may appear hot. However, when walking, the cotton clothing creates a type of air conditioning and causes cool air to circulate over the body. The full length cotton African garments are actually cooling. They help to prevent dehydration. If the African is partially naked or totally naked in hot weather, they must drink extra fluids to stop themselves from becoming dehydrated.

If the baby is kept clean and dry, there is no need for antiseptic soap, medicated concoctions, boric acid, starch powder, talcum powder, vinegar, oatmeal or bran baths, greasy, oily, lubricated wipes and other substitutes for good hygiene.

DRUGGING AN UNBORN BABY

Pregnant women given drugs or who take drugs must realize that all drugs go directly into the baby's body. Pica (drugs, junk foods) and poor nutrition cause the African baby to try to breathe before being born. Under-nutrition and drugs can cause the unborn baby to have a bowel movement in the amniotic fluid. The baby drinks the amniotic fluid that has a bowel movement (manure) in it. The baby's bowel movement before birth is caused by emotional and/or physical shock.

Drugs taken by the mother or given during hospital births retard growth, slow down learning and interrupt the baby's growth and development and ability to bond with its mother. Drugs cause a shock reaction in the unborn child. In a state of shock the baby attempts to breathe. Drugs cause the baby's immune system to get exhausted and deteriorate. Pica (drugs and junk foods) deplete the immunity because they over-stimulate the sympathetic nervous system. The sympathetic nervous system then decreases nutrients to the sex organs, digestive system and immune system. Drugs activate serotonin out of its natural cyclic pattern and depress melatonin. Melatonin is needed for growth and development.

ULTRASOUND AND BABIES

Hospitals treat menopause, pregnancy and birth as a disease. Their test standards are based upon White people's biochemistry. Their birthing techniques are an unnecessary interruption in the prenatal child's rhythm, biochemistry, hormonal level, emotions, and brain function. The child is subject to cancer-causing ultrasounds. The needles used for taking the amniocentesis fluid (determines whether the baby is a girl or boy) is guided by ultrasound. Fetal monitors that are strapped on the mother's abdomen use ultrasound. The internal metallic devices that are screwed into the unborn baby's head cause inflammations with pus-filled abscesses. The X-rays given to pregnant women cause a 50% increase in various types of cancer. Aside from this, the increase in electronics and computers has caused an increase in drug use, surgical procedures and Caesarean Sections (C-Section). C-Section babies have an increase in diseases, bonding difficulties and learning problems. Their biochemical "rites of passage" and bonding becomes dysfunctional and interrupted. The prenatal life and birthing process of the child influences their emotional and mental development. The process of birth shapes the child's personality. When it is interrupted or made into a disease-type procedure, the child becomes dysfunctional.

PLAYGROUND OR DEATH GROUND

The Caucasian culture's playgrounds are made with equipment, which makes the play area a death ground. Playgrounds usually have an unsanitary ground of concrete, chemically polluted sand, asphalt, outdoor carpet, dirt or wood chips, which can include broken glass, urine, parasites, ticks, fleas, fecal matter, fungus, etc. The playground toys and exercise devices can be made of steel pipes, wood or an assortment of plastic, pipes and/or jagged or razor-edged devices that are hazardous to health. The exercise devices are usually made for monkeys or pet animals and do not allow all muscle groups to exercise. The toys are un-holistic, do not have cultural symbolism or themes and are based on the Caucasian culture's idea of toys. The toys are militaristic and resemble the army's basic training devices.

African toys expressed cultural themes, science, astrology, spirituality, and were geared to help the child towards higher growth. The African play activities taught communal life, sharing, and Maat rather than individualistic or violent competitive play. There were the African games such as Kea (similar to tic-tac-toe) which was played with stones. In contemporary African American history, the Kea type play board was drawn on the ground and a shoe heel was used in similar fashion as a stone (moving piece). A game such a "Hop Scotch" has patterns drawn with chalk on the pavement or in the street (usually on an asphalt street) which were patterned after Kea. The Hop Scotch pattern had a large chalk drawn play board which incorporated the symbol of the Sun (Ra) at the apex, a pyramid shape inside a square, and symbols of the female and male principle as connecting boxes. This was played with a shoe heel as a moving peg. Asphalt is oil waste filled with cancerous chemicals.

Belenin (similar to marbles), Beleta (similar to jacks), Wali (count and capture) and action games such as Kele (chicken fighting) were played. Kele is an action form of Duck Duck Goose with participants jumping in a frog position and trying to push each other over. These games were played by African children until the early 1960's.

Caucasian toys and playgrounds are made so that the child becomes accustomed to hunting and capturing prey, hoarding goods and violence. The winner of a game hollers or shouts in order to degrade the loser. The Caucasian playground toy devices are not organized by gender nor do they reflect spirituality, cosmic reality or have any relationship to family life. Most playground accidents are influenced by the child doing whatever it takes to win. The games require violence and can lead to child abuse and accidents. Adults that allow children to watch violent movies or play violent computer games cause the child to mimic violence while playing – this causes the child to harm themselves and other children. This programs violence into children and causes them to associate sex, injury and pain with fun.

The playground is usually a fenced-in cage made of wood, plastic or steel pipes and wires. Falls and miscalculated play activities can cause injury and permanent harm or death. No professional athlete would consider training or exercising on the playground devices or under the conditions that children are forced to play under. In 1990, almost 80 percent of the children taken to hospital emergency rooms were between 5 and 14 years of age and the other 20 percent of the children were below 5 years of age. The climbing toys and monkey bars caused over 70,000 children to be taken to the hospital. The number of children treated by parents, teachers, school nurses, self-treated, treated by other children or that go untreated would increase the total of playground injuries. The number of injuries children inflict upon each other on playgrounds has not been determined. The injuries adults inflict upon children that they are helping to play at playgrounds increases the total number of injuries of children. As far as monkey bars are concerned, a safe way to decrease a child's risk of injury on them is to measure the distance between the bar rungs. If the child's leg is shorter than the distance between rungs, then they will have a higher chance of their foot slipping and causing an injury to their body.

The playground lacks instructions for proper use of the devices. The playgrounds do not have warnings for the appropriate distance to stand away from the swings nor is any child's exercise safety monitored by another child or adult. Play at the playground is usually designed for individual and not for group or family oriented play. The playgrounds do not have first aid kits available. Children can be scarred, maimed, mutilated or injured for life at the caged playground. Some of the children are on prescription drugs (asthma, hyperactive, or have taken illegal drugs) and can be in withdrawal or high (physically and mentally impaired).

The playground, with drugged and malnourished children form a doubly destructive combination against the African child. The child presents its body at the playground and the condition of that body is nutritional deprivation caused by a Pica (junk food) diet. The child is nutritionally crippled. The neuro-hormonal and neuro-physiological responses are slow, inadequate or degenerated. The child's mind and body reflexes can be near zero, muscle reflexes are slower or inaccurate, nerves are irritated, mood swings burst sporadically, near-arthritic and rheumatoid conditions exist, mild heart failure symptoms, sugar withdrawal and thought tracking disorder are present.

A child on a Pica diet can have their muscles, nerves and brain floating in liquid manure and lactic acid waste which irritates and slows down responses. The child is carrying around approximately 3 pounds of caked-up toxic manure impacted in the rectum (adults usually have 7 to 15 pounds). Ironically, impacted manure is calculated as part of the normal body weight. The internal organs, tissues, nerves and cells are clogged and activity-impaired by toxins, mucus or plaque, congested cells and nerves. A low energy hypoglycemic level can strike at any moment caused by the sugary breakfast or dessert or snack or soda or candy that they have eaten or they can be extremely hyper from sugar. This can instantaneously cause loss of muscle, brain and nerve control. A child sugar addict can be in withdrawal. The sugar drunkard can be having a mood swing, attention deficit episode or be unstable mentally and/or emotionally.

The obstacle courses called playground toys require 100% physical efficiency that the Pica junk food diet and sugary snacks and sodas cannot and will not provide. The child is taken to the playground dysfunctional and nutritionally crippled and asked to perform 100% on a nutritionless diet. It is not a matter of if they will be harmed but when will they be harmed because they are accident prone. To make matters worse, the parents, teachers, school nurses, doctors other children or extended family members are drugged or have eaten sugary snacks or have a Pica junk food diet or are dysfunctional and do not see the obvious dangers of the situation.

SOUND

Rhythm (circadian rhythm, natural cycles) is melanin dependent. Rhythm is complicated and unique. For example, pendulum operated clocks can all be started at different time intervals. However, they all will synchronize to one rhythm. This has been found true even in a house where several women live together. Each may have had a different menstruation period (cycle) before living together. When they live in the same house they will eventually have synchronized periods and menstruate at the same time. An African baby and mother will have synchronized heartbeats. Sounds become human cells in the baby's body. Since the ear matures first, sound is important because sound waves turn into chemicals, electricity and magnetism that are absorbed by melanin and translate into thoughts, feelings, emotions, spirit and ideas. Babies should not be exposed to sounds of arguments, hostility, fighting, violence, loud noise or music, White racism (cultural insults), and disharmony. European culture is anti-rhythm and anti-harmony for African. Caucasian medicine ignores the melanin rhythmic importance of the African baby and mother. The use of anti-melanin drugs and Pica junk foods causes a conflict within the body of the mother and child. Rhythm controls the growth of organs and bones. A baby can grow up to 1 inch in height in 24 hours. Growth cycles (rhythm) are controlled by melanin. When rhythm has been disturbed by the anti-melanin hospitals and medical procedures the melanin is deficient or insufficient which can cause a sudden growth spurt that can retard physiological growth of brain cells. This can result in sudden irritation as well as emotional and mental problems in a baby (Growth Research, University of Pennsylvania by M. Lampl, M.D., Ph.D.).

SUGARS CAUSE DISEASE

(Sweet N Low, Nutrasweet, Equal, Aspartame, White Sugar, Brown Sugar, Raw Sugar, Succanat, Maple Syrup, Honey, Molasses, Grain Sugars, Fructose, Stevia)

Aspartame (a form of Pica) is an artificial sweetener that is 200 times sweeter than white sugar. It is totally synthetic and is made with a toxic poison called methanol. Methanol (alcohol) is combined with synthetic aspartic acid and phenylalanine and called aspartame with the commercial trade name Nutrasweet or Equal. Methanol is toxic to the thymus while excessive amounts of synthetic aspartic acid and phenylalanine are toxic to the liver. It is cheap to make and yields high profits.

The U.S. Food and Drug Administration has reported that the common symptoms of excessive amounts of aspartame is dizziness, nausea, vision problems, seizures, malaise and recurrent headaches. The Center for Disease Control has reported that the majority of complaints about aspartame are nerve damage (neurological). Canada, one of the first countries to use it, has noted that aspartame causes menstruation problems, mood swings, numbness and migraine headaches especially among children and teenagers. When children stopped using it for 10 days, the teenagers that had migraine headaches, numbness, mood swings, and other symptoms cleared up.

Children are not tested for toxic levels of aspartame, nor are the secondary effects or permanently damaging effects known. Aspartame is a sweet way to use children as laboratory test animals that create economic profits for the food industry. Aspartame can be found in diet foods as well as the following products: chewing gum, wine coolers, sodas, instant tea, milkshake mixes, yogurt, drugs, laxative, cocoa mixes, cereals, candy, cake, instant breakfast, frozen deserts, gelatin deserts, breath mints, juice drinks, toppings, multivitamins, milk, instant coffee and most foods that say sugar free.

Aspartame is used in carbonated sodas and the word "diet" is put on the label. The work "diet" on the label indicates that the soda is part of a diet. It is never specified on the label whether the word "diet" refers to a junk food diet, vegetarian diet or weight gain or loss diet. The consumer assumes that the word "diet" means a weight loss food. Aspartame and other synthetic sugars have never been scientifically proven to cause weight loss. In aspartame diet sodas and all sodas, the carbon monoxide used to make carbonated sodas is a poisonous gas. The body exhales toxic carbon dioxide, in order to get rid of it. The soda drinker drinks the carbon dioxide that the body wants to get rid of. The consumer ironically buys trace amounts of carbon monoxide and carbon dioxide and drinks it in carbonated sodas. This is against good health. Carbonated sodas decrease oxygen to the brain, the phosphorus stops calcium absorption, de-mineralize the bones and body and cause cirrhosis (hardening) of the liver. Harmful synthetic sugars are in "sugar free" foods. If a food taste sweet a type of sugar is in it. The Food and Drug Administration only classifies white sugar (glucose) as an official sugar. The word "sugar free" means glucose sugar is not in the product. "Sugar free" means a synthetic poisonous sugar such as aspartame is in the food. Synthetic chemicals such as artificial sweeteners are addicting and harmful.

The aspartame users have moved from sugar addiction to aspartame addiction. They never get treated for the sugar (sweets) addiction. Sweets (aspartame, white sugar) doubles the disease-causing effects when combined with bleached white flour, white grits, polished (white) rice, salt, saturated fats, animal flesh and high cholesterol. White sugar is a synthetic chemical and bleached white flour is a chemical. The harm caused by each of these chemicals is known. However, when white sugar is combined with bleached white flour it forms a totally new chemical that is different from white sugar and bleached white flour. The diseases caused by this new chemical are not known. Heart disease, diabetes, varicose veins, senility, coronary artery disease, high blood pressure, cataracts, circulatory problems, cancer and many other diseases are directly related to refined carbohydrates such as white sugar, bleached white flour, white grits, white rice, concentrated sweeteners, etc. It was not until concentrated sweeteners were added to the traditional processed polyunsaturated and saturated diet that diseases increased. When aspartame is added to the combination of processed polyunsaturated and saturated fats, salt and hidden white sugar in Pica junk foods and "health junk food" that health problems increased. These foods are toxic (poisonous) to the pancreas, liver, pineal gland and the entire body.

Drugs such as aspartame are synergistic (enhancers) to other synthetic chemicals and junk foods. Books that can reveal more information on the subject are Sugar Blues, by William Duffy, Natural Health, Sugar and the Criminal Mind, by J. A. Rodale, Body, Mind and Sugar, by E. Abrahamson and A Pezet and Killer Salt, by Marietta Whittlesey.

White sugar comes in many forms. For example, brown sugar is white sugar dyed with caramel color. Natural raw cane sugar sold in health food stores is white sugar with caramel color. There are other harmful sweeteners such as corn syrup (white sugar's other name) fructose, sucrose, dextrose, honey, etc. All these concentrated sweeteners cause nerve damage. As a result of sugar consumption, over 50% of Americans are hypoglycemic and diabetic while the remainder are pre-diabetic.

White sugar over stimulates the pancreas, which in turn burns up all the starch energy. A diseased pancreas cannot get energy from starches, therefore, the body has to switch to burning fats (oils) for energy. In other words, sodas make you crave French fries (oil) and potato chips (oil) and then the salt on the fries and chips make you crave the drug white sugar which causes you to crave oil (French fries, oily potato chips).

White sugar is a concentrated sweetener. The body tries to dilute white sugar with fluids. It takes moisture (fluids) from the bones, organs, tissues, veins, arteries and nerves. The nerves become damaged causing blindness, chronic fatigue, kidney failure, Alzheimers, Parkinsons, cataracts, glaucoma, hearing problems, arthritis, infertility, high blood pressure, hyperactivity, mood swings and diabetes. The loss of fluids causes dehydration and thirst. White sugar makes you thirsty. In other words, drinking a soda makes you thirsty for a soda. Constantly buying sodas to satisfy the thirst sodas makes profits for the soda industry. The average child does not drink any water; they drink sodas or white sugar sweetened bottle water or some type of sugary beverage.

The only truly safe sugars are those found within the raw vegetable or fruit. The herb Stevia is a green natural sweetener. For those who want a fairly safe concentrated sugar that causes nerve damage use grains such as malt, rice or barley syrup or powders. They are used slowly by the body and cause the same damage as white sugar and are less toxic and harmful to the pancreas.

The health foods stores sell many foods that have types of white sugars as well as food items combined improperly. There is a large "junk health food" variety of sugary sweet foods. The problem with "junk health food" is that they use deceptive misguiding words such as "natural" when they actually contain artificial ingredients. A few wholesome ingredients are mixed with brown sugar, corn syrup, aspartame, disease causing canola oils, disease causing processed polyunsaturated oils, salt, hydrogenated oils, etc. Salad dressings and catsup have sugar in them and are equally dangerous. The need to add sugar to food has to be eliminated.

SUGARS
(Refined and Processed)

There are two types of sugars. When sugars are isolated and concentrated (processed) they are technically classified as a drug. The sugars naturally eaten within plants are safe. Refined (processed) sugars are dangerous to health.

1. Glucose
   Causes: dehydration, blindness, kidney failure, diabetes, fatigue, arthritis.

   - High blood pressure, hardening of the arteries and veins, hypertension
   - Activity, infertility, low blood sugar (hypoglycemia) mood swings
   - Glaucoma, cataracts, hair loss, gum disease, rotten teeth (cavities)
   - Senility, rheumatism, nerve damage, Alzheimers, Parkinson
   - Numbness, Tingling and addiction

2. Fructose
   When refined causes free radical oxidation (makes cells rust) causes the same diseases as glucose.

   Sugar Combinations
   - Sucrose - is a combination of glucose and fructose
   - Lactose - is milk sugar and a combination of glucose with galatose

HONEY

Contains: 70% Fruit Sugar (Fructose)
30% Sucrose Sugar (White Sugar)

CAUSES:
- Blood Levels of Insulin
- Blood Vessel Damage
- Contributes to uterine Fibroids,
- Endometriosis, Cystic Mastitis,
- Breast Cancer, Ulcers
- Gouty Arthritis
- Hardening of the Arteries
- Heart Attacks
- Hyperactivity
- Increases Blood Fats

Kidney Fatigue and Disease
Damaged and enlarged the
Liver and Adrenal Glands
Mood and Thought Disorders
Pancreas shrinks and deteriorates
Periodontal Disease (Teeth and Gums)

Strokes
Triglycerides, Cortisone, and
Cholesterol to increase

- Increases Uric Acid

SUGAR CRAVING REMEDY

Gymnema Sylvestre	=	prevents sugar craving
Bitter Melon	=	prevents sugar craving
Bilberry (Huckleberry)	=	increases insulin used for diabetes, heals pancreas
Guggulipid	=	prevents sugar craving
Vanadium (Vanadyl Sulfate)	=	heals pancreas
Chromium	=	increased energy, stabilizes blood sugar
Supplements called Natrol Cravex or Crave Less	=	stops the biochemical craving for sugar
Pau d'Arco	=	kills yeast

MENTORS

The mentor is the key agent for cultural and nutritional wisdom and the development of the Black child. Mentors are commonly called a "hero," a "shero," a famous ancestor, an educator, athlete, social activist, freedom fighter, scientist, relative or significant Black person. Mentors translate culture and serve as role models. They have three primary functions. First, the Mentor is a "coach" that encourages the child's highest [ability] good. Secondly, the mentor is a "Tutor" that instructs in the use of rules or theories or cultural values and norms as they apply to the child's ability. Finally, a mentor is a "Counselor" that gives guidance on the quality of life needed for that child's talent and ability. Ability has a broad meaning and includes talent, career, aspiration, family life, community life, business development, leadership and the child's individual concerns. An education is the primary expression of that ability. The origin of the Mentor demonstrates its significance in "family-centered" African life.

Mentors have a long history in African heritage and culture. Mentor in Greek means Divine Teacher. In African civilizations such as the Kush, Ethiopia, Nubia and Egypt, it is explained in mythology. The mythological God name Osiris (his name means "Guide of the Soul") was a great ruler. Before Osiris was born, the world had no order; there were no buildings and life was crude. Osiris left his country to travel all over the world to teach the laws of cycles, order, Maat, proper worship and technology. In his absence from his children, a highly developed person was chosen to teach his son Horus the laws of man, God, universe, Maat, science, ethics, nutrition, agriculture and holistic health. The person chosen was named Thoth. Thoth was a God in charge of the written laws of Maat. Thoth taught Maat to Horus. Maat is a word that stands for morals, righteousness, ethics, truth and justice which includes the divine image of humans, perfection, teachabililty, free will of humans and moral practice in human development. "Maat-Thoth (Mentor)" is also represented by the Kabala, Caduceus, Mancala or Ankh. These words and symbols mean "Tree of Life." The "Tree of Life" is symbolic of the utilization of 12 Melanin centers of the brainstem, the 12 cranial nerves, the 12 steps of Jacob's Ladder, the 12 steps on the God Shun's stairs, the 12 principles of Metutu, or the 12 cyclic degrees of the Zodiac (attributes of God). These 12 steps plus the Sun God equal number 13.

The "Rites of Passage" of growth and development are degrees of knowledge. This knowledge is called the Mystery System which was taught by Mentors. The mentor is a cultural technology and responsible for the fruit (child) of the "Tree of Life." A Mentor is part of the African extended family. Sometimes, the principles or steps are combined into the 7 principles of Kwanzaa or the 7 Halls of Osiris or they can be reduced to 3 steps or levels. For example, the Mystery Steps could be (1) "Mortal" - In this step there is no "inner-vision" and the person learns how to holistically participate in and care for his family-centered life, (2) "Intelligence" - In this step the person receives mind or consciousness and attains "inner-vision" and (3) "Creator" or "Suns of Light" or "Enlightenment." In this step the person becomes united with the light of God (RA) and received "super-vision." Mentors and Maat are used to make the Black child a technology that solves Black folks' problems. Children must be raised to solve their race's problems, reach their highest level of humanism and further African culture.

CHAPTER 14 PARENTING CONSIDERATION

What the family talks about in the evening, the child will talk about in the morning.

Oromo Of Ethiopia and Kenya proverb

BONDING WITH YOUR CHILD

Bonding is a biochemical, emotional, hormonal, spiritual and electromagnetic process. Bonding occurs between two living things. Bonding occurs between plants and humans, soil and humans, animals and humans as well as human to human.

Plant and human bonding has been verified by galvanometers which are a type of lie detector (polygraph) that is attached to the leaves of plants. In scientific research this type of lie detector device was attached to the leaves of plants and people were selected to think about hurting a plant by burning it (The Secret Life of Plants by Peter Thompkins). The people actually were going to burn the plant. Plants are able to recognize and respond to intentions to harm them from a thought of harm. Plants respond to storms and harm by making their sap go to the roots. If a person plans to harm a plant the plant will electro-magnetically respond to thoughts of harm by making a lie detector attached to its leaves move. Lie detectors have verified that plants get happy when their owner is on the way home, plants know when their owner is lying and plants respond to the owner's moods, injury, stress and negative and positive thoughts and behaviors. Once the owner of a plant bonds to the plant by taking care of it, singing to it, touching it and loving it, they become bonded. Consequently, the plant acts and reacts to owner's emotions and thoughts. If a person sits next to a plant and hates it, the plant responds by becoming weak and may cry and die from the negative effect of the negative bond. Bonding has a holistic effect on lesser life forms such as a plant and has a holistic effect on a higher life form such as a child.

In many scientifically documented experiments bonding has been studied by deconstructing socio-biological behavior. Bonding requires having feelings of attachment as well as adapting your personality to a plant or person while remaining true to your essential non-adapting Maat culture. Bonding requires understanding the nature of the child and being receptive to the child and being spiritually in touch with the child. Bonding is a training process for the child. The child is trained with the rules, taboos, morals, rituals, and ceremonies of their culture. Scientists have bonded with plants and taught plants to grow a certain way such as Mr. Burbank. He taught cactus plants to grow without thorns and did not genetically modify the cactus or use harmful synthetic fertilizers or hybridize (Training of the Human Plant by Burbank). Burbank discovered that it is easier to train plants if you bond with them, use love and mix play (culture) with work.

Metals respond to bonding. Metals can bond to a person that loves them and will change its electromagnetic response when the person's moods change. Metals have cycles. Each type of metal (i.e., copper, zinc, iron) has a unique electromagnetic personality. A plant or metal bonded to a person can get upset if the person is upset or acts dysfunction if the person is dysfunctional. For example, a plant that is bonded and treated negatively by a person will grow poorly. If Caucasian Acid Rock and Roll music is played to a plant, the plant will grow leaves in bunches and/or non-symmetrically, the roots will grow shorter, the plant will absorb excessive amounts of water and the plant will be stunted in growth. In other words, the plant will become dysfunctional (Plants Response as a means of Physiological Investigation by Jagadis Bose). Negative bonding has an effect on plant moods, growth, electromagnetic energy, and life.

A child is bonded negatively if taken out of its culture. The child will develop abnormally. Plants taken out of their natural habitat and plant culture and not allowed to bond with other plants that are the same as itself will develop abnormally. The works of Johann Wolfgang von Goethe (1786) in Metamorphosis of Plants and the book Effects of Cross and Self Fertilization in the Vegetable Kingdom by Charles Darwin point to the variations in plants grown outside of their plant culture and bonding environment. Aside from plants, amoeba, yogurt, yeast, blood and sperm when put in a liquid and attached to a lie detector type device response to human emotions. When these living things are bonded to a person they can identify when the person has told a lie and when something harmful has happened to the person. In fact, human sperm is bonded to its owner and can identify its owner. Bonding has far reaching effects, affects and emotional actions and reactions. Living things want to bond to living things. Living things have developed feelings and behaviors, which make the bonding experience pleasurable. Bonding is a type of electromagnetic pleasurable exchange between two living things.

Bonding between a mother and her child is a two-way biochemical, hormonal and physical process. When the child interacts with the mother, both of them secrete a morphine type chemical, which makes the body feel pleasurable. When the breast-fed baby sucks on the nipple a morphine type chemical called oxytocin is realeased. The hormone oxytocin makes nursing pleasurable for the mother (or wet nurse). This same type hormone is released in the body when friends and family members are together. It is also released during sexual intercourse as well as pregnancy. It makes intercourse and pregnancy pleasurable. The birth of a child causes the mother to have a drop in oxytocin. This sudden drop can cause Post Partum Depression (i.e., morphine type drug withdrawal). The morphine type hormone oxytocin and endorphine (released during exercise) is nature's way of rewarding a person for bonding and exercising. Aside from this nature uses behavior to insure bonding.

The baby must insure that the mother enjoys the bonding process by using specific types of behavior called "Fixed Action Patterns." The baby's "Fixed Action Pattern" consists of clutching, grasping, rooting the nipple, smiles, cooing sounds, clinging, and eye to eye contact behaviors. These behaviors make the baby attractive to the mother. The baby is not attracted to strangers and has a natural fear of strangers. When a stranger approaches the child, the child will cry if the mother is not near when a stranger approaches. This causes the mother to constantly stay with the baby and continue the bonding process which gives the mother a morphine-like high. Oddly enough, the baby does not have a natural fear of tigers, dogs, snakes or predatory animals. To further insure bonding the baby enjoys curves (i.e., eyebrows, cheeks, smiles, nipples), color contrast (i.e., iris and pupil), acute angles (i.e., corners of the eyes, smiles), high pitched melodious sounds (i.e., songs, baby talk), movement in a frame (i.e., lip movement on a face), and symmetry (i.e., similar size and equally aligned two eyes and two ears). The sum total of the baby's enjoyment amounts to a human face and breast. The baby likes symmetry in facial structure. Physiologically, symmetry is equated with a normal healthy human being while asymmetrical (out of alignment and balance) facial structure or one eye lower or slanted or on an off angle equates to poor bone structure and ill health. In other words, the nature of the baby seeks a healthy adult. Incidentally, movie idols that are considered attractive have symmetrical facial features (i.e., Denzel Washington, Sidney Poitier, Halley Berry, Lena Horne).

The bonding process essentially is the same for all types of bonding be it mother/child, male/female, sexual male/female bonding, non-sexual male/male, and non-sexual female/female. In bonding there is a biochemical change, morphine-like chemicals are released. Pheronomes (hormone vapors of odorless fumes) are released, the histo-compatibility complex is stimulated, (a sensation of feeling good or bad), and bio-potential of skin changes and Fixed Action Patterns are involved. There are "Fixed Action Patterns" during sexual intercourse because there is clinging, grasping, cooing type sounds, kissing replaces rooting of the nipple, and morphine-like chemicals are released during sex. The Fixed Action Patterns of non-sexual male/male bonding are basically the same. For example, men bond when playing sports, or having mock boxing matches. They grasp, cling, touch each other making cooing type sounds and release the morphine type chemical called endorphins. Since Fixed Action Patterns are essentially the same, the culture separates one type from another by using taboos, morality, and different sets of rituals and ceremonies to limit the physical behavior used. Caucasians use Fixed Action Patterns when bonding to their pet dogs and seem to have no limits on physical behaviors with pets. In any case, the absence of adult Fixed Action Patterns in parent/child bonding causes the child to have dysfunctional behaviors such as timidity, social withdrawal, fear, insecurity, relationship problems and intimacy dysfunction.

The child enjoys bonding and prefers bonding with relatives that have bonded with its parents. The child has a hierarchy of bonding preferences. When a child can equally socialize with kinfolk, the child will invest more bonding time with their nearest relative rather than a distant third or fourth cousin. This is mostly the result of the child being genetically closer to their nearest kin. The approximate ratio of genes the child has is ¼ genes of the mother and ¼ genes of the mother's ancestors and ¼ genes of the father and ¼ genes of the father's ancestors. Consequently, the parent and child are 1/4 genetically related. Genetically the child is more related (3/4 genetically) to its sisters and brothers than its parents. In the parent/child bonding process, the child is interested in itself and getting its needs met. The parents' awareness of the child's neediness is not as clear, precise and focused as the child's awareness of its neediness. The child spends the vast majority of its time in a state of neediness. It is totally dependent on the parents for all its needs. The parents' focus and attention is divided between household maintenance, E-mail, work, friends, relatives, their mate, traveling to and from work, telephone conversations, sex, social issues and problems. The child with their total focus on their neediness and the parent with partial focus on the child's neediness means the parent is put into a position of being manipulated by the child. Since the parents want an emotional and social reward for investing time in their child, this sets them up to be manipulated by the child. The child uses Fixed Action Patterns to manipulate the parent and to make the parents invest time, money and dreams in them. This means the child is looking out for its own needs. Aside from this, the child's bonding and Fixed Action Patterns stimulate the parents' biochemistry to secrete morphine-like chemicals (i.e., endorphins, oxytocin) that cause a pleasurable sensation in the parent. Consequently, the child's manipulative techniques bring physical pleasure to the parent despite the parents' conscious efforts to avoid manipulation. The nature of the child is to use Fixed Action Patterns and love to attach to the parent and manipulate the parents. The problem is manipulative techniques are the same as Fixed Action Pattern. However, in healthy, bonded children they know the limits of manipulation while damage bonded, dysfunctional children do not know the limits or abuse the limits.

The Black Child becomes damaged and/or dysfunctional because bonding is not complete. Bonding is the emotional attachment the child has to its mother, father, and culture. Bonding starts before birth with the child's placenta and the unborn child. The placenta allows two different people (child and mother) to attach and form a relationship. The placenta forms the umbilical cord and attaches the child (fetus) to the uterus of the mother. It provides nourishment, air and blood to the fetus. The placenta has a personality and spirit. The placenta's lactogen hormone can stimulate can stimulate the mother to increase nutrients in her blood. A mother with an inadequate nutritional diet can stress the unborn baby and herself. This can result in hypertension (preclampsia) and a low birth weight and high placenta weight. A low birth weight can cause hyperactivity in the child and as an adult the child can develop high blood pressure. A large placenta can indicate bonding problems as well as a malnourished child. Bonding problems can lead to dysfunctional emotions and behaviors, relationship problems, and the child can become an adult that has problems relating to jobs, money, people, parents and themselves. Bonding problems can biochemically start with the mother's egg before conception.

The egg communicates to the follicle that surrounds it in the ovary. The follicle makes a nutritional evaluation of the mother and communicates to the egg. The egg can then decide to speed up or slow down its development. The egg divides four times before the sperm fertilizes it. This indicates that the egg has a type of emotional and intellectual biochemical personality that can be influenced by the mother's moods, thoughts, nutrition, spirit and dysfunctionality. The quality of the egg as well as the quality of the sperm can predispose the conceived child to have dysfunctional bonding. Both egg and sperm are subject to the electromagnetic, neuroelectrical, and neuromagnetic pulses that stimulates the nervous system and facilitate communication between the brain cells formed by the union of the egg and sperm. In other words, the sperm and egg are influenced by the physical, mental, and spiritual health of the adult. This means a sick man has sick sperm. The quality of egg and sperm are a reflection of the quality of the life of the adult. Poor quality eggs and sperms can predispose a conceived child to have bonding problems as well as psychological, physiological, and emotional difficulties.

The ability of the baby to bond as well as intelligence and emotions are influenced by social and physiological factors. For example, the birth order can impact a child's intelligence. Usually, the first born will have an IQ (intelligence quotient) 3 to ½ points higher than the children born later. The decline in IQ is probably caused by the child receiving more bonding time from the parents. The birth space which is the time between the birth of children impacts IQ. Children born 2 to 4 years apart have a higher IQ than those born less than 2 years apart. The birth space coincides with the natural 2 to 4 years of breastfeeding each child should receive – the average in the world is 3 years. Children that have sisters and/or brothers to bond with have a higher IQ than children without siblings (an only child).

Bonding is damaged by social life relationships, emotional, mental, physical and/or spiritual stress. Stress causes the sympathetic nervous system to react by releasing catecholamines (epinephrine = fight, norepinephrine = flight) and steroids (i.e., corticosteroids). Stressors on the pregnant woman causes decreased oxygen and nutrients to the unborn child. This can cause the baby to be easily irritated and develop altered sexual behavior, unstable emotions, mood swings, learning problems, and a decrease in social skill – dysfunctionality. Maternal stress decreases the head size, and birth weight of the child and the bonding ability. Stressors and anxiety in pregnant women increases corticosteroids and catecholamines in the unborn. This can cause the eczema, respiratory problems, ulcers, ear infections, miscarriages, neonatal death, Sudden Infant Death Syndrome (SIDS), cleft lip, Downs Syndrome, premature birth and bonding problems.

Social stressors can be direct or indirect and the child or parent can be aware (conscious) or unaware (unconscious) of the stress. The effect of the stress causes hormone imbalances and neurological brain malfunctions which result in dysfunctionalilty. For example, unborn, overstressed prenatal girls and girl infants tend to release adrenal hormones (i.e., adrenaline, noradrenaline) which decreases her sex hormone balance. This imbalance lessens the feminization of her brain, resulting in tomboyish behavior. Stress hormones (adrenaline, cortisol) interfere with the testosterone production . In infant boys (3 to 4 month old) the testosterone rises until the end of the first year. The testosterone rise stimulates the hypothalamus region of the brain (men have twice as many neurons in the area than women). However, pregnant women that are stressed have increased adrenal hormones which decrease the testosterone level in boys. This alters instinctive behavior, manhood and fatherhood ability and causes some type of dysfunctionality. In girls the testosterone hormone takes a default nerve pathway and does not masculinize their brain. However, stressors tend to cause similar dysfunctionality in girl.

Children that are bond damaged are insecurely bonded. The electrical signals in the brain are usually altered with abnormal electrical activity in the frontal and temporal regions of the brain, especially the left frontal region which is associated with having a "feel good" feeling. The brain's cortex frontal region (lobe) is associated with personality. The brain of an unborn child is affected by unconscious and conscious stressors of the mother. A bond damaged child's brain is under-stimulated. This restricts the emotional vocabulary and intelligence. For example, a child that is physically restricted by being locked behind gates or playpens (jail), constantly told "no", "stop", "don't do that," "keep quiet", "sit still", or left alone in a playpen, subjected to loud music constantly or is raised by one parent, or is not on an eating or sleep schedule, or is restricted to the same toys (should rotate toys or trade with other parents), will have an under stimulated brain. The child with an under stimulated brain will develop dysfunctionalities.

Bonding reflects society and is attached to culture. Bonding gives the child gender. Gender is behaviors a culture attaches to the male sex and female sex. Children learn gender before they are one year old. In European culture, mothers during the genderfication process smile more at girls than boys, pay more attention to boy's anger and less attention to boys' smiles. Boys are taught that they are supposed to "sew their oats" – having promiscuous sex before marriage, prey upon virgin girls, etc. Girls are taught to always protect themselves from male sex predators and girls are taught that being raped by males is always a possibility. Physiologically in boys the brain's orbito-frontal region grows faster than girls. This means that boys have a higher degree of emotional restraint (i.e., not easy to cry). The bonding problems and Caucasian gender rules of Black children can be eradicated if Maat cultural values are used instead of European social and cultural values.

A child cannot be totally bonded and cultureless nor can a person have freedom and be cultureless or healthy and cultureless. Culture provides the emotional, social, spiritual and psychological language that allows a person to define themselves and reality. Culture provides a biosocial computer program that transmits and translates reality. Culture prescribes and defines what bonding can be and should be. If a Black person uses an alien culture (European) to bond to their child, then the child is bond damaged permanently. For example, the European "abandoned child" themes are the foundational stories and myths. Children abandoned by their parents are dysfunctional. The study and use of an abandoned child's interpretation of love, marriage and social life forces dysfunctionality upon a Black child. The "abandoned child" themes and philosophies are abundant in European (Caucasian) culture. Some Caucasian characters that are abandoned (unloved) children are Hercules, Paris, Cadillac, Snow White, Superman, Hansel and Gretel, Cinderella, Oedipus, etc. The Oedipus myth is the foundation of European psychology. Europeans (Caucasians) believe the mind was abandoned by God and therefore cannot be trusted. The "abandoned child" themes mean that nature, your mother and father, love and God cannot be trusted to provide or to bond. The constant use of the "abandoned child" themes read to children in the form of fairytales or used in cartoons or movies or video games maintain bond damage. In abandoned and/or abused children, the Hippocampus brain tends to be smaller. The Hippocampus is associated with long term memory (i.e., a computer memory stored on a CD-ROM or disk). In abandoned and/or abused children, the emotional temperament and fear, anxiety, distress and social withdrawal are increased. The Limbic Region (emotional center) is abnormally affected. The limbic region (cerebral cortex) and the brain's Amygdala and Temporal Lobe are associated with memory, knowing the difference between right and wrong (discrimination), recognizing faces (reality), controlling emotions, etc. The "abandoned child" themes rewire the normal thought process and reward a child for being abandoned. Each "abandoned child" character becomes a "hero." A "hero" is a person rewarded for being a person (abandoned). They are "rewarded" for not having parental guidance, control, discipline and love. They are rewarded for being dysfunctionally bonded. An abandoned child has no investment of time from the parents.

Bonding requires an investment of time and unconditional concern and care for the child. An adult can decide not to invest in the child. There are two types of non-investment (1) abortion and (2) adoption. Abortion is the murder of a child before birth or murder of the child after its birth – infanticide. There are two types of adoption (1) adoption before conception and birth and (2) adoption of the child after birth. Adoption of the child before birth occurs when a woman sells or donates her eggs and a man sells or donates his sperm and then their egg and sperm are united outside the womb and placed in a test tube or womb of another woman. In abortion and adoption, the parent of the child or egg or sperm does not invest in the child.

Bonding requires a complete investment in the child. Total (complete) bonding requires that the mother and father act as complimentary pairs that provide unconditional care and undivided attention to the child, attach the child to its culture and the mother breastfeeds. A child that does not get total bonding is at risk. No amount of quality time or love changes the risk. In nature there is no negotiating with bonding. Either the child is bonded or not bonded. Either the child is undamaged or damaged from bonding. Parents tend to assume they can negotiate or compromise with nature by giving their child so called "quality time." Quality time means "good enough time" or "the best I can do to squeeze you into my schedule." African culture gives the best example of bonding.

The mother and father in the Aka tribe of Central Africa completely bond to the child. The Aka father spends 20% of the time with the child and the mother 80%. He provides emotional, spiritual and physical support by being physically and emotionally near the mother 50% of the time that she is with the child. This is total bonding with the child. It must be kept in mind that in mammals the mother tends to do more parenting. She provides breast milk and her milk will let down (secretion) in response to the baby's hunger cry. The mother has a prolactin hormonal response and responds to baby's cries quicker than fathers. A total bonded child develops an extensive emotional vocabulary and healthy social skills. The child bonds to the parents and the parents bond the child to the culture. Thus, total bonding transmits and translates culture. Any deviation or incomplete bond will cause an aspect of the child's emotional, social and spiritual life to be dysfunctional forever. The impact of incomplete bonding cannot be overcome or cured by love or therapy. For example, a child born in jail or chattel slavery with loving parents cannot escape the impact of slavery or jail on their life. Love cannot erase the damage slavery has caused to the child. A child denied access to their culture's language, rituals, ceremonies, spiritual system and freedom is damaged forever. Nature has strict rules. Ignorance or intelligence does not help avoid nature's rules. For example, if you are shot in the head with a canon you will die. It does not matter to nature whether you are a child, intelligent, senile, ignorant, old, or accidentally stepped in front of the cannon ball. Nature has rules that must be obeyed (i.e., stop breathing, you die, etc.) Oppression/Slavery denies total bonding and nature's price for this is some type of spiritual, emotional, and social dysfunctionality. Obviously the solution to the problem is to be free of oppression/slavery. Nature will not compromise, negotiate or delay the penalty. The impact of incomplete bonding is called partial bonding.

Partial Bonding occurs when the child is not breastfed and/or the mother and child spend long periods of time away from each other and are inattentive to each other. Bonding activities can be the mother talking or singing to or with the baby or cuddling or being quiet and alert to each other, playing together, massaging each other, etc. Partial bonding occurs when the mother and child are physically together but emotionally and mentally apart. For example, the mother or father is physical with the child but instead of emotional and social bonding activities, the child and/or parent are separately or together playing video games, watching television or talking on a cell phone. Today mothers can be with their child and talking on a cell phone while shopping, driving to and from school, fixing dinner, etc. The end result of such emotional detachment from the child is partial bonding, which causes a dysfunctional child. There are typical characteristics of a partially bonded child.

A partial bonded child tends to cling tightly to mother, develops distress, tension, mistrust and anger, lacks appropriate social skills, seeks and avoids intimacy and/or takes unnecessary risks. A partial bonded child becomes an adult that has difficulty establishing and/or maintaining intimate relationships, avoids looking the parent in the eyes, has unexplainable fears, is unaware of emotional limits, has episodes of confusion, tends to be disorganized and/or disorientated, etc. Total bonded children have obvious good behavior and partial bonded children have obvious problems that have been scientifically proven by a test called the "Strange Situation Test." African children are totally bonded with healthy African centered parents and have holistic behavior are in the book Infancy in Uganda, Infant Care and the Growth of Love by Mary Ainsworth. She created the "Strange Situation Test."

Partial bonding can be less of a problem and not produce dysfunctionality if it occurs in an African cultural setting. In African culture each adult is a parent and practices parenting skills with all children. Mothers that work have caregivers that are bonded to her and/or related and bonded to her. The baby feels emotionally secure with caregivers bonded to the mother. The caregivers are usually of the same ethnic group (i.e., Akan, Hausa, Yoruba, Twa) which means the child is exposed to rituals and ceremonies consistent with the mother. Children bonded under these types of cultural conditions do not exhibit bonding problems. When the child is old enough to attend school, the teachers are usually of the same ethnic group and/or are a relative and are seen as a parent by the child. The adults and teachers are extensions of the mother/child bond. However, today the Black child is damaged by partial bonding (Mother Love/Mother Hate: The Power of Maternal Ambivalence by Rozsika Parker). Bond damaged children were observed among babies in Israeli Kibbutzim (day care centers). Jewish mothers that did not spend bonding time with their babies caused dysfunctional behaviors in the child. The Jewish working mother that took time off from work to breastfeed and bath their babies and their babies sleep with them at night caused at least 10% of the babies to be damaged by partial bonding. It must be kept in mind that the mothers were totally free to practice their culture's rituals, ceremonies, diet, health system, birthing practices, religion, dance, music, language and marriage, and yet 10% of the children partially bonded were dysfunctional. The Black women and men in slavery, oppression (so-called Black Experience) do not breastfeed, allow strangers to care for their children, do not have a natural foods diet, use Caucasian hospital birth rituals, have slavery trauma and/or adopt European culture are causing children to be bond damaged. Bond damaged Black children do not have the culture, emotions, thoughts or spirituality to access Black intelligence. What these children do have is some aspect of their emotions, feelings, desires, wants, needs, sexuality, diet and lifestyle dysfunctionalized permanently. In order to avoid producing dysfunctional children that become dysfunctional adults (so-called normal Black folks) social and biological bonding factors need to be understood.

Mother/child bonding has many social and biological factors that influence the bonding success. Bonding is influenced by the food supply, gender preference, economics, colonialism, slavery trauma, sex, demographics (ratio of men to women), biochemistry, breastfeeding, environment, "Nature" and "Mother Nature" philosophy. Each culture has a different definition of Mother Nature. Mother Nature philosophy is consistent with the rituals, ceremonies, spirituality, social customs, morality and taboos of a people's culture. Mother Nature philosophy transmits and translates culture and in many ways is a self-serving deception. There is a difference between Nature and Mother Nature.

The Mother Nature philosophy says that all women instinctively love their children. This idea is supported by the maternal love philosophy and maternal instinct philosophy. However, in nature mothers kill their children, abandon, abuse, neglect, many foster out their children (give them to relatives to raise), some mothers have poor parenting skills and some mothers do not invest parenting time in the child. This can indicate a lack of maternal love or a lack of mother instinct. One out of three Ghanaian women and approximately 40% of Liberian woman between the ages of fifteen and thirty "Foster Out a Child." "Fostering Out" is low in Sudan, Kenya and Nigeria. Fostering out is high in Sierra Leone (46%) between ages thirty to thirty four. In South Africa 50% of the children of unmarried mothers and 32% of married mothers foster out their child. In "Fostering Out" Another parent becomes the child's foster parents. The fostered out children usually live with their grandmother. Fostering out occurs in nature. However, Mother Nature philosophies say that a mother would not do it. Mother Nature philosophies basically define women as breeders and their sole desire and purpose in life is to stay home and raise children and if necessary sacrifice their own health, career and dreams in order to make their children and husband happy. Mother Nature philosophy says that there is a deep mystical mother instinct that naturally creates in women the desire to be mothers and make children the main purpose of their life and center of their happiness. Mothers work (farm, factory, etc.) to create income to support the child and family. Mother Nature philosophy says a mother will die for her child, not give up her child for adoption or foster out or abort her child. Nature and nature's rules do not cooperate with Mother Nature philosophy, nor does Nature operate in a vacuum. Nature operates within the environment, food supply, social environment and the changing social options. Fostering out children is nature operating within the social limitations and options society has given women. A woman that fosters out allows herself to be single and unattached to a child and available for marriage. If the mother is a teenager then fostering out allows the teenage mother to mature, find her purpose in life and gives her a second chance to have a successful relationship and have a baby with a father that lives in the household. Nature allows women and mothers to evaluate and use various choices and types of relationships based upon a woman's environment, social needs, food supply, economic necessities, sex preference of the society, gender rules and emotional needs.

Women have to consider the bonding needs of the child, the over 70,000 calories of energy needed for a pregnancy, the high caloric demand of breastfeeding, the spacing of pregnancies, emotional and social energy needed to maintain her marriage, her health and pending menopause, her social support system and the unstable resource called a Black man. He is considered a possible unreliable/unstable resource because of his high rate of degenerative disease, dying at an early age, high unemployment, murder, addiction, jail, prostate cancer risk, adultery rate, high rate of divorce and the possibility that he may leave her causing her to be a single parent. Women and female mammals generally do not sacrifice their needs and welfare for the survival of their children or species. Mother Nature philosophy says women sacrifice their needs and life for children and a husband. However, nature makes decisions about life over and beyond a culture's Mother Nature philosophy. In nature the only time a woman will sacrifice her life for that of a child is when she is close to menopause or is not capable of having another child. Nature provides options so that a woman does not have to sacrifice her life unless the social conditions dictate it.

The man/woman pair bond is influenced by the marriage options available. Man/woman bond has an impact on the mother/child bond. The mother must provide security and be a stable resource for the child or else the child suffers from the negative effects of an unstable bond. The female has a personality and must decide how to satisfy her personality needs and get a return on her investment in her culture. The female must choose between various types of man/woman pair bonds relationships such as monogamous, polygamous, mistress, sexual liaison with unmarried or married men, serial relationships, single with a consistent male relationship and single and/or married without children.

The man in all types of man/woman pair bonds is considered a potential unstable, unreliable and/or unpredictable resource for the mother/child bond. This means he may choose to leave the woman, which means he abandons supporting the mother/child bond causing bond damage to the child. Women have to emotionally maneuver around and with the male as a resource. They must find ways to address their sexual personality, cope with the sexuality imposed upon them by nature and cope with the gender rules for her sex (i.e., women wear lipstick, nail polish and dresses; men do not, women stay home with the children; men do not).

Nature has defined and created sexuality in women despite Mother Nature philosophy and mother/child bonding. Women are faced with the task of realizing and satisfying their sexuality without jeopardizing the mother/child bond and without being misused by the man/woman bond pairing. Women's sexuality is unique because nature has given women a clitoris. Its only purpose is for sexual pleasure while men do not have such a physical part. In men the penis is not strictly for sex. It has three functions: sperm and urine delivery and the head of the penis is for sexual stimulation. Men do not have any body part designed strictly for sexual pleasure. Women can have long periods of sexual arousal because the clitoris can sustain orgasm pleasure. Men cannot sustain orgasm pleasure and it is doubtful that they can have an orgasm. Men have a pleasing sensation from ejaculation, but this is not a physiological orgasm. During sexual intercourse, the rubbing of penis against the vagina, the thrusting of penis against the uterus, the hip thrusting against the clitoris and the swinging back and forward motion of the uterus ligaments cause the uterus and vagina muscles and ligaments to rebound. This rebounding sustains the orgasm pleasure for the woman. Physiologically women are built for sex while men are not. Women can have longer episodes of pleasure arousal because they have higher levels of stimulation to reach a sexual turn on (threshold) while men have a low threshold. Females have higher smell sensitivity for men's odorless fumes of sex stimulating hormones called pheromones. Therefore, they can easily sense fertility in men. Women during ovulation have increased aggressiveness, self confidence, orgasm easier and have increased sex fantasies. Women sexually enjoy male/female bonding rituals and ceremonies called romance while men tolerate romance or do not enjoy it. Women have outward signs of fertility such as large non-lactating breast (other females' breast are flat when not nursing), and excessive fatty tissue on the hips which makes their waist smaller than the hips, indicating availability for pregnancy. Women during pregnancy are hormonally triggered to enhance their sexually attractiveness and flirt (i.e., are romantic) more in order to keep the male bonded to them. In women ovulation is concealed. Women do not have an outward fertility sign similar to other female mammals like the monkey whose buttocks turn bright pink. Concealed ovulation allows women to exercise more selectiveness in choosing a mate while unconcealed ovulation would make her the mate of the most aggressive and dominating male. Essentially, women are physiologically better built for sex and gain more pleasure from sex and bonding than men. Their bodies secrete the morphine like chemicals oxytocin and endorphins which give them a pleasure (drug high) from sex and bonding. Sexual stimulation of the clitoris sustains the drug-like high. Nature has psysiologically defined women's sexuality and Mother Nature philosophies have in many ways tried to redefine the woman's nature. Despite the conflict or in spite of the conflict between Nature (what is) and Mother Nature (what isn't) women have to find ways to pair bond (male/female bond) and bond with a child (mother/child). Women are focused on bonding to their own nature, their man's nature and child's nature which require using the culture to define the bonds and the best method for using and coordinating the bonds.

Women bonding with men as well as men bonding with their child are affected by the brotherhood. The men's bond with their child is affected by the brotherhood. The men's brotherhood consists of a man's significant group of friends or male alliances to other men or men only clubs and/or gangs. The brotherhood defines for the men their sex role, how to have sex with women, defines manhood, how to be a husband and father and how to keep your manhood on jobs and in society and in female relationships. The brotherhood can be a formal (organized) or an informal group or a combination of both. Men in their brotherhood constantly exchange information and evaluate each other's emotions and behaviors in a casual or joking manner or while gossiping or while engaged in an activity (watching sports, playing computer games, basketball, at parties or night clubs, etc.). The male's significant circle of male friends (brotherhood) updates each other on the trends in parenting, romance, methods of sexual female conquest techniques, slang words, ways to avoid parenting or social time with wives or girlfriends, jobs available, movies to watch, exchange stories, jokes and myths (lies), talk about sexual conquest, ways to avoid police or beat the system, methods of adultery, etc. Men in the brotherhood rate each other (rank) and classify each other's skills and manhood ability (file) and reaffirm each other's manhood. A man's bond with other men (brotherhood) is in many ways more important than his bond with his wife and/or girlfriend because the brotherhood gives him his value as man and meaning for life as a man. In many ways male bonding is similar to male animals.

In male animals the male must first have power and control over the males or control land (resources) before he can mate with a female. It is the male brotherhood that gives him power or takes away his power. Men fight (compete) with each other for control of resources (land, food, women). Women are considered a resource or a type of property or trophy for achieving power. Men constantly devote time to the brotherhood by doing brotherhood related activities. Men watch sports in order to emotionally feel connected to the brotherhood and they gossip about sports in order to emotionally maintain the male bond. Men will abandon (leave, divorce, separate) their significant female but will never abandon the brotherhood. When they abandon the female they also abandon the total bonding activities needed to have a healthy child. The brotherhood therefore makes the male an unstable resource for the female and child bond. Consequently, women must maneuver with and around the brotherhood (male bonding to males) in order to maintain father/child bonds. However, in most instances the brotherhood damages the child because it is usually established with European culture as a model. The Black man's brotherhood must be formed with Maat as the basis not power (ego), resources and/or land as the foundation. Men in the brotherhood tend to brag about sexual conquest and coach each other to be promiscuous or rape.

Physiological male sexuality begins when he can ejaculate sperm and achieves bone and muscle mass (size) while a woman's sexuality is triggered by her physical ability to store fat and this triggers ovulation. Fat is stored around the hips, buttocks, under the skin (makes it feel soft) and breasts. In any case, men must have physical size (muscle mass) in order to protect themselves from other males. The man's ability to fight to protect himself, mate and family is a typical mammal characteristic. In male animals their horns, antlers, tusk, and fangs are almost exclusively used for violence/combat with other males. Male to male violence is higher than male violence to wives and girlfriends. In Caucasian culture and Black men that follow Caucasian culture, men are physically assaulted, murdered and raped by other men at twice as high a rate than men to women. It is a code of the brotherhood that violence (fighting) is a way to protect and show off your manhood. For example, male dogs and male monkeys that sexually mount other males do it to show off their dominance (manhood power) and to maintain their status in the brotherhood. The rape of men by men is a negative form of dominance and showing off manhood.

Men have to devote time to the brotherhood. They usually have to reduce the time needed for bonding to their mate and child in order to maintain their brotherhood group. Usually, men invent excuses to avoid spending bonding time with their girlfriend/wife and/or child in order to spend more time with the brotherhood. If the male fails to spend time with the brotherhood he has no way to maintain or evaluate his manhood. And, females evaluate their male mates based upon how many males make positive comments about him, how much other males recognize him, give him a rank or file status or pay attention to his abilities. The more the brotherhood gives recognition to the male or the more male positive social activities of recognition (i.e., church/mosque attendance, knowledge of politics, computers, sports, culture, etc.) the more attractive he is to women. It is the quality of male brotherhood recognition that gives him status/manhood. The recognition can be through control or violence or combat type sports (War Before Civilization by Keely). Recognition can be negative (gangs, materialism) or positive. However, the recognition has to be indirectly (good job, promotion on job, male superior) or directly given by a male. Recognition is a reward received and valued by other men which makes him sexually appealing to women. It is a paradoxical situation that the female is in because the more recognition the male has the more time is required to earn it (i.e., socializing with the fellows, long hours at work) and the less time he has to bond with her or his child. The end result of European cultural type bonding is a child damaged by lack of bonding time from the father.

The male to male bonding groups (brotherhood) and the female to female (sisterhood) groups are similar. They are an outgrowth of the culture, sustain the culture, and are rigidly protected by the rewards and punishments of the members. The members of the brotherhood as well as the culture do not tolerate males that try to do activities outside of the brotherhood's spoken and unspoken system of rewards and punishments. The rewards for staying in the brotherhood are the male membership giving the male a feeling of manhood, power and respect. The membership gossips positively about things its members have done or make jokes about each other's manly type behaviors. The punishment for a member doing activities not approved by the brotherhood is the male member accidentally being uninvited to social activity or the member being left out the dozens game, etc. This punishment causes the offending member to feel lonely and powerless. Offending male behavior for the brotherhood can be: a father attending shopping trips; parties, field trips, with his child along with married or single female parents, chauffeuring his child along with other children to social activities where single and married female parents are in attendance, participating in predominately single and/or married female parent groups, telephoning single and/or married female parents in order to exchange parenting skills or food recipes, cornrowing a daughter's or son's hair, talking non-sexually to single or married female parents casually while with your child, etc. These are related father/child bonding activities and necessary. However, the father or worse yet a big brother (non-blood related mentor) that engages in such activities will directly and indirectly cause problems with the single and married females' mate and girlfriends (i.e., sisterhood). The brotherhood and sisterhood will question the father's motives and assume he is trying to make a sexual conquest of one or a few of the mothers or they will assume he has mental problems (crazy) or assume he has gender issues (i.e., homosexual), etc. The brotherhood and sisterhood will punish the father by spreading harmful character assassination gossip about the father or accidentally forget to invite him to brotherhood activities because they will assume he is too busy being a parent or they will emotionally torture him by telephoning him to brag about the fun the brotherhood had at a social activity or insinuate that he missed an easy sexual conquest or an exciting sports activity, etc. These are tactics the brotherhood uses to punish a male for doing father/child bonding activities and bonding related activities. The brotherhood does not tolerate total father/child bonding and in many ways treats it as a sign of manhood weakness. They emotionally torture a father that attempts total bonding. The brotherhoods conscious and subconscious punishment of a father bonding results in unspoken approval of partial bonding. The African-centered brotherhood should re-define itself and offer rewards for total bonding. However, the sisterhood, gender, demographic, the culture's sex preference and marriage institution will view a male participating in total bonding as a problem. Society and culture can overcome this disadvantage built into the brotherhood by basing the brotherhood on the principles of Maat and/or Kwanzaa and Cultural Virtues.

The problem built into the European cultural centered sisterhood of Black women is European gender. It is commonly taught to girls by their mother and accepted by Black women that Black men are only interested in having sex with any available female. The social phrase is "black men are only interested in what's between a woman's legs = pussy". It is felt that given a chance or opportunity, any Black man will have sex with a woman if presented with the opportunity. Young girls are taught this and shape their emotions, way of thinking, behavior, posture and words to be a defense against a male sex predator. The obvious facts of the Black man's sex behavior are revealed in countless anthropology books. These books about African centered sexuality within African cultures uncontaminated by European culture's sex rules and gender document that Black men are primarily concerned about their family (wife, child, relatives) and resources (land, craft) not sex. No anthropology book states that African centered Black men are solely interested in being a sex predator. When European culture's sex ideations (men are only interested in sex) are taught to girls it Europeanizes them and causes them to be alienated from Maat and holistic sex. The girls become mothers who disease the bonding process of children with a foreign Caucasian philosophy. It is difficult for a Black child to access their Black (African centered) intelligence with a White social and sexual (European) program. The sisterhood has to re-evaluate its philosophy about Black men and black men have to re-evaluate their brotherhood. There are many imperfections in the sisterhood and brotherhood that require a holistic healing.

The sisterhood (adolescent, teenage and adult peer groups-cliques) maintains bonds between members with rewards and punishments. The females in the group bond with the group and with each other. The members compete with each other to maintain and/or gain rank (status). Rank gives the member value (reward) and power (reward). Rank can be achieved if the school/college age female student has high grades ("A" student), is known to know a lot of personal secrets of others, owns expensive sneakers, clothes and jewelry, has the ability to win fights, possesses physical beauty, etc. The group functions as a dictionary that translates society, parents, sex, boys, politics and life. The females maintain their bonds with various rituals and ceremonies such as putting on make-up together, going to shopping malls together, exchanging gossip, doing homework together, maintaining E-mail and chat rooms with each other, etc. Adolescent and teenage group members grow up to be adults that use the group experience to help them to bond positively, negatively and dysfunctionally with other females and/or males.

The group is a miniature version of the "Illness and Goodness" of the larger society, it is created by the society and functions to maintain society. The peer groups (sisterhoods/brotherhoods) maintains the values of society along with a mixture of non-genetic factors, genetic factors, European culture and castrated African culture(so called Black Experience). A negative experience in an adolescent and/or teenage peer group or an experience of being a victim of non-aggressive or aggressive attack of a peer group can cause dysfunctional male and/or female relationships in adult life. Group abused adolescent and/or teenage females become women that cannot completely trust other women or a woman that prefers to enjoy men's company (companionship) over women, or they become women that cannot develop unconditional close relationships with other women. Young girls become women that do not trust other women because they have experienced or witnessed females unprovoked violent sneak attacks or character assassination attacks, malicious gossip, lies, slurs and/or negative rumors which were started to demonstrate power or achieve power or to break up two female friends or a boyfriend and girlfriend relationship.

The passive aggressive, non-verbal, and physically violent aggression is part of the tools (tactics) groups use to maintain bonding and to recruit new members. New members join the group to share in the group's power or because they have observed the fear others have of the group or they join the group to use it as a surrogate family or they join to be with others of like mind, troubles, drug/alcohol use, and dysfunctions. In many ways the individual, the group and society are one and the same. Individuals, groups and society depend upon bonding for survival. It must be kept in mind that the brotherhood is just as flawed and dysfunctional as the sisterhood, they both are victims of a miseducation, and use deceit (back stabbing) type behaviors and gossip to stay alive. Girls do unto girls the same as boys do unto boys.

The teenagers are in puberty and are fertile and ready to breed, they have sex hormonal stimulated feelings, thoughts, behaviors, and desires. The sex hormones cause them to focus on sexual intercourse, sexual fantasy, sex gossip, pornographic type music videos, dancing and movies. Teenagers enjoy exhibiting sexual availability (so called flirting). The girls' toy Barbie Dolls and the boys' computer games and G.I. Joe type toys of adolescents (pre-puberty) were used to practice social and sexual manipulation and violence and power. The adolescent becomes a teenager that uses people to socially and sexually manipulate instead of dolls and computer games. The girls teach each other that nice guys, sensitive men and/or male friends are the type males to talk with or use for free psychotherapy or counseling; but are not the type of males to sexually lust for or fall romantically in love with or commit adultery with. The boys in groups teach each other that a nice girl is one to marry but not to have erotic sex or hang out with. The social and sexual schizophrenia of adults is alive in the group bonding process, the adult phrase "do as I say, not as I do" reveals the relevance of the double standard (social schizophrenia). The females' double standard is not sexually or behaviorally unique to females or males. However, females tend to use social schizophrenia (smile in your face and stab you in the back with slander about you to others) and indirect and passive aggression. The females tend to have emotional tantrums and mood swings that a non-sensitive male will be unaware of or ignore. A sensitive male in a relationship with an emotionally sporadic (hot and cold) female will be aware of the emotional tantrums and mood swings and react by getting upset and eventually won't tolerate them by discontinuing the relationship or will avoid interpersonal contact but not sexual contact. Consequently, it may be to the female's advantage to lust for the non-sensitive, macho man and profess to need a sensitive man. The social schizophrenia is essentially practiced by males and females and makes an unconditional bond problematic or dysfunctional.

The female groups use indirect, covert, passive aggressive behavior, deception, sex, misdirection, violence, cursing, money, manipulation, and emotionalism as a tactic to operate the strategies of power and control. The females' individual bonding and group behaviors are distorted by the erroneous assumptions and beliefs of a Mother Nature philosophy. Mother Nature philosophy essentially defines females as primarily innately nurturers, passive, cooperative, nice, caregivers, gentle, focused on mothering rather than ego and endowed by heredity to be emotionally superior to men. Nature (socio-biology, chemistry, genetics, etc.) contradicts Mother Nature philosophy. Nature does not explain or excuse that females are killing machines (soldiers, police), athletes, boxers, wrestlers, lack parenting skills, tomboys, murderers, egotistical, competitive, selfish, murderers of children (birth control pills, abortions) and basically are human beings with flaws, perfections, and inadequacies. The sisterhood groups function like Nature and accept females for what they are and what they want to be. The group gives an outlet for flaws, violence, greed, sex ideation, power, niceness, liars, corruption, normalcy and the need to bond.

The sisterhood and brotherhood both use military tactics and strategies. The groups do not see themselves as military units. Historically, the Black Experience (oppression, segregation, colonialism, and slavery) is a military experience and an experience of being bonded and socialized in groups (plantation slaves, breeding slaves, soldier slaves, etc.) by military people (Caucasian gangs of invaders, terrorist, rapist, soldiers, colonizers, slave traders, etc.). The slave masters facilitated the group experience of slave plantation workers and slave breeders with group techniques universally shared through the slave merchants and slave master's bulletins, newsletters, planters conventions and consultants (i.e., Willie Lynch). The slave groups were taught to value light skin over dark skin, lie (malicious gossip) on each other to get rewards and praise from the slave master (group leader). The slaves maintained temporary relationships and maintained the power relationship roles of slave (Black wife) and slave master (Black husband), the slaves constantly mistrusted each other and were constantly suspicious of betrayal (i.e., Uncle Tom, adultery) and they were taught (miseducated) to adopt Caucasian group dynamics as the ideal. Today, the adolescent, teenage and adult group members relationship with each other are copies of European tribes, European gangs, slave plantation workers and European military behaviors. Ironically, enslavement of Africans requires bondage. Black people (Africans) were bonded together with chains and were called chattel slaves. Society wants its people "bonded" to it, to support it and work and live for it and kill for it (soldiers) and invest in its "stocks" and "bonds." Obviously, the Wall Street Stock Market sells "bonds" to subliminally keep people physically and economically and mentally bonded to society. Therefore, people are the "stocks" used to make "bonds" that build and maintain society. The stock market psychologically and economically keeps people attached (bonded) to society. The group experience of adolescents and teenagers is a "bondage" experience which can be positive and/or negative. Bonding for Black folks can be positive if it is attached to their culture. An African centered group bonding experience for the young functions with Maat/Kwanzaa principles, adults, elders and ancestors' wisdom (i.e., Harriet Tubman, Marcus Garvey, Malcolm X, Fanny Lou Hammer, Martin King). The group is a living, holistic bonding experience that covers a full range of functions.

The adolescent, teenage and adult group socializes individuals and helps them to create attitudes, bonds, behaviors and methods to have social and sexual relationships. The group is not an isolated entity, it is a collection of individuals created by being bonded to culture. Bonding is a political, educational and economic device of culture. The group and the individual are one and the same. They both bond to society to transmit and translate culture. The male group functions as if it is one male entity while the female group functions as if it is a single female entity or a single family entity bonded to a culture. A group grows and learns like it is a child growing to be an adult. The number of people in a group can vary. A group is a family unit. One individual member unconsciously functions as a father or mother or eldest child, youngest child, bad child, good child, talkative or shy child or as an adopted child. Within the group there can be emotional, spiritual and mental (the brain) leaders, a disciplinarian, counselor, sex police, a spy, recruiters, fashion police, rumor and gossip spreaders, thugs, Miss Nice, a beauty queen, fight planners, etc. The problem with a negative group experience is that it can cause permanent emotional scars. From the group experience females can negatively learn how to bond, as well as be deceitful, learn how to steal boyfriends, break friendships and/or love affairs, be a player (non-romantic sex), learn how to agitate, plot sneak attacks, etc. Females in the group collaborate to define what a man should be and learn how to be the ruler and authorizer of feelings and emotions in a relationship. Men learn from a consensus of opinions of group members when to and how to neglect women's feelings and emotional needs. Both the female and male groups provide negative and positive bonding and power for its members.

The sisterhood can consist of any size and combination of casual, steady or plutonic female friends, school friends, work place (job) friends, and/or family relatives. The group can be formal, informal, organized, unorganized, a clique, gang, housewives, junkie friends, church friends, etc. Membership in a female youth (adolescent, teenage) group gives members recognition by bestowing a high rank (status) for being socially popular, a sexual predator (player), rapper, dancer, having the ability to get money from a boy or use his car, stealing from stores, stealing test or homework answers, having a boyfriend with high rank, etc. The group uses offensive and defensive tactics to protect members and to be more popular than another group and/or develop a reputation. Some of the youth group tactics are attacking a designated female victim with malicious gossip, telephone a female, then don't speak and hang up, non-verbal aggression, condescending looks, teasing, spreading a rumor that a girl is a slut that freely gives oral sex to boys and/or girls, silent treatment (failing to greet or speak to the victim and/or ignoring the victim), saying the girl has V.D., beating the girl up, etc. Many of the tactics used on someone that is not approved by the group, or the attack can be a sneak attack that leaves no evidence of who committed the attack or a justifiable reason for the attack.

Victims of a group attack can be emotionally scared for life. The victim usually feels ostracized, isolated, violated, lonely, confused, angry or depressed. The victim may attempt to do anything (social, money, or sexual favors) to stop the attacks or have the group accept them, they can develop low self-esteem, start using illegal drugs and/or abuse alcohol, need medication, attempt suicide or develop an eating disorder or their grades will drop or they become truant.

Girls as individuals or group members are forced by society to stay slim and look sexually available (so-called attractive). Consequently, Black girls want to look like a music video whore, so they consume diet sweeteners (Aspartame) in foods and sodas. Aspartame (artificial sweetener such as Nutra Sweet) causes nerve damage, memory loss, attention deficit, violence, rage, hormone imbalance, menstruation problems and mood swings which cause girls to get in more fights than boys. Added to this girls regulate their periods and avoid pregnancy by taking birth control drugs or using the birth control patch. The drugs and synthetic estrogen used for birth control cause weight gain (more Aspartame use) and water bloating, menstruation problems, mood swings, attention deficit, cancer and skin outbreaks (bumps on the face and more make-up use). Consequently the ovulating teenager has added motivation for violently, emotionally and socially abusing each other.

The manner in which group members bond with each other and the manner in which individuals bond with individuals is created by an individual's prenatal life, non-genetic factors, genetic factors and hormones. People feel good being bonded to friends, family members, gang members, and love ones because natural morphine-like hormones (i.e., oxytocin, enkephalin and endorphin) are secreted in the body. This is nature's morphine-like hormonal method of causing people to enjoy bonding and wanting to bond. The thoughts, behaviors and feelings used to bond are developed logically and/or illogically when the senses are stimulated during your prenatal life. The unborn child (fetus) uses its senses of taste, smell, sight, hearing and touch to constantly create spiritual, mental and emotional thoughts (intelligence). These different types of intelligence cascade (develop) into part of the adolescent (pre-puberty), teenage (puberty) and adult feelings, moods and behaviors. In fact, the senses are used constantly to transmit and translate into thoughts and behaviors which are erroneously called traits and innate ability. For example, it has been scientifically verified that during the early growth of a baby chicken, if it is not allowed to see its feet (feet were covered with cloth), it will not eat worms. Until this was proven, it was erroneously assumed that the act of chickens eating worms was an innate ability and a genetic, programmed trait. It is erroneously assumed that the senses have no function in personality and thought development and bonding.

When the senses are stimulated they participate in the development of moods, thoughts, feelings, sex, behaviors, bonding and participate in the spiritual and physical personalities. The senses are not an isolated part of an individual, they are a holistic part and participant of bonding with yourself, nature, the environment, God and your culture (culture is a group with the same ethics, morals, rituals and ceremonies and classified by skin color). The quality of the group and an individual's life is dependent upon the quality of bonding, especially prenatal, infant, toddler, adolescent (pre-puberty) and puberty (teenager) bonding.

A culture has imperfections and must be willing and able to make adjustments and find solutions. Obviously, European cultural centered mother/child and father/child relationship has problems. The Family Institution and Marriage Institution is dysfunctional. A Black person that uses European institutions is walking into a house on fire—doomed to dysfunctionality. This is clearly validated by the children's high suicide, homosexuality, drug abuse, sex addiction, gang activities, learning problems, crime rate and disrespect for parental authority. There are certain factors and influences that are not healthy for the parent/child relationship to change. It is natural for the parent/child relationship to change. And, it is natural for parents and culture to have a crisis, healings, social and emotional ups and downs and adaptations. A problem or problems with a people have to be solved by that people. A problem within a culture has to be solved by the people of that culture;

it is not a responsibility of "nature". Nature cannot be relied upon to help people with a people problem.

Nature (not to be confused with Mother Nature philosophy) is clear about its purpose and survival. Nature will let two homeless drug addicts get married and have children and will let two healthy people get married and have no children. Nature is concerned about nature's survival, greyhound dogs are concerned about greyhounds, eagles are concerned about eagles, the cosmic is concerned about the cosmic, etc. These living things within certain limits will adapt to people. However, a specific living (i.e., cat, rat, frog) is primarily concerned about its own survival. People create a Mother Nature philosophy to explain, excuse, and/or accept Nature, but nature is not concerned with a people's philosophy. Nature is not perfect and is a creation. Only God is the uncreated perfect. All creations have imperfections, only God is perfect. For example, Nature has imperfections—birthing of a child would be easier and more practical for the infant to come through the abdomen rather than squeeze its large head through the small pelvic area and vaginal shaft. The large caloric expenditure of energy for the female's pregnancy and child birth makes it energy efficient for males to breastfeed, the retina of the eye attached to the back of the eyeball causes a visual blind spot. It would be better engineering to avoid the blind spot by the retina being attached to the side off the eyeball near the nose. Female infertility (menopause) would be socially, physiologically and sexually logical if males became infertile and their infertility should be synchronized with the female infertility. Large trees are a waste of metabolic energy. It would be more energy efficient for them to be the size and height of a three feet bush. The anus and sex organs are too close together and cause hygiene problems, large breast on non-lactating women would be more energy efficient if the women had a flat chest until they breastfeed, etc. Nature has the ability to correct such imperfections and has performed more impossible tasks and miracles. However, Nature does not have to explain itself to humans and if Nature did explain itself it is doubtful people would understand. Nature provides people with intelligence but does not explain to the brain how the brain works or lets the brain know the time and place of its first thought. Nature survives with many variables and many solutions and many unknowables.

Nature can maintain two types of solutions. There can be two losers or two winners or a winner and a loser. In nature, winning does not have to based upon an opponent losing. In nature a solution does not require a problem. No single solution is a best or worse solution to nature's winners and losers game. Obviously, partial bonding does not work in the best interest of nature, children or society. Nonetheless, Nature will not provide the solution. Culture is obligated to create a Maat bonding solution for the children damaged, neglected, abused, misused and sexually, physically, emotionally and spiritually harmed by parents. The solution has to contain Maat and/or Kwanzaa principles or Cultural Virtues in some form.

The problem with bonding and clusters of un-bonded children (gangs) can be solved if and only if a culture's moral principles (Maat/Kwanzaa) are applied to the children early in life. The child during prenatal and infancy life senses culture from the mother. The infant and mother have synchronized emotions which stimulate each others corresponding brain regions. What happens to the mother (culture) happens to the baby (culture). When the mother has regular confrontations with white racism, economic problems, crime, disease, relationship problems, negative attitudes, junk foods, stress, drugs, and there is a lack of inner peace and culture, the brain's frontal lobe gets under stimulated. When a child's left frontal lobe of the brain is under-stimulated, they tend to be disobedient, easily frustrated, lack initiative, have emotional outbursts and are not easily controlled by rewards and punishments (culture). The frontal cortex of the brain tends to be necessary for applying cultural and social rules and information. A mother under stressors cannot devote the necessary time needed for healthy bonding and this causes the frontal lobe to be under-stimulated. In other words, the child's brain is a computer with hardware and inadequate (dysfunctional) software to operate the brain. The bonding technology the child requires during infancy is not available when the mother's attention is diverted away from nurturing and allocated to stressors. In many cases, a mother or father with a low income have higher stressors and Black folk with high income have high stressors because their income (economic status, living condition, social life) isolates them from other Black folks (culture). In any case, stressed people tend to be around others that talk to them about the negativity in their life which increases stress. Being stressed by others causes stress to build up over time which leads to an increase in relationship problems, diseases and emotional and mental problems. This results in dysfunctional children being bred in a stressed family unit and these dysfunctional children form cliques (gangs) that create a dysfunctional community and dysfunctional leaders (dysleadership). Stressed parents' bonds crack and brake causing their children, marriages and relationships to become casualties. A stressed child has a stressed emotional center of the brain (limbic system, amygdala) which sends signals of danger causing thoughts of "get out of the home," "stay away from your parents," "protect yourself," "I want to do what I want to do before I get hurt," etc.

The emotional center of the brain's limbic system especially the amygdala needs bonding to function normally. The amygdala senses whether a person has good intentions or bad intentions as well as when a bond is good or bad. However, a limbic system inadequately nurtured or exhausted because of drugs, disease, junk food, or emotional abuse will not develop normally. This can cause a child with an under-nurtured childhood experience to become an adult that thrives on dysfunctional relationships or makes a functional relationship into a dysfunctional relationship. A stressed baby that gets loving, nurturing responses or has parents that react to stress without becoming emotionally abusive or violent learns emotional skills needed to be normal. When a child does not experience good parenting skills or nurturing, they tend to be emotionally impoverished, unsure of themselves, emotionally inadequate in relationships and in some spiritual way dysfunctional.

Children that are unbonded, negatively bonded or grow up in dysfunctional families tend to have a higher likelihood of diabetes, depression, learning disorders, suicide, cancer, hepatitis, strokes, bronchitis, venereal disease, drug and alcohol abuse and dysfunctional relationships. They tend to lack control of the boundaries of acceptable aggression which means aggressive play can lead to a fight. They have genetic problems because they have a short nerve alleles 5HTT inadequate information reception center and lack control of the boundaries of acceptable aggression which means aggressive play can lead to a fight. They have genetic problems because they have a short alleles 5HTT which influences normal serotonin levels. Consequently, they have low serotonin, which causes irritability, lack of impulse control and depression. If they were bonded positively and nurtured they would have normal serotonin levels and be able to regulate the flow of chemical information in their brains. An inadequate serotonin level can compound problems with girls (females). Females tend to take longer to defuse emotions. They tend to nurture good and bad feelings before they release them. This may be caused by their body fat storing hormones (i.e., serotonin) and/or releasing them slower. Hormones are contributors to girls' and boys' emotions and playtime behaviors.

Boys and girls must use playtime to develop social skills. The passive aggressive behavior and violent aggressive play (rough and tumble, mock fighting) of boys and girls allow the child to emotionally define what feelings and actions are appropriate or inappropriate in social settings. The pretend (mock) fights and cooperative and/or competitive, physical activities are needed so that children can learn social limits of behavior or word usage, evaluate others strengths and weaknesses, develop evidence and avoidance skills, adapt to change and challenges in a relationship and learn how to calm down after a conflict as well as develop the ability to resolve physical, emotional and verbal conflicts. The child's desire for playtime activities is partially caused by the oxytocin hormone (morphine-like high) which causes people to seek bonding to others. The feelings of bonding and social confidence are associated with another hormone called serotonin. Hormones such as norepinephrine and vasopressin in the correct proportion with the hormones of oxytocin, prolactin, serotonin and the endogenous (bodily made) opioid peptides help people to have friendly bonds with others and help social memory. When the child feels unloved or has negative bonding feelings or a negative bond experience, prolactin levels decrease and anxiety, stress, and irritability increase. If the child had a negative prenatal experience caused by their pregnant mother being sexually, emotionally, socially, economically, spiritually, physically abused or having relationship stressors, then the child will tend to be aggressive, bond negatively with others as well as find it difficult to talk, will walk later and be difficult to toilet train and nurture. The infant and prenatal experience contributes to the dysfunctional behaviors of the child in gangs and relationships and in many ways creates dysfunctionality.

A poor quality bond experience such as participating in a gang of dysfunctional youth with dysfunctional gang behaviors leaves a lasting impression. A child can become addicted to the gang and gang activities. When a child or adult is addicted to a gang (i.e., clique) they convince themselves that the gang's negative behaviors do not have a destructive effect on them. Addiction to gangs, relationships, drugs, material objects as well as other addictions indicates that the addicted person is demanding that someone else or something else must be responsible for their happiness.

A child addicted to dysfunctional friends or a dysfunctional gang becomes an adult that is addicted to dysfunctional relationships. And, a relationship addict (junkie) is an adult that is constantly in a series of bad relationships or they are in a good relationship which they subconsciously make bad and then leave the relationship. The problem with adult relationship occurs because the relationship addict subconsciously uses the dysfunctional gang's bonding experience or their dysfunctional family as the model for bonding behaviors. The gang experience provided the pleasure of bonding. However, the bond was dysfunctional. Children bonded dysfunctionally to their parents or a gang eventually become "bad relationship junkies." The relationship junkie enters a new relationship to feel the high from the bodily made morphine-like hormone chemicals (opiodes-enkelphalin, endorphins, oxytocin) that the body naturally makes when bonded people are together (friends, parent and child, sister and brother and/or sister, relatives, gang members, etc.). The addicted persons new relationship (drug-like high) provides temporary relief from the inner personality dysfunctions. When the newness of the relationship wears off or the bond is broken, the addict seeks another relationship or gang activity to get high off. Addiction to a relationship high gives a false sense of power.

A false sense of power is demonstrated when a male dog homosexually mounts another male dog and starts thrusting his penis at the dog underneath him as if the male dog is a female dog. The dog that is on top is in the male position, the dominant, controlling, superior and power position. The male dog on top is demonstrating power. Homosexual type behaviors in the animal kingdom and with human animals are related to power. The need for power or a sense of powerlessness is the dysfunctional subconscious driving force of a person's homosexual behavior while sex pleasure is a conscious secondary dysfunctional desire. Sex and sexual rape are usually used to satisfy the need for power. Addiction is a dysfunctional form of power in which the addict get power by raping themselves with drugs, gambling, food, relationships, homosexuality, pornography, talking, sex and gang activity.

Bonding to a gang gives an individual the power that the group represents. The gang addicted child spends increased amounts of time with the gang and gets high off the activities. The addicted person's emotions cooperate with the addiction by telling the addict that they feel good. Each contact with the gang causes a craving for more contact. Nothing satisfies more contact but more contact. Eventually the person's behavior and the gang's behavior become one and the same. The addict's identity is the gang's identity. The addict constantly invents and re-invents excuses (alibis) for staying in the gang or bad relationship and the addict denies the addiction and believes the unreal alibis (lies) for the addiction are true. For example, a person addicted to bad relationships will use the alibi (excuse) that they stay in the bad relationship because the sex is good. The bond to the gang (or bad relationship) is an addiction to the gang and an addictive bond. This addictive bond alters the person's biochemistry and affects the emotions. The addict's behavior in a gang is messed into the natural playtime behavior of boys and girls.

Children's hormone levels and bond to their parents (or surrogate parent or parental figure) shape their emotional thinking and physical behaviors. For example, boys that have a positive bond to their fathers or a significant adult male tend to learn how to substitute social skills for violent aggression. Boys bonded positively with adult males have higher testosterone and serotonin hormone levels. The negatively bonded or unbonded boy (teenager as well as young males) tend to have high testosterone and low serotonin levels and are more physically violent and sexually aggressive. The lack of a positive bond has an impact on hormone levels and social skills.

The more physically aggressive boys and older males in groups (i.e., gangs) tend to lack nurturing abilities and do not achieve high ranks in groups. For example, the male with the most nurturing, conflict resolution, reassurance, reconciliation and appeasement social skills tends to become the leader. In other words, the male that can utilize his Female Principle is made the leader or given some type of high rank. The leader usually has high serotonin and normal testosterone levels. Male gangs (groups) that have high testosterone and low serotonin usually do not have a definite leader or a clear rank and file picking order (hierarchy).

Gangs without a clear hierarchy or that have many males that had negative bonds have internal violence and social problems plus they do acts of violence on the community (society). Oddly enough, the unbonded males form dysfunctional gangs that serve a negative and positive social purpose. Gangs tend to be a fixed part of Caucasian culture and a fixed part of the Black folks that follow Caucasian culture. The dysfunctional gangs are usually a collection of members that are not viable to society and in many ways left over people (social waste). The gangs are a social institution and no amount of social programs will change or uncreate them. The gang members that had negative bonds or were never bonded join together to dysfunctionally bond together. They suffer from internal violence, sell drugs to others and sell to each other, they kill each other, steal from each other and the community, rape members and others, have poor health, come from broken homes, have learning disorders, high unemployment, AIDS, addiction, a poor education and are preyed upon by the police. Gang members share emotional, spiritual, and social misery. Their shared dysfunctionality, social and family misery keep their bond alive with chaos, violence and casualties. They are created by society and are mirrors of the worst of society. They represent society's inabilities to solve bond damage and inability to save the unfortunate dysfunctionals.

When society rejects the unbonded and dysfunctionals by not solving their problems, society indirectly creates gangs. Gang members only have one social institution that accepts them and that is the gang. The gang as an institution destroys its own members with violence, drugs, murder and disease—they exterminate themselves. And, because they exterminate themselves, they solve society's problem by getting rid of society's dysfunctionals. Therefore, the gangs are created by society to exterminate society's problem. Consequently, the gangs are society's solution for its social waste. The gang serves as a social garbage disposal system for society's unwanted social waste. In fact, the gang members become adults that are dysfunctional that have children that they make dysfunctional that eventually join the social garbage trash container called a gang. The gang acts as a buffer to protect society from society's unwanted social garbage. Gangs are a self creating perpetual motion machine that serves an economic function for society. The gangs' dysfunctional and anti-social behavior is a feeder system that generates income for the criminal justice system, department of welfare, adoption agencies, abortion clinics, psychologists, lawyers and the drug, gun, junk food, clothing, music, special education, car dealerships, fast food, home protective systems, cell phones, computer games, pornography, prostitution, alcohol, funerals, jewelry, surveillance and hospital industries. Consequently, the gangs sustain the economy and will continue to be a social fixture of Caucasian culture. Society feeds on the gang, the gangs feed on society and act as feeders for society. Gangs in Caucasian society are a negative/positive, mutual cooperative and dependent dysfunctional unit that is forced upon Black folks that do not follow Maat or Kwanzaa principles or Cultural Virtues persistently and consistently. Within African culture lies the solution to gangs, bonding problems and the unbonded (i.e., Maat/Kwanzaa, Cultural Virtues, Rites of Passage Group-gangs).

Culture cannot solely create solutions nor does a gene solely create behavior. Behavior is very complex and its creation is partially environmental, nutritional, social, colonialism, hormonal, neurological, conditioning, slavery trauma, gender, genetic, cultural and racial. Genes give you the biochemical possibility to have a behavior but genes are not behavior. A gene simultaneously has different functions, it can be for taste, color, characteristics, and at the same time emotional. Genes predispose you to do stupid things as well as good things. Genes do not always work in your best interest. They can create a mutation (freak) as well as a genius. Genes do not evolve humans so they can be better in the future. In order to do that the genes must presently know about the future, then change for it. They cannot change for a future that does not exist. Genes allow you to adapt to your current condition. Adaptation can give the right or wrong solution for your current condition. Culture, genetics, evolution, gravity, adaptation, science and art are a people's attempt to explain beliefs about life. At best they explain life or excuse life. For example, in evolution the belief is the fittest survive, therefore, those that are surviving (living today) are the fittest (healthiest people). Fitness does not create survival (life) or natural selection (adaptation). Survival of the fittest reveals a person's ability to live (survive). Survival of the fittest assumes that the White race in control of the planet's resources is the fittest race. The White race's fitness is based upon power (guns, military, ability to mis-educate others) and power does not make one the fittest. A child with a loaded gun has the power to tell unarmed adults what to do and the adults will obey the child because if they don't they will be murdered by the child. Since the child is in control and in the power position it can be assumed that the child is the fittest. The ability to control and own violence only means you control and own violence. The survival of the fittest is not solely determined by violence and genes. Genes and fitness do not solely determine behavior nor does bonding solely determine mother/child relationship. Bonding is a device of nature to ensure nature's survival. And, people mix their culture's values into bonding to ensure their culture's survival.

The culture provides rituals and ceremonies for bonding and nature has socio-biochemical rituals and ceremonies for bonding. These two are often confused because each culture has a Mother Nature philosophy based upon its spiritual beliefs and morality. Bonding is a unity, covenant, agreement, and harmony between two people. When two people unite or a person is united with a culture, it is called bonding. For example, a man and a woman in love can be emotionally united together with social and sexual rituals and ceremonies called romance. Romance is a social term for mating rituals and ceremonies. Nature uses biochemical changes and physical rituals and ceremonies to bond two people or two living things together. The two people can be a mother and child, two friends, two relatives, a person and a plant, and a person and an animal. The difference between Nature and Mother Nature philosophy must be clear in order to understand bonding. Nature and Mother Nature are two ways to view life. Nature can be considered the science of living and Mother Nature the art of living. Nature can be considered the Male Principle and Mother Nature the Female Principle. The Child is the technology produced by Nature and Mother Nature. The child is a fission or type of unity of the man and woman. This unity or technology has to be raised to create solutions to the problems that the man and woman need solved. Maat is the foundation of raising the child and the culture provides the vision for the child to see the solution. If the child is not properly, totally bonded and reality not correctly defined, then the correct solution to the race's problems will not be reached. The first step to developing the child as a problem solving technology is the parents seeing bonding as an essential building block for the race's future. However, bonding cannot take place without good parenting skills and parenting knowledge.

SEXUAL ABUSE AND RAPE

Heterosexual and homosexual abuse, molestation and rape have infected Black culture. Black folks that are dominated by Caucasian culture or oppressed, colonized, educated or enslaved by Caucasians are performing heterosexual and homosexual rape, molestation and sexual abuse with their relatives, children, brothers and sisters (incest) and strangers. Caucasian medias of newspapers, movies, textbooks, fairytales, video games, and advertisements promote molestation, sexual abuse and rape. Black music videos use heterosexual and homosexual intercourse dance movements, mimic rape, masochism, sadism and mix violence with sex. In Caucasian culture, sex is subliminally used as a military technique in which the powerful (victor) sexually abuses and rapes the loser (defeated). Television shows have overt and obvious heterosexual and homosexual language and physical activities that stimulate both types of sex. Wrestling entertainment uses subliminal homosexual movements that stimulate sex ideation. Football and basketball use cheerleaders to stimulate sex; volleyball and tennis use sexually stimulating clothes and camera angles. The sexual social climate is charged with an atmosphere that promotes sexual abuse and rape of children. In Caucasian culture, sex is a material object and a commodity; it is not a Godly activity. The concept of sex has been colonized by Caucasians. This causes people to be viewed as sex objects to be used for pleasure, molestation, rape and sexual abuse. Children are valued as sexual virgins that must be raped and sexually abused.

The children's beauty pageants are advertisements for pedophiles (adults that rape children). In beauty pageants, little girls dress as if they are women, sing sexually suggestive songs and sensually parade in adult clothing styles. The children's movies and television shows promote puppy love (sexual activities between children). The Caucasian culture constantly stimulates and subliminally suggests the rape and sexual abuse of adults and children. The largest selling pornographic videos and Internet sites are those involving child prostitution and pedophile activities. A child is endangered by potential homosexual or heterosexual pedophile predators that may be a male or female school teacher, neighbor, relative, schoolmate, friend, police, babysitter, stranger, clergy or their brother or sister (incest). Anyone with genitals can be a potential sexual abuser or rapist of children. Therefore, parents have to be aware of the symptoms and behaviors of sexually abused and raped children.
Because it is built into Caucasian culture to constantly promote sexual thoughts and behaviors, this causes adults and children to physically act out their sexual desires and fantasies. Children that molest other children are modeling adult behavior and are themselves victims. Sex is a language of culture. Sex transmits and translates culture. In Caucasian

culture, sex tends to be a form of power. Caucasian culture's sex rituals tend to be predator and prey orientated and non-spiritual. In African culture, sex is viewed as a spiritual activity and a prayer is said before sexual intercourse. In African culture, sexual abuse of someone is the same as abusing God and to rape someone is the same as raping God. In African culture sex is defined by nature. According to the laws of nature, sperm is meant to fertilize an egg; not manure in a man's anus or saliva in a man's mouth. The female's mouth does not have a sex gland or reproductive function and is not designed for licking or sucking and spitting in another woman's vagina. The mouth has teeth in it for eating food. It is not designed for eating vaginal secretions and spitting into another woman's vagina. The African culture with spiritualized sex and Cultural Virtues, Maat behavior totally eliminates heterosexual and homosexual abuse, molestation and rape of children. Children are not intellectually aware of sexuality but are aware of God, Maat and culture.

Children that have been raped and/or sexually abused do not have the vocabulary to tell someone or they do not know that they have been sexually attacked. A child that has been sexually violated may feel weird or differently inside. They are suffering from a mental illness called post traumatic stress disorder. Their body has become the scene of a crime and parts of their body and emotions cause the feeling of the crime to be re-stimulated. They cannot run away from the assault because their body is the crime scene. If they are not immediately treated they develop emotional, mood and behavioral psychological sex scars. The longer they go untreated the deeper the scar. The sex abuse and or rape has taken away their normal childhood forever. The child may feel ashamed, trapped in an emotion that haunts them, they may have flash backs caused by the particular colors, smell, body part, touch, clothes style, sounds or pain associated with the rape, they may feel dirty, embarrassed, hate their parents for not protecting them, blame themselves, or fear that they or their parents will be harmed if they tell. If untreated they will become adults that have dysfunctional sexuality and dysfunctional relationships and some type of mental illness. Children that have been assaulted sexually must be treated by a professional and legal action must be taken against the person that committed the crime and the criminal must get psychotherapy and if the perpetrator was another child, then psychotherapy is required. The parent must use good parenting skills and be able to talk with the child that has been violated.

A child that is able to talk should be talked to in a calm, relaxed manner. Calmly ask the child if someone has touched them in the genital area or in their underwear area, or touched them with the mouth, hands, a device in the genitals, anus or nipples. Assure the child that she/he is loved, safe and protected. Tell them it is alright to talk about the attack. You may have to use dolls to demonstrate the inappropriate behavior of the attacker and seek professional help in order to help the child talk about the attack. Let the child know that they are not bad because something bad (rape) was done to them. Children feel that if a good person has done something bad to them, then it must be their fault. The child should be told that friends, parents, strangers, children and adults should not touch their penis, vagina, anus and/or nipples with the mouth, hands or an object or device. Using the correct names for the genitals, anus, nipples, etc. instead of saying "pee pee", "wee wee", "pocketbook (clitoris)", "poo-poo (manure)", "kitchen (vagina)", "stinky (manure)" and "accident (urinated in your clothes)" makes ineffective communication about sexual abuse. The child should be told to yell "stop", "no" or "help" whenever someone touches their genitals with their hands, mouth or an object. The child should be told to yell very loudly and run away from the person (child or adult) that is sexually abusing them. The child must be told that the parts of their body that are covered with underwear are not allowed to be touched by children or adults. The child should be told that they should never be asked to take off their clothes and allow someone to take their picture. The child must be told that they should not be asked to watch someone do sex acts (watch masturbation) or others touch genitals (have sex). The child must be told that others should not tell them to touch themselves (masturbate) while the other person watches.

Symptoms of Sexual Abuse (Rape)

*Swelling and/or bleeding from the sex organs or anus
*Pain during urination
*Pain while walking or sitting
*Sore in the mouth can indicate sexually transmitted disease (STD)
*Constant rubbing or touching of genitals
*An increase in bathroom use
*Blood stains in underwear or in or on the toilet or toilet seat
*Recurring urinary tract infection (UTI)
*Itching in genital area

Behaviors That Indicate Sexual Abuse (Rape)

*Unexplainable moodiness
*Physically harmful behavior
*Nightmares
*Telling make believe stories that involve the genital areas
*Suicide attempts
*Constant masturbation
*Easily becoming irritable and hostile
*A potty-trained child that bed wets

*Running away
*Tending to avoid socializing
*Avoids ordinary hugging and/or kissing
*Anxiety
*Reverting to babyish behavior
*Drawing pictures of sexual activities of people or animals
*Change of appetite
*Constantly trying to please others
*Excessive crying
*Depression
*Lack of cleanliness
*Sexual adult behavior
*Decreased self-esteem
*Excessive Anger
*Inability to sleep through the night (Sleep Disorder)
*New fears of people or places
*Age-inappropriate awareness or knowledge about sex
*Compulsive lying
*Abnormal increase in headaches
*Wanting to sit in the laps of adult strangers
*Wearing many layers of clothes
*New fears about going to a doctor
*Changes in school behavior or performance
*Tends to touch others genitals

If your child has been sexually abused, molested or raped or you suspect they have contact professional help. If you suspect someone else's child has been sexually assaulted, notify the parent. Remember that the victim and victimizer must both have psychotherapy.

Suggested Resources

Rape, Abuse and Incest National Network (RAINN)
www.rainn.org
info@rainn.org
800 656-4673

www.brokenspirits.com provides online help for past and present rape victims.

Stop Prison Rape 323 653-7867
www.spr.org
info@spr.org

National Crime Victim Bar Association
www.victimbar.org

victim@ncvc.org Refers victims to attorneys in their area

National Sexual Violence Resource Center
www.nsvrc.org
resource@nsvrc
877 739-3895

Men Can Stop Rape
www.mencanstoprape.org
info@mencanstoprape.org
202 265-6530

SEX, ETC
www.sxetc.org
732 445-7929

Incite! Women of Color Against Violence
www.incite-national.org
415 553-3837

The Dinah Project
www.metropolitanfrc.com/dinah_project.asp
metrofrc@aol.com
A resource that educates about sexuality, violence and appropriate relationships to prevent violence in the Black community.

Committee for Children
www.cfchildren.org
info@cfchildren.org

Contact Mobile
helpline@mobilecan.org
Help line 251 431- 5111

Child Abuse Hotline
www.childhelpusa.org
800 4 – A – CHILD (800) 422-4453

RELATIONSHIP AND EMOTIONS

The basic component of a relationship is communication. The three methods of communication are:

1. Talking
2. Teaching
3. Treading (emotional).

"Talking" is usually unfocused random conversation.

"Teaching" is focused and usually sequential and a step by step way of delivering information.

"Treating" is using emotions to move the person's feelings and then delivering the information.

This method is primarily used by preachers, psychologist, coaches of sports teams, and motivation speakers.

When you fail to deliver information by "talking" then try "teaching" and if the "teaching" method fails, the try "Treating".

If you want to be effective in communicating to someone you must know your own listening style, thinking style, learning type and learning style and you must know the same about the person you are in communication with. Most parents fail to use this scientific way of communication.

The three major listening styles are:

1. Informational
2. Enhancer
3. Critical

The "Informational style" is typical of a person that listens to subjects and topics that add to their knowledge base. They are gathers of data that makes them seem knowledgeable and intelligent. "The Enhancer" style is typical of a person that listens for subjects and topics that they can use to improve their life or the lives of others or relationship. "The Critical Analytical" style is typical of a person that likes to debate subjects or argues the correctness or incorrectness of an idea, event, person or thing.

The four major "Thinking styles" are:

1. Idealistic
2. Harmonizer
3. Critical/Analytical

4. Realistic

The "Idealistic Style" focuses on thinking about things that should have or should be happening for an ideal (perfect) purpose.

"The Harmonizer Style" focuses on everyone else's opinion and/or behavior and wants a peaceful solution to people's differences.

The "Critical Style" tries to improve all situations and sees faults in everyone else's thinking and/or behavior.

The "Realistic Style" sees that human errors are a part of all situations and ideas and accepts that the way an event is planned will not necessarily be the way an event will happen.

The Three major Learning types are:

1. Auditory
2. Visual
3. Rhythm/touch

The Auditory Learner" uses words associated with hearing such as "that sounds stupid", "sounds funny", "hear what I am saying" etc.

The Visual Learner" uses words associated with vision such as "It is not clear...", "That's unclear", "I see what you are saying" etc.

The "Rhythm/Touch Learner" uses words associate movement and the physical body such as "that doesn't move me", "I don't feel that" "it is touching" "that is a touchy subject" etc.

The Four major "Learning styles are:

1. Sequential
2. Random
3. Concrete
4. Abstract.

The sequential Learner" uses a step by step approach tends to, and finishes one task or subject before starting another.

The "Random Learner" tends to multitask, move from one subject to another unrelated subject or starts a task and does not finish and then stops and starts another task. The 'Concrete Learner" usually likes to be shown an activity or task rather than be given oral instructions, if they see a picture or are told a detail description then they can perform the task.

The "Abstract Learner tends to require written instructions or directions then they can perform the task.

The first and primary language is emotions. It is a language that requires development and each person must have an Emotional Vocabulary, Emotional Expense account. Before birth the emotions are active. Each unborn child is a complete emotional package. The unborn child has the emotion of love, anger, fear, joy, depression, hate, shyness, regret, grief, exhaustion, confusion, disappointments, guilt, creativity, hopelessness, despair, jealousy, disgust, surprised, contempt, boredom, peacefulness, sadness,. Etc. The emotions are not felt or expressed in an adult manner they are expressed as an unborn baby would. The baby must use each emotion as if it were a toy. They must play with their emotions to establish their comfortable emotional range and weak emotional levels. This helps them to develop an Emotional Vocabulary and to feel when and when not to use an emotion's negative and positive powers. The unborn child's biochemistry changes with each emotion.

Emotions are a bodily process. For example, anger causes the potential of the element hydrogen to change. Anger causes an electrical change in the body called acid while joy causes an electrical change called alkalinity. In other words, if you are happy and become tearful, your tears are alkaline, while if you are sad and cry your tears are acid. Each state of consciousness and emotion is a biochemical state because the fat and protein ratio, vitamin and mineral ratio, and hormone level will change when your emotion changes. The unborn baby emotionally talks to the mother with its shift in fat and protein, vitamin and minerals and hormone emotional shifts. The mother bio-chemically and hormonally

Detects emotional shifts in the child and the child detects emotional shifts in the mother while the father detects and reacts to emotional shifts in the mother and child.

For example, the unborn baby wants the mother to feel good during pregnancy. Therefore, the baby stimulates the "morphine-like" hormone oxytocin in the mother. Oxytocin is the hormone that causes bonding and makes a person feel good around family or friends or lovers. The baby makes the mother feel good, then the mother makes the father feel good by nurturing him, the father feels good and nurtures the mother, then mother feels good (oxytocin feeling) and enjoys and nurtures the baby. He emotions travel from child to mother to father, then back to the mother and then to the unborn child. It is an unbroken circle of emotional communication driven by oxytocin. Oddly enough if the circle is broken then the child, mother and father, will have an area of their mental, emotional and spiritual vocabulary become dysfunctional or distorted. The emotional circle facilitates the unborn baby develop limits to each emotion a sort of stop and go for emotions.

This hormonal and emotional connectness has been typical of girls that are raised by their mother and father will menstruate late in puberty while girls raised only by their mother menstruate at an earlier age. The father's presence in the menstruating girl's life has a hormonal effect. And hormones are connected to emotions such as fear, which can cause the release of adrenalin which is used to fight the fear or run away (flight) from the object that caused fear.

The unborn child takes the man and woman on an emotional journey (Rites of passage). The unborn child causes the man and woman's feelings and emotions to touch the unborn child inside themselves. The unborn child is birthing the man and woman as mother and father (parents). The child is not being born emotionally it is the man and woman that are being born as parents. The unborn child helps to complete the parent's emotional vocabulary. The parents learn to feel emotions as they shift in the unborn child and shift in each other. It takes the emotional unborn state of the parents to emotionally communicate and connect with the unborn child's emotions.

CHILDHOOD DEVELOPMENT

This chart indicates behavior and problems caused by trimester stress on an unborn child.

Behavioral Development	Behavior Action/Reaction	Dysfunction Caused by Trimester stressors
FIRST TRIMESTER		
Bond (attachment)	Clinger/Avoider (people, relationship)	Scary/Fear (enjoys scary movies, likes fear stimulation in video games)
Retachment (re-unite after separation)	Pursues/Isolate (relationships, social activity)	Anger (Cannot control temper, easily gets mad)
SECOND TRIMESTER		
Identity	Controlling/Manipulators (controls others, lets others control or influence them)	Anxious (In a hurry or rush to do things, nervous
Competence	Competitor/Manipulators (Wants to compete or manipulate others)	Embarrassment (Easily embarrassed, too shy)
THIRD TRIMESTER		
Concern	Caretakers/Loners (likes doing for others, avoids others doing for them)	Sad (Easily gets sad or worried)
Intimacy	Rebel/conformist (in conflict with others or avoids confrontations)	Introvert/Extrovert (Enjoys social activities, always breaks rules, easily influenced.

Emotions have an effect on the brain. For example, the emotion of joy and happiness causes thinking to expand. When you are happy you can think of many activities to do such as going for a walk, dancing, singing, reading, talking to friends etc.

The emotion of anger and hate narrows your thinking. When you are angry with a person you can only think of the person or the activity that caused the anger or doing something to hurt the person. In other words, anger decreases your thinking and makes you dumb while joy increases your thinking and makes you smart.

Also, emotions cause a change in the thought process because they alter nutrients and hormones that the brain uses. For example, sexual intercourse with a pregnant woman causes the testosterone hormone to rise and lowers the progesterone hormone that the baby needs for growth and development and the building of stability in the emotions. This causes the occipital lobe of the brain to have decreased nourishment due to sexual activity during pregnancy.

BRAIN NOURISHMENT

(Cerebrum lobes=sections)

Lobes	Nutrient/Hormone
Frontal (Near Forehead)	Tyrosine, Phenylalanine Testosterone
Parietal (Middle of head)	Acetylcholine, Lecithin, Estrogen
Temporal (Around ear)	GABA, Glutamine, Lipoic Acid Progesterone
Occipital (back of upper neck)	Melatonin, Serotonin, DHEA, 5HTP (Tryptophane) Pregnenolone

Emotions are more powerful than intellect, logic and rational reasoning. Emotions will over ride the intellect and dominate your mood and state of consciousness. Emotions rule while the intellect is relegated to an inferior place. In many situations emotions are only satisfied with emotions not logic. In other words, the only thing that satisfies the emotion of love is love given in return. And, the emotion of love demands more love. No intellectual reasoning can satisfy love. The emotions must work in the company of other emotions to achieve balance. This requires an Emotional Vocabulary which is nurtured in the person before birth and after birth. The Emotional Vocabulary is established by the mother and father's synchronized emotions. If this does not happen then love is misappropriate, misguided, dysfunctional and compromised and viewed as an object. Love becomes ill defined and is used the same as money and the person wants their market value for their love. Usually, they have fixed a price on the dysfunctional love and want the receiver of their love to spend too much to get it and too much to maintain the love. Love is build by an Emotional Vocabulary and this starts as an unborn child that does not have Trimester Stressors from the mother and/or father.

Emotions have a journey to reach maturity. They start similar to an unborn child and search for ways to express themselves. The mother and father must help guide, protect and teach and nurture each of the child's emotions. An emotion that is interrupted or damaged on the path to maturity will not mature and may harm the child as well as others. The emotion seeks maturity and tends to pull the person back to the emotional point where the interruption or stressor of emotional growth occurred.

For example, an alcoholic may have drunk alcohol from 12 years old to 30 years old and then stopped drinking until they were 50 years old. At the age of 50, the alcoholic starts drinking alcohol again, The moment they started drinking their emotional state, reversed to a drunk emotion and went back to age 30. This has been evidence by Alcoholic Anonymous Organization. The drunk emotion was scarred soberness at 30 years old and lost its flexibility to move in a sober state and therefore had to return to 30 years old to repair its self and heal itself so it could move forward. The person's Emotional Vocabulary has lost the emotional ingredients needed to heal and has become frozen at 30 years old and must return to a 30 year old drunk state to start the healing to grow older. The emotional deficit must be paid by emotional currency not intellectual currency. No amount of physical or intellectual growth can make an emotion grow, Emotions grow through emotions.

Emotions hunger from a lack of growth and a healthy satisfied connection to other emotions. Emotions are often disguised by other emotions. A person may smile in your face as if they are your friend and when your back is turned speak to others about how much they hate you. Or, for example, a person may hate themselves and subconsciously want to kill themselves. They may enjoy using a drug (crack, alcohol, heroin) and use their drug habit as a means to kill themselves. In other words, self hate is disguised as a drug habit.

Another example, a girl or boy connects the need to be nurtured by love with their mother's naked body or breast. Because as a young child, when they were nurtured by the mother, the mother would dress and undress her naked body in front of the child. Thus, female nudity was associated with the emotion of nurturing the child's emotion. A young child (especially boys) is allowed to express raw emotion, such as crying feely, saying they hate someone or a toy etc. In other words female nudity (the mother undressing and exposing her nakedness) became associated with emotional freedom. The child was emotionally free to cry, show disgust, anger, hate etc., without a penalty. Consequently, the child grew up to become an adult in a mature adult's emotional straight jacket.

The adult's only way to recapture the feeling of emotional freedom was to seek female and male heterosexual nudity activity which also included nude sex organs This inadvertently causes adult males to emotionally recapture their child-like emotional freedom with pornography. They also emotionally seek to punish their mother for allowing adulthood to take away their child like emotional freedom so they masturbate which is self rape. The act of rape allows the rapist to have power to overcome the lack of emotional freedom caused by the adulthood's emotional constraints so called acting emotionally mature. The child wants emotions to be timeless and endless.

Consequently, if a child is having fun they won't stop to drink water, will try until the last minute to stay up all night having fun, instead of going to bed. Adulthood dictates rule and restriction on emotions making them conform to time and having an ending. The adult with an inadequate or dysfunctional Emotional Vocabulary will use pornography and masturbation to recapture the timelessness and endless state of Emotional Freedom. These perverted activities indicate the failure of the parents to develop an emotional Vocabulary for the child prenatally and during childhood. Sex and pornography and masturbation are over 90% an emotional activity. Those children and adults that participate in pornography, masturbation violent rape, petty rape (sex performed for social or money grain) seductive rape (seduced into sex by music, drugs, peer influence etc.) and fornication (sex as an object not as a spiritual activity) are emotionally ill.

There are very, very few people with a Mental Illness. Mental illness is the failure to use the mind for rationalizing, reasoning and logic. People usually do not have a mental illness, they have an Emotional Illness. When a person is presented with a logical reason to stop a behavior and they continue the negative behavior, then the problem is emotional. If intelligence does not solve a problem then the problem is emotional.

People are Emotionally Ill primarily because their parents or parent was and is Emotionally Ill, Emotionally Dysfunctional. The Parent's culture defines functional and dysfunctional behavior and emotions.

The culture's belief about what is right and wrong sets boundaries for behavior, emotions, feelings and polite conversation. The culture gives a person their beliefs, a person's reactions to beliefs are called emotion, a reaction to an emotion is a feeling and a feeling of long duration is a mood. Only a culture intact can produce a healthy Emotional Vocabulary. A culture is intact if the parent in the culture can practice their culture at all times and in all situations. The culture guarantees and protects a person's life, liberty and pursue of happiness. A culture is a large group of people that have the same rituals and ceremonies and the same beliefs and behaviors. An individual must have a group to guarantee and protect their life, liberty and pursue of happiness. A law on paper does not give you life, liberty and pursue of happiness. Only a group can grant human rights not a law. Essentially, a law is a ritual and/or ceremony enforced by violence or some type of penalty. In any case, a culture that is controlled or perverted or alter (oppression, slavery and colonialism charge/adulterated African culture) can not produce the parents that can produce a healthy Emotional Vocabulary for a child. The culture (which means people) must be free for the children to be Emotionally healthy Because an Europeanized altered African culture is an unhealthy emotional culture, it can not produce the product called healthy child. The unadulterated Ancient African culture has been replaced with a Plantation Culture. The Plantation Culture is the universal culture of Black People. And, continental, European, Caribbean, North and South American, East Indian and Asian Black folks all have been infected with the Plantation Culture.

The Plantation Culture is a distorted Black culture dominated by White culture and has adopted white rituals and ceremonies, laws, education, medicine, foods, sexuality, dancing, morality, religions, marriages and child rearing. Plantation culture has taught black folks to mistrust each other, not to be able to get along together and has taught one black group to feel more superior than another black group. And, it has caused a limited Emotional Vocabulary in which the slave Master taught the slave to fear the Master and love the Master for saving him from the dark primitive African country and hate himself for being the color black with kinky non-white hair, thick lips, a big flat nose and horrible African accent.

MY CHILD DOES NOT UNDERSTAND ME

The failures in communication between parent and child are between digital vocabulary and analogue vocabulary. The child's digital vocabulary usually consist of text message symbols, sounds and words, incomplete fragment sentences, rap music slang, corrupted bastardized English, and the use of letters instead of words.

The use of letters (KFC, ADHD, TMI, LOL, BLT, SOB etc.) has taken the place of words. A letter is now a word. This means words now have the value of sentence and a sentence has the value of a paragraph. The use of letters, sounds of symbols and symbols (i.e. 24 times 7) has reduced the child's attention span and ability to stay focused on a task. The analogue vocabulary of parents consists of words, sentences and paragraphs with very few digital vocabulary words. The parents essentially use Standard English which demands a long attention span with digital children that have a short attention span. Added to this, the high amount of nerve damaging processed sugars, aspartame, caffeine (in energy drinks) glucoronolactgone (in energy drinks0 guarana (high in caffeine) and combinations of these ingredients in sex stimulants cause nerve and brain damage, hyperactivity and cause short attention spans and juvenile senility.

Juvenile senility is erroneously called Attention Deficit, forgetfulness, inability to remember school work, inability to stay on task, restlessness, forgets directions, etc. This causes parents to repeat and repeat instruction and spend hours helping with school homework. In a 70 year old that can not remember a task or instruction, forgets simple things, forgets directions and task it would be labeled senility while in a child senility is labeled Attention Deficit. In any case, the child's digital vocabulary fails to translate the parent's analogue vocabulary.

The conflict between the digital and analogue vocabulary is socially engineered, The white society has slowly increased its use of letters and symbols (i.e. KFC, CVS, BOGO, ADHD, HD). This increase if letters has caused the use of fragmented sentences which results in fragmented incomplete thinking. Added to this black youth have the highest percentage of High School and College drop outs. Therefore, they have dropped out of the whole world and complete sentences vocabulary needed to access their analogue parents. Sadly the Black historical and African centered information and books and speakers are all analogue. Consequently, the digital black child has white culture's digital education. This white intelligence (programmed/engineered] can not access black analogue intelligence. The parent (and single adults) can not successfully communicate to the child. Therefore, black parents fear that they are losing their children.

Fear is the emotional driving force of white culture's relationship to black culture. Historically, enslaved and colonialized blacks feared their slave master and militarily powerful colonial rulers. Black people were forced to adopt the Caucasian religions where the fear of God is taught. Currently, Black people fear they may lose their jobs, fear they won't be successful, and are fearful their marriage or love affair may not be successful. They are fearful, that if they do not buy the fashionable clothes, tattoos gadgets (flat screens), computer games, cars, rims, grills, illegal drugs, sneakers, sex toys, do not participate in the latest sex perversion, go to a popular night club, movie or church and join a peer group, club, sorority, fraternity or sex club they won't be accepted as normal. The emotion of fear causes the body to release a morphine-like neurotransmitter chemical called Dopamine. The constant stimulation of fear causes a high dopamine level which results in physiological addiction. The Black person's addiction to Dopamine (calm fear) causes an addiction to those things associated with fear. The only thing associated with white culture's created fear is white culture. Therefore, fear is used to attach black people to white culture. In other words, Black people are addicted to White people.

Black parents are addicted to using white culture's parenting skills. Black parents use the fear of violence to control their children. If the child violates a rule, the child must be physically beaten. Therefore, the child's good behavior is done to avoid violence. The child is afraid of a beating, so fear is the negative motivating force for good behavior. The child's Emotional vocabulary is limited to the emotion of fear and the avoidance of fear is called the emotion of happiness. The child's limited emotional Vocabulary does not allow the other emotions they need to emotionally inner talk to themselves or talk and feel emotionally connected to others. The child becomes an adult that is emotionally constipated and emotionally raped by white culture. This results in the creation of Plantation Culture and Plantation Behaviors and Emotions. And, the child can only emotionally serve the plantation owner by working for white culture. The child desires to get an emotional reward by obtaining a college/University degree. The college degree grants the child emotional approval of the Slave Master's culture.

The college degree validated that the black person has earned a degree of under-standing on a subject. It is a garmented incomplete understanding. The understanding of the subject can be one degree, two degrees, fifty degree or one hundred degrees of know-ledge but never three hundred and sixty degrees of understanding. It is not holistic understanding (i.e. body, mind, spirit). The degree makes a partial person that can not and will not relate any subject (chemistry, astronomy, mathematics, art, architecture, music etc.) to body or spirit. For every degree of understanding a black person gets from a white sub-ject, the Caucasian culture take ten degrees of the Black person's holistic understanding.

Thus, the Black child goes to a white school and is made degree (credit) by degree a miseducated partial person. The black child loses their holistic black intelligence and gains partial (one degree) intelligence. The White miseducation has done its job and created a Plantation Negro that can only serve the Slave Master. The plantation emotionality and mentality of the Black child is a partial degree educated emotionally castrated servant of white culture.

The only way for the Black child to escape emotional death is for the Black parent to provide an African centered education either after Caucasian school hours or on the weekends or in an African culture school. If this is not done by the Black parent, then fear consciously or subconsciously is controlling the parent. The Black parent that does not try to give their child a complete Emotional Vocabulary either is a traitor to the Black race, or a coward.

Fear is merely the emotional tool that White Domination supported by the emotional false belief of white supremacy which is protected by White Racism which is an emotional driven device used to protect a psychopathic racial personality of Caucasians.

The emotions rule the world not the intellect and the Emotional Vocabulary of the Black child must be healthy so they can become the holistic rulers of the world. If the parent is not emotionally communicating with a complete Emotional Vocabulary then the child will not understand the parent. And, if emotional understanding is partial, the parent won't understand the child. The final result of the collision of digital and analogue communication is a parent that will say "My Child does not understand me".

SUGGESTED READING

Asante, M. — Afrocentricity African World Press – Trenton, NJ.

Ashanti, K.F. — The Psycho-Technology of Brainwashing Tone Books – Durham , NC.

Ashanti, K.F. — Africentric Funerals and Burials Tone Books - Durham, NC.

Ashanti, K.F. — African Royal Weddings: A Guide Tone Books – Durham, NC.

Phyllis Balch, CNC
James F. Balch, MD — Prescription For Dietary Wellness Using Foods To Heal

Brown, Dennis and Toussaint, Pamela A. — Mamas Little Baby: The Black Woman's Guide to Pregnancy, Childbirth and Baby's First Year Plume Printing/Penguin Group 1998.

Beal, Anne; Villarosa, L. and Abner, A. — The Black Parenting Book Broadway Books division of Random House 1999.

Dandy, E. — Black Communications: Breaking Down the Barriers African American Images – Chicago, IL 1991.

Davis, A. — Let's Have Healthy Children Harcourt Brace Jovanovich Inc., 1951.

Fiengold, B. — The Feingold Cookbook for Hyperactive Children Random House – NY 1979.

Frazier, C. — Parents Guide to Allergy in Children Grosset and Dunlap – NY 1973.

Grad L. Flick, Ph.D. — Power Parenting for Children with ADD/ADHD: A Practical Parent's Guide for Managing Difficult Behaviors. The Center for Applied Research in Education – West Nyack, New York, 10994 1996.

Geldard, D. — Counselling Adolescents: The Pro-active Approach

Healy, J. Your Child's Growing Mind: A Practical Guide to Brain Development
Learning from Birth to Adolescence

Hill, P. Coming of Age: African American Male Rites of Passage African American Images – Chicago, IL 1992.

Howarth, V. Children and Young People Who Sexually Abuse Others:
Challenge Responses

Kindlon, D. Raising Cain: Protecting the Emotional Life of Boys

Kunjufu, J. Countering the Conspiracy to Destroy Black Boys Vol. I, II, III
African American Images – Chicago, IL 1986.

Kunjufu, J. Developing Positive Self-Image and Discipline in Black Children
African American Images – Chicago, IL 1984.

Bryan Lask, M.D. Overcoming Behavior Problems in Children: A practical guide.
(ARCO Publishing, Inc. – New York 1985).

Liddle, T.L. Why Motor Skills Matter: Improving Your Child's Physical Development
Enhance Learning and Self-Esteem

Miller, A. The Drama of the Gifted Child: The Search for the True Self.

Mindell, E. Vitamin Bible for Your Kids Rawson, Wade Publishers Inc., NY 1981.

Jane Nelsen, Ed.D. Positive Discipline: The classic guide for parents and teachers to help children develop self-discipline, responsibility, cooperation, and problem solving skills. (Ballantine Books – New York 1981, 1987, 1996.

Karen Renshaw-Joslin Positive Parenting from A – Z Fawcett Columbine – New York 1994.

Sahley, B. Control Hyperactivity A.D.D. Naturally Pain and Stress Publications – San Antonio, TX 1996.

Shandler Ophelia Speaks: Adolescent Girls Write About Their Search for Self

Sharry, J. — Counselling Children, Adolescents and Families: A Strengths-based Approach

Shelton, H. — The Hygienic Care of Children Natural Hygiene Press – Chicago IL 1970.

Simmons, R. — Odd Girl Out: The Hidden Culture of Aggression in Girls

Smith, L. — The Encyclopedia of Baby and Child Care Warner Books, 1972.

Smith, L. — Improving Your Child's Behavior Chemistry Pocket Books – NY 1976.

Stern, D. — Diary of a Baby: What Your Child Sees, Feels, and Experiences

Julia Stewart — Proverbs from: African Proverbs and Wisdom (A Collection for Every Day of the Year, From More Than Forty African Nations)

Talkington, A and Hill, B — To Save A Child: Things You Can Do to Protect, Nurture and Teach Our Children Avery Pub., Garden City Park, NY 1993.

Stanley Turecki, M.D. and Leslie Tonner — The Difficult Child: A new step-by-step approach by a noted child psychiatrist for understanding and managing hard to raise children. (Bantam Books – New York 1985).

Wasse, G. — Maat: The American African Path of Sankofa Mbadu Publishing – Denver, CO 1998.

Weiner, Michael A. — Healing Children Naturally

Wilson, A. — Awakening the Natural Genius of Black Children Afrikan World InfoSystems – NY.

Wilson, A. — Understanding Black Adolescent Male Violence Afrikan World InfoSystems – NY.

Wilson, A. — Blueprint for Black Power Afrikan World InfoSystems – NY 1998.

Zand. O.M.D. Janet Walton, RN, Rachel Roundtree, MD, Bob	Smart Medicine For A Healthier Child

SUGGESTED PRODUCTS

Herbal Tame (Herbal Hair Relaxer)
800 324-7136
www.goldmedalhair.com
Safe relaxer for those children and parents that want straightened hair)

Electronic Itch Stopper
800 669 0987
www.4LF.com
(Helps stop children from scratching itchy skin)

Raw Food Recipes contact:
Raw Power 800 205- 2350
www.nature@rawfood.com

Protection from disease causing radiation from cell phones, computers, electronic devices and games order:
Quantum Byte
Cell Phone Diode
800 456-9887
www.ToolsForWellness.com

Clean clothes and dishes without harmful chemicals
T. Wave Laundry Cleaning Disk
800 752-2775
www. natural – lifestyle.com

Eczema/Psoriasis/Dandruff Products
DermaZinc
800 753-0047 or 888 700-8482

Toilet stool for correct position for bowel movements
Life Step – Toilet Stool
800 830 4778 Extension 3

Moon Calendar
800 GO-LUNAR
(40) (58627)

Dyslexia
Color transparencies that help with reading
813 441-2270
Life As A Black Man
877 BLAC GAME
(2522) 4263)
Educational board game based on today's Black Experience. Boys and girls enjoy it.

Natural Better Vision
877 778-8296
www.bettervisions@ad.com
Improves vision. Can help you stop wearing eye glasses and/or contacts.

Why Cry Analyzer (identifies type of cries; hungry, upset, cuddle, etc.)
800 669-0987
www.4LF.com

ABOUT THE AUTHOR

Llaila (La-ee-La) O. Afrika was born in Baltimore, Maryland. He was formerly a psychotherapist and group facilitator at Eastern Pennsylvania Psychiatric Institute and Georgia Baptist Medical Center, and Counselor for Addictive Services of Pennsylvania's Department of Probation and Parole as well as the Veteran's Hospital Drug and Alcohol Unit in Atlanta Georgia.

Llaila has a Doctorate in Naturopathy and is a Certified Addictionologist (C.A.D), Certified Acupuncture Therapist, Medical Astrologist, Massage Therapist and Drugless Practitioner. He is on the Board of the African Traditional Thinkers, Priests, Healers and Religions. Llaila is essentially self-taught and obtained diplomas and certifications because his clients like to see the cosmetics of the professionalism. In the Medical Corp of the US Army, he was a Psychologist Specialist and later became a Nurse. He was discharged from the Army National Guard because he omitted information and he says, "It was a blessing."

Llaila lectures on a broad spectrum of topics such as Stress, Parenting, Hyperactivity, Diabetes, Changing Children's Behavior, Controlling Teenagers, Relationships, Computer and Electronic Diseases, The Difficult Child, Fibroids, Holistic Sex Laws, Cocaine, Anthrax and AIDS Remedies, Weight Loss, Child Growth, Gay Children, Nutrition, African History, etc. He offers workshops, seminars, classes and nutritional consultations. Llaila designs lectures and classes for schools, churches and a variety of groups.

Llaila conducts Gullah Sea Island Black History Tours. He has a wide selection of health and related subjects on videos, DVD, CD's and audios. He can be reached at:

P.O. Box 2475
Beaufort, SC 29901
Telephone: (317) 216-8088

Website www.geocities.com/afrika7_2000

Email llailaafrika@juno.com

INDEX

DATE

DATE	
5/19/17	
11/25/17	
1/24/18	

PRINTED IN U.S.A.

Made in the USA
Middletown, DE
14 February 2017